DRUG ADULTERATION

DETECTION AND CONTROL
IN NINETEENTH-CENTURY
BRITAIN

By Ernst W. Stieb
with the collaboration of
Glenn Sonnedecker

LTERATION

ON AND CONTROL

CENTURY BRITAIN

"In the existing state of society do you think that *caveat emptor* should be changed into *caveat venditor?*" "Yes." In the dramatic simplicity of his reply, a central figure in the English movement for pure foods and drugs signaled the start of a revolutionary change in social philosophy. The response was that of Arthur Hill Hassall, chief witness appearing before the Parliamentary Select Committee on Adulterations of Food, Etc., in 1856.

Did no one before 1856 seek to protect the consumer from the adulteration of medicines and drugs, a protection we take for granted today? In this study, two leading historians of pharmacy, Ernst W. Stieb and Glenn Sonnedecker, have answered the question. They have investigated the development of controls in Great Britain between 1820, when Fredrick Accum publicized the problem in his *Treatise on Adulterations,* and 1906, when the United States enacted its first pure food and drug law.

A preliminary discussion of more primitive efforts to detect and control adulteration before 1820 emphasizes the importance of emergent scientific and technical means of detection. It was with the use of the microscope and the maturing of analytical chemistry and physics that society was provided with weapons with which to win the fight against adulteration.

The development of controls over adulteration was, as the authors show, a long, slow struggle. Although the prevailing official attitude was one of laissez faire, the reforming spirit of Victorian England caught fire in some individuals who began agitating for legislative control. The successful operation of such con-

DRUG
ADULTERATION

DETECTION AND CONTROL
IN NINETEENTH-CENTURY
BRITAIN

ERNST W. STIEB

WITH THE COLLABORATION OF GLENN SONNEDECKER

THE UNIVERSITY OF WISCONSIN PRESS

Madison, Milwaukee, and London, 1966

Published by

The University of Wisconsin Press

Madison, Milwaukee, and London

U.S.A.: Box 1379, Madison, Wisconsin 53701

U.K.: 26–28 Hallam Street, London, W.1

Copyright © 1966 by the Regents of the

University of Wisconsin

Printed in the United States of America

by Kingsport Press, Inc.,

Kingsport, Tennessee

Library of Congress Catalog Card Number 66–22859

trol depended on the rise of specialized groups to solve in a systematic and scientific manner the many problems encountered. A professional organization of pharmacists was formed in 1841, and the Society of Public Analysts was founded in 1874; other groups and individuals joined the fight, and in 1899 the Sale of Food and Drugs Act gave the Local Government Board sufficient power to see that laws were uniformly administered. Thus toward the end of the nineteenth century, through the combined efforts of scientists and social reformers, the control of drug adulteration was becoming a reality.

ERNST W. STIEB

Ernst W. Stieb, registered in 1953 as a pharmacist in Ontario, Canada, received his Ph.D. from the University of Wisconsin, where he is currently Associate Professor in the departments of Pharmacy and the History of Science. He has published numerous articles on pharmacy and the history of pharmacy.

Glenn Sonnedecker, Director of the American Institute of the History of Pharmacy since 1957, is Professor of Pharmacy and the History of Science at the University of Wisconsin.

TO CATHY

In the existing state of society
do you think that *caveat emptor*
should be changed into
caveat venditor?

Yes. —Arthur Hill Hassall
in testimony to the
Parliamentary Select Committee
on Adulterations of Food, Etc.,
1856

PREFACE

The adulteration of drugs has always been of public concern; and the problem significantly stimulated the development of organized pharmacy as a countervailing force, especially in Great Britain and the United States. Yet no systematic study of this chapter of social and pharmaceutical history has appeared. The parallel and often interconnected problem of adulteration of food has been studied historically, although the best publication even on that side of the subject appeared thirty years ago and has long been out of print.

However incidental and buried, the discussion of drug adulteration in the introductory chapters of textbooks on chemical analysis of foods and drugs constituted, until now, the main source of historical information. The subject also has received incidental mention in connection with the history of food adulteration.

The present study focuses upon Great Britain because among the Anglo-American countries Great Britain was first to control the adulteration of drugs by comprehensive legal means and influenced the development of controls in other parts of the Anglo-American world. Our approach to this historical topic has been influenced by the author's background as pharmacist and as historian of pharmaceutical science. While reflecting the special significance we see in the subject for the development of the profession of pharmacy, the book shows the significance of the subject within both a technologic and social context.

The period chosen for detailed study (1820–1906) seems pivotal for that aspect of British history which here comes into focus. In

these years man finally came to grips with a problem that had
plagued him for at least two millennia; the form these measures took
largely shaped the present methods of control. The year 1820 marks
the appearance, amid much furor, of Fredrick Accum's *Treatise on
Adulterations,* which signalled the beginning of more and more serious attention to adulterated food and drugs in Britain; and 1906 marks
the year in which the United States enacted its first federal statutes.

What happened before 1820 on the Continent is introduced for
background and comparison, but in general it lies beyond the scope
of the present investigation. We attempted, however, to discover
what circumstances determined that just this particular period would
bring solutions, of a sort, to problems of drug adulteration.

The author's work has been extended and refined considerably in
recent years; on the other hand, the interested reader can find additional details in his doctoral dissertation (1959), which was prepared
under the direction of Professor Glenn Sonnedecker of the University
of Wisconsin. Help and advice also is gratefully acknowledged from
other members of the History of Science Department of the University of Wisconsin, especially Aaron J. Ihde, who shares interests in the
history of adulteration—his being more particularly in foods. Professor Ihde generously allowed the author to read (in manuscript) the
chapters on analytical chemistry in his *The Development of Modern
Chemistry* (New York, 1964). Gratitude is also expressed to Mrs.
Gordon K. Johnson for typing the manuscript.

Appreciation is also due a number of libraries and their librarians
who were generous with their services, particularly Mrs. Elsa Reich
and Miss Dolores Nemec, successive librarians of the University of
Wisconsin Pharmacy Library, and the interlibrary-loan librarian of the
University of Wisconsin Memorial Library, Miss Marguerite Chris-
tensen. Other libraries that have been particularly helpful are The
National Library of Medicine (Bethesda, Maryland), The Library of
Congress, The National Archives, Lewis Library, Yale University
Medical Library, John Crerar Library of Chicago, and those of The
Pharmaceutical Society (Great Britain), The University of Michigan,
The United States Department of Agriculture, The University of
Minnesota, The State University of Iowa, The Peabody Institute,
Princeton University, The University of Virginia, The College of
Physicians of Philadelphia, The University of Chicago, and the Mid-
west Interlibrary Center. The Edward Kremers Reference Files at the
University of Wisconsin, maintained jointly by the American Institute
of the History of Pharmacy, have also provided valuable information.

Appreciation is expressed to Dean Arthur H. Uhl and the School of

Pharmacy for kindly curtailing my teaching duties during a semester to allow completion of the work.

Research has been supported in part by the Research Committee of the University of Wisconsin Graduate School from funds supplied by the Wisconsin Alumni Research Foundation. Publication is supported in part by a grant (NIGMS–RGB GM 09132–02) from the National Institutes of Health, Public Health Service, Department of Health, Education, and Welfare.

Madison, Wisconsin   ERNST W. STIEB
January, 1966

CONTENTS

ILLUSTRATIONS

PART I

PROLOGUE

1.

BEFORE 1820:
DRUG ADULTERATION
AND ITS DETECTION
OVER TWO MILLENNIA

Effective solutions to the problem of drug adulteration did not evolve until the nineteenth century; and yet, the same problem, with only minor variations, had been facing mankind for several thousand years. The significance of nineteenth-century developments in Britain can be appreciated fully only if we first know what came before. The extant records of adulteration, from the fourth century B.C. to the nineteenth century A.D., are so numerous and often so repetitive that we should select and mention only a few of the important or representative developments of the preceding 2200 years.[1]

The concept of "adulteration" as applied to drugs varies in different times and contexts; but here the term will mean any practice which, through intent or neglect, results in a variation of strength and/or purity from the professed standard of a drug. ("Drug" here means any substance, or combination of substances, intended to diagnose, cure, or mitigate disease in man or animals.)

From the sixteenth century onward, official pharmacopeias increasingly set standards that guided the preparation and evaluation of drugs. Before such explicit guides appeared, standards were largely implicit and varied with place and time. The writings of early authorities, such as Dioscorides, were often used as guides, but they largely lacked precision (as did the early pharmacopeias) and the force of legal authority.

3

Lacking defined standards, the term "adulteration" may be considered to have included, always in association with intent or neglect: secret addition of extraneous substances, whether deleterious or merely to increase bulk and weight; the subtraction of constituents usually considered part of the substance; deterioration from an accepted standard of strength or quality. Adulteration may also include preparing a substance to conceal its defects and to make it appear better than it is. Besides the *fact of adulteration,* as discussed here, we are even more concerned with the *means of controlling it;* and thus efforts to deal with the question of drug identity and quality are relevant.

It would be conjecture to say when, where, or why, the practice of adulteration originated. Yet when the Roman author Pliny (A.D. 23–79) remarked that "nature has revealed . . . most remarkable properties to mortals, were it not that the fraudulent propensities of man are apt to corrupt and falsify everything" [2] it suggests that fraud —and adulteration in one form or another—probably has been recurrent since the beginning of social history. As Walden suggests, analytical procedures probably already had been developed in Greco-Roman times as a defense against adulterated articles of trade (drugs included).[3]

ANCIENT GREECE AND ROME

In the Greco-Roman period, famous writers who dealt with medical and technical subjects—such as Dioscorides, Pliny, and Galen, along with Archimedes and Theophrastus—represent well informed opinion. The tests at their disposal for detecting drug adulteration, with some exceptions, were primarily sense-perceptions. Such empirical and subjective methods prevailed until the middle of the nineteenth century and still play some role in pharmacognosy.

Theophrastus.—Theophrastus (*ca.* 372—*ca.* 288 B.C.) discussed "Differences in Taste," in general and specifically with respect to drugs, in a chapter entitled "Of roots possessing remarkable taste and smell." [4] He concluded his discussion on myrrh by noting that the myrrh "of better quality is tested by its taste and they select that which is of uniform colour." [5]

Among many factors contributing to the quality of drugs, Theophrastus recognized the age of the plant, method of collection, portion of the plant used, and geographical origin; [6] also proper storage and preservation.[7] In spite of thorough knowledge of qualitative distinctions, he was aware that inferior varieties were sometimes confused with the best specimens because they were the same in appearance though different "in their virtues." [8]

In the *Enquiry into Plants*, Theophrastus referred only once to adulteration, saying that balsam of Mecca was readily adulterated and therefore seldom procurable in a pure state. He indicated that its market price was proportional to its purity, and a pure sample might be worth double its weight in silver. Theophrastus indicated no means of distinguishing the pure from the "mixed" gum,[9] but his qualitative descriptions for differentiating one plant from another might serve as guides for the discernment of falsifications. He used similar means to distinguish between minerals.[10]

About a year after Theophrastus' death, Archimedes was born. The "earliest detection of adulteration" might be credited to Archimedes, Blyth and Blyth have suggested, because of his specific-gravity method of detecting base metal in King Hiero's crown.[11] Archimedes' development of this physical constant and its consequent application to adulteration acquired added significance when contrasted with the empirical qualitative methods of Theophrastus, or even those of Dioscorides.

Dioscorides.—The significance for this study of the Greek surgeon Dioscorides (1st C.), like that of Pliny and Galen, goes beyond the value or validity of his writings. It rests rather on the fact that Dioscorides' *Materia medica* was used widely and persistently throughout the Middle Ages, leaving traces even into the modern period.

In his *Materia medica*, Dioscorides mentioned, among a thousand or more entries, forty examples of adulteration. For thirty of these he gave definite methods of detection; in eight others his qualitative descriptions of the pure substances were probably sufficient to differentiate the true from the adulterated sample.

Simple organoleptic tests accounted for 70 to 75 per cent of the total and covered a wide range of delicate, sometimes ambiguous, degrees of qualitative distinctions, as in the case of adulterated myrrh.[12] Where he gave no tests he provided qualitative descriptions as criteria for purity. In some cases the geographic origin or botanical description of drugs served the same purpose.[13]

Besides organoleptic tests, chemico-physical methods account for many of Dioscorides' procedures of detection, although ambiguity makes it difficult to decide how accurate these tests were. For example, one method of deciding whether a sample of balsam was adulterated or pure was to apply it to a piece of wool: the specimen was pure if the cloth showed no stains after it was washed. In addition, pure balsam easily diffused in water or milk, whereas sophisticated balsam floated, like oil, on the surface.[14]

In the monographs dealing with frankincense, we are told that the pure substance was readily flammable, had a pleasant sweet smell, and gave off clear, airy smoke.[15] In the case of soda, solubility in oil was the criterion for purity, while for wool fat, the formation of lanolin upon rubbing with water is mentioned.[16] Other tests of the chemico-physical type show a similarly empirical approach.[17]

Of the chemical tests, Dioscorides used most frequently the flame test (almost half the drugs for which he indicated chemical tests) and flammability (one-third of the time). Of the physical tests, solubility was used for one-third of the substances involved.

Dioscorides, like Theophrastus, frequently alluded to proper methods of storage and preservation, and to problems of deterioration; [18] also to varying degrees of quality and to processes of preparation or purification.[19]

For the detection of adulterations, Dioscorides relied mainly upon simple organoleptic methods, but by his time chemico-physical tests also held a place. Such tests were more prominent still in the *Natural History* of his contemporary, Pliny.

Pliny the Elder.—The similarities between Dioscorides and Pliny, the Roman gentleman and civil servant, went beyond their encyclopedic style to actual content. The great interest in the *Natural History* lies not so much in Pliny's methods or their relative scientific merit, but in the insight he gives us into one facet of the social history of his and earlier times. We discover some of the "whys" concerning adulteration practices, as well as the "hows," if we look beyond some of his strong personal biases.[20]

Pliny repeatedly charged his fellows with greed, "fraudulent propensities" or "disposition," as he phrased it,[21] and implied that human avarice was the common basis for fraud and adulteration. Numerous references to adulterants and processes for adulteration indicate that they constituted a social problem of some dimension.[22]

Pliny recognized profit and scarcity as responsible for adulteration practices [23] and mentioned the price of substances in many cases as a criterion of genuineness.[24]

Even more critical than Pliny's outbursts against the fraud and ignorance of the physicians, were those against *seplasiarii*, a term that might be translated "druggists": [25]

[The physicians] trust entirely to the druggists, who spoil everything by their fraudulent adulterations. For this long time past . . . [the physicians] have even purchased their plasters and salves ready made, and the consequence is, that the spoiled and adulterated wares in the druggists' shops are got rid of.[26]

Pliny, like Dioscorides, relied heavily upon simple organoleptic tests for detecting adulteration,[27] yet his reports include a discernibly higher proportion of chemico-physical tests. It would be misleading to assume, however, that Pliny was more advanced than Dioscorides. In addition to the use of gall infusion, which Browne interpreted as "the first historical reference to the use of test paper," [28] the following types of chemico-physical tests may be distinguished in the *Natural History:* the *flame test,* used at least fifteen times in descriptions covering some thirty substances, with note being taken of the color and odor of the smoke as well as the color of the flame or the process of decrepitation; [29] *ring tests;* [30] *acid reactions;* [31] a *tannin test,* which Browne perceived in Pliny's statement that "the mode of detecting whether or not alum has been adulterated, is by the application of pomegranate-juice; for if genuine, it will turn black on combining with the juice." [32] Other tests which hold some interest are: water-oil solubility, assay by means of incandescent gold or iron, viscosity, volatility, the touchstone, and density.

The insight that Pliny's *Natural History* gives us concerning the level of ancient methods to detect drug adulteration, particularly chemico-physical methods, complements his candid delineation of the social scene in which this adulteration took place. Galen, who lived and wrote in the century following Pliny, approached the problem of adulteration in a different spirit.

Galen.—Galen of Pergamum (*ca.* A.D. 129–201), body physician to the Emperor Marcus Aurelius, devoted several books and portions of others to drugs, yet his chief concern, as a physician, lay in therapeutics. While he showed concern over the purity of his drug supply, the number of cases of adulteration he specifically mentioned was small, and the methods he used to detect these adulterations were again limited largely to the simplest organoleptic tests. The extent of drug adulteration was revealed in general comments concerning his methods of obtaining drug supplies and in his disparaging remarks about drug dealers. Galen's admittedly hypercritical and contentious disposition perhaps affected the hues of the pictures he painted.

Medical men served as both pharmacist and clinician, although later in the Roman period they purchased certain types of compounded drugs from the *seplasiarii,* and others. Galen distrusted these various types of drug-dealers, calling them "roguish dealers of petty wares," but he related that they in turn were betrayed by the

merchants bringing drugs and by the root gatherers (*rhizotomoi*).[33]
Galen, in fact, told how in his youth he had been taught by a man
who profited greatly by his skilled falsification of costly drugs.[34]
Galen declined, however, to reveal any methods of adulteration, for
fear they might be misapplied by the unscrupulous. Instead, he
stressed the necessity of being able to distinguish true and genuine
drugs from the adulterated.[35]

Whenever possible, Galen obtained his own personal supplies of
drugs directly from the proper geographical sources, to insure the
purity of his medications.[36] He advised others to do likewise.

He cautioned his readers to be certain when buying from Roman
dealers in unguents (*unguentarii*) that they be able to distinguish
the products of best quality. Indeed, for almost every item of the
materia medica he treated, Galen described just how to distinguish
drugs of optimum quality, whether by their taste (see Plate I), odor,
appearance, pharmacologic potency, or geographic source.[37]

Galen's methods for detecting adulterated drugs were much like
those we have noted for other Greco-Roman authors. His test for
pepper,[38] which was for centuries one of the most heavily adulterated
commodities, exemplifies the influence such authorities had on later
periods. The maceration test for the purity of whole pepper described
by Galen remained standard until the middle of the nineteenth
century, when the application of the microscope to adulteration was
first fully realized.

Aside from the adulteration Galen reported for specific drugs, he
made a number of references to the adulteration of medicaments in
general and to pills and theriac in particular.[39] The passage concerning theriac designated pharmacological activity—purgative action—
as the means of determining adulteration. Here, as elsewhere, Galen
stressed the necessity for physicians to be familiar with their materia
medica. He emphasized that the repeated examination of drugs was
necessary to distinguish those which at first glance—like twins—
seemed to be alike, but which upon closer examination turned out to
be different.[40]

Although Galen had his own sources of pure drugs, he was well
aware that not all physicians were so fortunate. Consequently, in his
work entitled *De substitutis medicinis* (or *De succedaneis*) he listed
drugs, accompanied by the names of other drugs which might be
substituted when those of first choice were unavailable.[41] Writers on
materia medica followed this practice up to the nineteenth century
when more certain transport made the *quid pro quo* unnecessary.

The influence of Galen can be traced through botanical and medical writings up to modern times, as can that of Dioscorides and Pliny. These writings, with few exceptions, reported no noteworthy advances in the detection of drug adulterations. Viewed in this light, the level of achievement reflected in the works of ancient authors takes on added interest. A few treatises from the medieval and early modern period will serve to illustrate how much the authors depended upon Greco-Roman sources, and how little they had advanced beyond their ancient models.

MEDIEVAL ISLAM

The Arabs of medieval Islam played a significant role in the transmission of Greco-Roman thought to the medieval Latin West, including an important influence on the development of European pharmacy by way of southern Italy, Spain, and France. Not only were the works of such authors as Dioscorides and Galen translated, but they were assimilated into the works of Arab scholars.

It was during the Islamic period that those who prepared medicine apparently first achieved sufficient autonomy from medicine to establish privately owned, yet government-supervised, shops.[42] Already then, the problem of unqualified practitioners and fraud had manifested itself sufficiently to require controls.

These systems of control created manuals dealing with al-hisbah, a function of the police officer in charge of markets (muhtasib), which included testing the genuineness of goods and the accuracy of weights and measures.[43] These hisbah treatises contained separate chapters devoted to various trades and industries, including the pharmacists, spicers, and vendors of juices and syrups.

These various dealers in drugs apparently caused the muhtasib particular troubles, so that he appointed an assistant (amīn) from within the specialized groups to supervise their activities. Frequent inspections and exhortations were needed to keep violations to a minimum. Furthermore, medicinal compounds were required to be prepared in the presence of the amīn himself; and to further guarantee their ultimate purity, an oath was sworn that no further admixture would take place after the compound left the amīn's surveillance.[44]

Shayzarī and Ibn Bassām.—We shall look briefly at the treatises of two Arab authors: the Nihāyat al-Rutbah fī Ṭalab al-Ḥisbah (freely translated, "Book of the Highest or Ultimate Standard in Acquiring Knowledge of al-Ḥisbah") by 'Abd al-Raḥmān ibn Naṣr . . . (al-'Adawī, al-Shayzarī); and the much augmented version of Shayzarī's Nihāyat by Ibn Bassām.

The *Nihāyat* of Shayzarī, an Egyptian author thought to have flourished in the time of Salāḥ al-Dīn (1169–1193), was a manual of *ḥisbah* with 40 chapters, of which chapters 17, 18, and 19 were devoted to the inspection of, respectively, pharmacists, spicers, and sellers of medicinal juices and syrups.[45] The *Nihāyat* was augmented by Ibn Bassām, in the thirteenth or fourteenth century, from 40 to 114 chapters, of which chapters 38, 40, and 39 corresponded to 17, 18, and 19 of Shayzarī.[46] Chapters 4 and 91 respectively of Shayzarī and Ibn Bassām dealt with false weights and measures, and inaccurate scales or balances, which are beyond the scope of the present discussion.[47] Ibn Bassām made nine additions to the chapters on drugs, but these are not significant enough to merit separate comment.

The preliminaries to chapter 17 of Shayzarī advised the inspectors, as an obligatory duty, to fill the pharmacists with a fear of God, lecture them and threaten them with punishment and corporal chastisement (see Plate II), and examine their drugs weekly. A religious allusion also enters the chapter's concluding passages, where the author refrained from giving many details of adulteration for fear that they would fall into the hands of unbelievers, who would be only too ready to practice these deceptions against the Muslims.[48]

The introductory portion of the corresponding chapter in Ibn Bassām stressed the need for the *muḥtasib* to appoint someone to watch over the pharmacists who knew well their ways and doings. It stressed the fact that of the three thousand drugs in existence, many resembled one another outwardly but were decidedly different in action.[49]

An examination of chapter 17 of Shayzarī's *Nihāyat* (and chapter 38 of Ibn Bassām) soon reveals inescapable similarities to Dioscorides' *Materia medica*. The passages dealing with adulterated verdigris (copper acetate), balsam, and opium, for example, are in many cases so nearly alike that they could be regarded as coming from a single work.[50]

In 8 of 29 instances in which Shayzarī mentioned adulterations he gave no means of detection; Ibn Bassām reported no method of detection in 11 of the 38 cases of adulteration he mentioned. In Shayzarī chemico-physical tests accounted for about the same number of tests as did organoleptic, while in Ibn Bassām the balance was slightly in favor of chemico-physical ones.

From the evidence presented, and from more cited by Wiedemann and Behrnauer, it appears that such Arab writers as Shayzarī and Ibn Bassām knew, used, and elaborated on Greco-Roman sources dealing directly or indirectly, with drug adulteration, particularly Dioscorides and Pliny. If Ibn Bassām used Ibn al Bayṭar (d. 1248) in his elaboration of Shayzarī, this might well strengthen, not lessen, the connection with Greek and Roman sources in view of Ibn al Bayṭar's known use of Dioscorides and Galen.

THE MEDIEVAL LATIN WEST

Just as the Arabs had relied mainly on their Greek predecessors for methods to detect drug adulteration, so did the authors of the Latin West, during the medieval period. The herbals and medico-botanical writings of the medieval and early modern period are interrelated in a most complex fashion, though their sources can be shown to be ultimately Greek, often through Arab intermediaries.

Of the many examples of this genre, we shall examine only the *Circa instans* (mid-12th C.) and the *Grete Herball* (1526). Although chronologically the latter work falls in the early modern period, its approach is medieval. The *Grete Herball* was in fact little more than a commentary upon the *Circa instans*.

Circa instans.—The *Liber de simplici medicina* (*incipit: Circa instans*), attributed to Matthaeus Platearius (12th C.), seems to be a revised and enlarged edition of *De gradibus simplicium* by Constantine the African.[51] The *Circa instans* was copied extensively by subsequent writers from the thirteenth to the sixteenth century, and consequently it influenced the development of later herbals (such as the *Grete Herball*) and pharmacopeias into modern times.[52] It was recommended for the use of pharmacists by the fifteenth-century physician Saladin de Asculo and required for *herbiers* (spicers) by a Charter of the University of Paris (October 2, 1422).[53] There were in fact 2 concurrent variants of the *Circa instans,* one with 432 chapters and a smaller one with only 273.[54]

Tests of the organoleptic type (see Plate III) predominated in the *Circa instans*, outnumbering the chemico-physical ones by more than three to one. But chemico-physical tests are indicated for balsam— references to a flame test and to crude relative density or specific gravity determinations. There is a striking similarity between the first of these tests and that already noted under the discussion of Shayzarī.[55] In another relatively simple and efficient method, the author noted that balsam was assumed to be adulterated if it was not two or three times heavier than the same measure of turpentine. Presumably adulterations with heavier substances were detected by the other methods.

A similar method applied to musk showed that the adulterated was twice as heavy as the pure. In the same monograph one interesting passage gave the actual method for adulterating musk and made an accusation against the Arabs ("Saracens").[56]

Among the reasons given for adulteration in the *Circa instans,* repeated in the *Grete Herball,* we find price and scarcity of supply,[57] while the extent of adulteration practices may be inferred from remarks that in forty pounds of a certain drug it was hardly possible to find two ounces of good substance; or again, if one found a certain other drug pure it was good for stomach disorders.[58]

In some cases, although there might be no mention of "meddling," distinctions were drawn between different qualities of drugs to guard against the acceptance of inferior or deteriorated ones. The word "pure," which was used occasionally, probably was intended in the sense of "clean." [59] Considerable attention was given in the *Circa instans* to the subject of proper collection and storage of drug plants. Repeated stress was laid upon the length of time plants might be stored without impaired activity.

Although the *Circa instans* offered little if any advance with respect to detection of adulteration over Dioscorides or Pliny, it was decidedly more comprehensive than most works of the period dealing with herbs.

The Grete Herball.—Even though the *Grete Herball* (first edition by Peter Treveris, London, 1526) relied heavily upon the *Circa instans,* via the intermediary of the *Grand Herbier,*[60] it had an influence of its own.

The monographs dealing with Aloes (1) and Aloes ligno (2) not only mentioned adulteration but indicated the methods of adulteration as well as those of detection. These latter methods, as in the *Circa instans,* were almost exclusively organoleptic. In fact, in 24 of the 25 cases of adulteration in which means of detection were provided, the tests of the organoleptic type outnumbered the chemico-physical by about 9 to 1 and, if anything, were inferior to those cited by Dioscorides.

Pharmacists were occasionally accused in connection with adulteration,[61] as were the "Saracens" (also mentioned, in the *Circa instans*).[62] Aside from their association with foreign drugs, which in all times have been claimed to be most often subject to adulteration, the "Saracens" were regarded as "unbelievers" and so capable of all sorts of unethical practices. We recall that Shayzarī also laid the blame for adulteration on "those without religion."

The fact that earlier authors served as sources for later ones does not merely illustrate that an examination of history is a natural antecedent to the serious study of any discipline; rather (except for a few isolated examples) in the Middle Ages, this was not merely the starting point, but the whole point, without additional comment or observation.

FROM BOYLE TO FAVRE

In chemistry, the modern revolution was not to come until the time of Lavoisier, but modern chemistry had its beginnings at least a century earlier; and it is of the man often called the founder of modern chemistry, and one of the founders of qualitative analysis, that we must first speak briefly here.

Robert Boyle: Medicina Hydrostatica.—Just a year before his death, Robert Boyle (1627–1691) published a little work entitled *Medicina Hydrostatica: or Hydrostaticks applyed to the Materia Medica.*[63] (See Figure 1.) Not only does this seem to be the first tract in English to deal with specific gravity, but it was also, so far as we know, the first work in English to discuss a means of detecting adulteration in drugs.[64]

Boyle was not the first, of course, to realize the potential of specific gravity as a physical constant,[65] and he readily acknowledged his debt to Archimedes for the underlying principle.[66] Boyle's *Medicina Hydrostatica* was significant because it made available, to those who wished to take advantage of it, a relatively precise tool for detecting drug adulteration. A century passed before this tool found wide application for this purpose, and even then its over-all effect upon controlling drug adulteration was limited by the fact that the materia medica was largely botanical. Yet Boyle's *Medicina Hydrostatica* remains important because it represents the beginning of the effective harnessing of science to expose drug adulteration.[67]

Boyle appeared confident that specific gravity would help "discern genuine Stones, whether Animal or Mineral, from Counterfeit Ones; which too often [passed] for true, to the great prejudice of Physicians and Patients," because few qualities were so basic in nature and difficult to alter unperceivedly as specific gravity.[68] Even beyond "Stones or Minerals," he saw a practical use for specific gravity in estimating the "Genuineness, or degree of Purity of Several Bodies, that [were, or might,] usefully be imployed in Physick." [69]

And indeed, Boyle described, in simple language and practical detail, various methods for determining the specific gravity of solids (water-soluble as well as -insoluble) and liquids. Also to simplify matters for his readers, Boyle annexed a table listing in alphabetical order the weight (in grains) of certain substances in air and in water

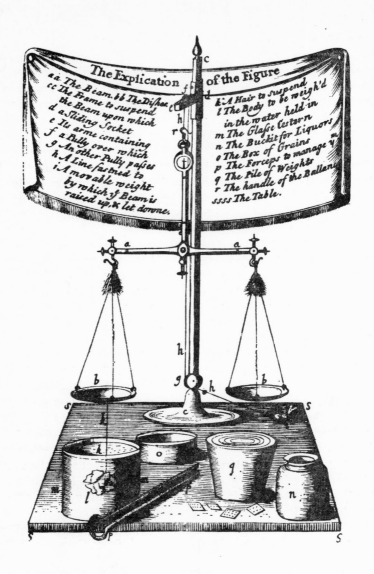

The Explication of the Figure

aa The Beam. bb The Dishes.
cc The Frame to suspend
the Beam upon which
d a Sliding Socket
e Its arme containing
f a Pully over which
g An other Pully passes
h A Line fastned to
i A movable weight
by which y Beam is
raised up, & let downe.

k A Hair to suspend
l The Body to be weigh'd
in the water held in
m The Glasse Cestern
n The Buckit for Liquors
o The Box of Grains
p The Forceps to manage y
q The Pile of Weights
r The handle of the Ballance
ssss The Table.

Figure 1. Frontispiece of Robert Boyle's *Medicina Hydrostatica* (1690), showing a balance of the type probably used by Boyle to carry out his specific gravity determinations. (University of Wisconsin Memorial Library.)

and the specific gravity or "proportion," as he called it. He expressed this constant as a ratio rather than in decimal form as we are accustomed to see it, thus 4 $\frac{7}{100}$ to 1, for example, in the case of "Antimony good and supposed to be Hungarian One." [70]

Aside from its value for determining purity, Boyle recognized the usefulness of specific gravity for distinguishing between the same substance in lots of different geographical origin, especially where one source was preferred over another.[71] He also realized that it was sometimes possible to detect deterioration, in juices for instance, by the change in specific gravity caused by fermentation.[72]

Although we regard specific gravity as a constant, Boyle cautioned his readers to think of the values obtained as only approximately constant or "Estimates." But he did not believe that this detracted at all from the usefulness of the values obtained. This also explains why Boyle considered it unnecessary to use "very Good and tender Ballances," since small variations would make little difference and, besides, there would be differences in the substances themselves.[73]

In spite of the apparent lack of precision this suggests, the specific-gravity methods Boyle outlined in his *Medicina Hydrostatica* for detecting drug adulteration were considerably more precise than other methods included in many contemporary works, particularly those that dealt predominately with vegetable drugs, such as Pomet's *Histoire générale des drogues* (1694).

Boyle's concern for the purity of drugs and chemicals—particularly the latter, as it influenced the possible outcome of his experiments—antedated and surpassed, of course, the printed manifestation of that concern expressed in the *Medicina Hydrostatica* of 1690. At least thirty years earlier, the same year the more famous *Sceptical Chymist* first appeared (1661), he expressed such concern in his *Two Essays, Concerning the Unsuccessfulness of Experiments.*[74]

Boyle's pioneer contributions to analytical chemistry in general, particularly the systematization of identification tests, flame tests, color-reaction tests, etc., added immeasurably to the battery of effective weapons available for the detection of adulteration.[75] The weapon provided, however, by specific gravity as outlined in the *Medicina Hydrostatica* remains one of Robert Boyle's outstanding contributions to the ultimate control of drug (and food) adulteration.

Pierre Pomet: Histoire générale des drogues.—Published within a few years of Boyle's *Medicina Hydrostatica* and described as "one of the classics on drug adulteration." [76] Pierre Pomet's *Histoire générale des drogues*—also titled *Le Marchand sincère* [77]—can perhaps be more accurately described as a book on materia medica, with considerable emphasis on adulteration and its detection. Interestingly, in view of problems Fredrick Accum faced a century later, the English edition was dedicated to Sir Hans Sloane, physician to Queen Anne and Secretary of the Royal Society, apparently for fear of retribution at the hands of adulterators.[78]

When Pomet treated drugs of animal or vegetable origin, he was forced back upon rather tenuous descriptions of purity and adulteration that depended largely upon simple organoleptic tests. While those monographs that dealt with minerals or chemicals, such as calomel,[79] reflected advances in analytical chemistry, even here the attack was often strongly empirical.[80]

Pomet considered certain dealers in drugs guilty of practicing adulteration, and pointed out the necessity for all those concerned with the drug supply (physicians, pharmacists, non-pharmacist dealers in drugs, and grocers) to master, through practice, the differentiation of the genuine from the adulterated.[81] According to custom, he blamed the foreign supplier—the "Levanites" or Near Easterners —for certain adulteration practices; he apprised his readers that "the great Cheats committed . . . in sophisticating of Medicines or Druggs, [were] not done by the General Merchants, or the Wholesale Dealers, but the little Retail Traders, who [imposed] their pernicious Commodities, upon honest well meaning People, without Honour or Conscience." [82]

Of necessity, Pomet probably goes but little farther beyond Dioscorides, one of his acknowledged sources, than did other medico-botanical writers up to the eighteenth century.

Mors in vitro *and* Mors in olla.—A few years before the English edition of Pomet, there appeared the first of the so-called "Death" treatises—the *Mors in vitro* (1709) by N. B. Noel, followed in 1722 by Jo. Henr. Schulze's *Mors in olla*. These treatises heralded a long series of works of the "scare" or muckraking variety that culminated a century later in Accum's famous *Treatise on Adulterations* (1820) and the anonymous *Deadly Adulteration* (1830?), attributed to John Dingwall Williams.

Although this class of literature was usually treated with near contempt by scholarly authors, it probably did more (because of some exaggerations) to make the public aware of the seriousness and extent of adulteration practices than many serious works on the subject. Neither the *Mors in vitro* nor the *Mors in olla* are relevant here, except as a genre of literature, for the former deals principally with brandy, the latter with contamination from certain metal containers.[83]

A. G. Richter: De corruptelis medicamentorum.—Only ten years separate the *Mors in olla* from Adolf Gottlob Richter's *De corruptelis medicamentorum cognoscendis tractatus medico-chymicus pharmacopoliis accommodatus et triplici indice instructus* (Dresden and Leipzig, 1732). (See Figure 2.) Yet Richter's little treatise of less

ADOLPHI 𝕲𝔬𝔱𝔱𝔩𝔬𝔟 RICHTERI

PHILOS. ET MED. D.

DE
CORRUPTELIS
MEDICAMEN-
TORVM

COGNOSCENDIS
TRACTATVS
MEDICO-CHYMICVS

PHARMACOPOLIIS ACCOMMODATVS
ET TRIPLICI INDICE INSTRVCTVS.

DRESDÆ & LIPSIÆ,

IN OFFICINA LIBRARIA HEKELIANA.
MDCCXXXII.

Figure 2. Titlepage of Adolph Gottlob Richter's *De corruptelis medicamentorum* (1732). (National Library of Medicine.)

than 100 pages is written in quite a different spirit, has an impressive bibliography, and is generous in its documentation. Topically subdivided with respect to pharmaceutical preparations (distilled water, oils, essences, tinctures, elixirs, etc.), the work also has comprehensive subject and author indices.

Here, as in the works we have examined thus far, the author—who was both M.D. and Ph.D.—again stressed organoleptic tests, though he gave some chemical tests for chemical compounds. Nevertheless, Richter's work stands out as something of a landmark. If we regard Boyle's *Medicina Hydrostatica* (1690) as essentially the description of one type of test and Pomet's *Histoire des drogues* (1694) as primarily a work of materia medica, then Richter's *De corruptelis medicamentorum* emerges as one of the first works devoted exclusively to revealing the adulteration of drugs and their detection.[84]

J. E. Gilibert: Anarchie medicinale.—Probably more deserving of the designation "first" in a modern spirit is J. B. Vanden Sande's *Falsification des medicaments dévoilée* (1784). We shall examine this work presently, but first look briefly at a curious work extensively quoted in Vanden Sande's preface, Gilibert's *L'Anarchie médicinale, ou la médecine considerée comme nuisible à la société.*[85] The work seems to have considerably influenced Vanden Sande's thinking concerning the persons most responsible for adulteration practices, the reasons for it, and the solutions to the problem.

Gilibert appealed for general medical reform, which he apparently wished to achieve by control and education of the various classes dealing in drugs and medicines, such as the herbalists, non-pharmacist dealers, or wholesalers, and pharmacists.[86]

Although Gilibert seemed to blame each class in turn, the non-pharmacist dealers, or wholesalers, perhaps fared worst. Gilibert described the nefarious practices in the port of Marseilles, where the merchandise, already adulterated in the countries of origin, and deteriorated in transit, underwent further changes at the hands of non-pharmacist dealers. "The abuse is pushed to such a point," wrote Gilibert, "that certain articles quadruple in mass on leaving Marseilles. There is sold, for example, one hundred times more cinchona than America could furnish and fifty times more manna than arrives at Marseilles." [87]

The abuse became generalized, according to Gilibert, because pharmacists were alleged to be ignorant of chemistry and bought chemical drugs ready-made from the non-pharmacist dealers, or wholesalers, and often from disreputable manufactories at Marseilles. Being equally ignorant of natural history, they were also easily deceived concerning vegetable drugs and fell easy prey to the herbalists' wiles. But the most serious consequence, in Gilibert's opinion, was that the blame eventually fell upon the physician, who lost faith in imported drugs that were ineffective as the result of adulteration and deterioration, and who might be equally disillusioned by indigenous drugs that were mishandled by ignorant herbalists.[88]

Perhaps Gilibert's associations with the medical faculty of Montpellier and the medical college of Lyons—he was a professor of botany, anatomy, and surgery—explain his stress upon education as an answer to the problems he discussed. Perhaps it merely reflected the prevailing philosophy of the Age of Enlightenment in which he lived, or his personal opinion that legal attempts to control pharmacists were fruitless, since the pharmacists knew "how to elude the laws." [89] The author's repeated stress upon the pharmacists' need for chemical knowledge reminds us that just at this period analytical chemistry began to assume its modern form.

J.B.A. Vanden Sande: La Falsification des médicaments dévoilée. —Carrying on Gilibert's ideas, Jean-Baptiste-Augustin Vanden Sande (1746–1820), master apothecary of Brussels, intended his *La Falsification des médicaments dévoilée* (1784) (see Figure 3) for a wide audience indeed—physicians, surgeons, pharmacists, non-pharmacist dealers in drugs, and the sick. Its approach was straightforward and scholarly, yet it seems doubtful that the lay public was competent to use the work effectively.[90]

Although Vanden Sande said relatively little about whom he considered responsible for adulteration practices, he seemed to indicate that non-pharmacist drug dealers, pharmacists, and physicians all shared responsibilities in different ways, along with a group of generally unqualified vendors (*marchands*). Physicians and pharmacists were held responsible largely on the grounds of their ignorance concerning drugs, while the merchant classes, in addition, were accused of letting profit motives direct their practices.[91]

Vanden Sande repeated Gilibert's charges that some pharmacists relied for their chemical preparations upon merchants who often had no more knowledge about these preparations than they themselves. Furthermore, these merchants bought them from Dutch Jews who took care to adulterate them to be able to supply them at a low price.[92] The indictment of Dutch Jews undoubtedly parallels that of certain Marseillans made by Gilibert, and later by Favre, for at this time the Dutch were still prominent traders in spices and drugs from the East.

Vanden Sande also seemed to agree with Gilibert that much of the

LA FALSIFICATION
D E S
MÉDICAMENTS
DÉVOILÉE.
O U V R A G E

dans lequel on enſeigne les moyens de découvrir
les tromperies miſes en uſage pour falſifier les
Médicaments tant ſimples que compoſés, & où on
établit des regles pour s'aſſurer de leur bonté.

Ouvrage non-ſeulement utile aux Médecins, Chi-
rurgiens, Apothicaires & Droguiſtes,
mais auſſi aux Malades.

Par J. B. VANDEN SANDE,
Maître Apothicaire de Bruxelles.

A LA HAYE,
chez Van Clef, Imprimeur-Libraire.
Et ſe trouve à Bruxelles chez Æ. De Bel,
Imprimeur-Libraire, *Marché au Bois.*

M. DCC. LXXXIV.

Figure 3. Titlepage of J. B. A. Vanden Sande's *La Falsification des médicaments
dévoilée* (1784). (National Library of Medicine.)

difficulty lay in the great number of uncontrolled, ignorant practitioners and merchants, not to mention *religieuses*, and in the complacency of some physicians in such a situation.[93]

More than any other author we have discussed thus far, Vanden Sande detailed what he saw as solutions to the problem of adulteration. These included, usually in the form of some sort of government-supervised control, limitation of the number of pharmacists; compulsory qualification and examination of pharmacists; regular, systematic tours of inspection by qualified inspectors of pharmacists, nonpharmacist dealers in drugs, and *religieuses;* price schedules; central stores; standard weights and measures; and supervised pharmaceutical education.[94]

As might be expected, and upon Vanden Sande's own admission, the majority of the drugs he discussed were imported. As might also be expected, he relied very heavily upon sensory-perceptive tests, though he used others whenever possible.

In the section dealing with pharmaceutical preparations Vanden Sande made a significant observation about the difficulty of determining the quality of certain extensively vitiated powdered drugs, such as jalap root or cinchona bark. He resolved the difficulty by considering the quantity of resin or extract obtained as the criterion of quality. Vanden Sande undoubtedly realized the great variation of active constituents among different samples of the same drug, regardless of how good these were, but the method was certainly a great advance over others that relied mainly upon taste, color, or odor.[95]

Vanden Sande did apply some quantitative determinations, such as the one for certain powders. Blyth and Blyth therefore placed special emphasis on this author's importance, though perhaps exaggerating his role as "the pioneer of applied quantitative chemistry." [96]

Though we grant some truth in Blyth and Blyth's evaluation, nevertheless Vanden Sande did rely upon organoleptic tests not dissimilar from those used for centuries.[97] He used as a guide, where he could, solubilities in various solvents, principally alcohol and water,[98] but in the main the physico-chemical tests applied to the animal and vegetable drugs remained elementary.

One of the most interesting monographs dealing with vegetable drugs concerned Mecca balsam. For Vanden Sande here discounted accepted tests of purity, some of them passed down from the time of Dioscorides and Pliny.[99] The influence of these ancient authors assumes full meaning with this fact, for it shows the acceptance, virtually unquestioned, of their pronouncements for eighteen hundred years.

By far the most modern section of Vanden Sande's work is that
dealing with mineral and chemical preparations.[100] This reflects the
time in which the author worked, as does his use of the phlogiston
principle in these discussions.

We have seen, then, that although Vanden Sande deserves recognition for having written one of the first comprehensive works dealing
with drug adulteration and its detection, it came just before the full
exploitation of analytical chemistry.

W. H. G. Remer: Lehrbuch der polizeilich-gerichtlichen Chemie.—
Reminiscent of the ḥisbah manuals of medieval Islam, W. H. G.
Remer's *Lehrbuch der polizeilich-gerichtlichen Chemie* (Helmstädt,
1803) was a manual for physicians employed by the government, or
for criminal judges and the police. Remer treated a variety of subjects, including false money and falsified documents, in addition to
food, beverages, and drugs. Each section or subsection concluded
with a brief bibliography of suggested sources (primarily German)
for further information and the tone of the book was serious and
conservative throughout.[101]

The brief section dealing with drugs and medicines also discussed
the problems of secret remedies, quackery, dispensing physicians,
and prescribing pharmacists. The drugs included those that might be
tested by chemical means, that is, largely chemical compounds.[102]

Remer's list of reasons for drug adulteration included, beyond the
factors usually mentioned, inadequate surveillance of pharmacies
and pharmacy apprentices and inadequate knowledge about drugs by
those handling them. Remer's solution revolved about a comprehensive system of official visits of inspection and reflected the German
(and Continental) approach to the problem rather than the Anglo-
American.[103]

The general plans envisaged by Remer for the visitation were
perhaps too thorough to be practicable except at great expense. For
instance, in his opinion, visitation required at least three physicians,
the chief of police, a sworn pharmacist, and a police officer to serve
the verbal summons.[104] Remer qualified his views concerning the
necessity of such measures, by remarking that not all pharmacies
required inspection and that some in fact were very well conducted,
but it was not for these that visitations were necessary.[105] He was also
aware that drugs were occasionally too hastily judged to be adulterated because the organoleptic character of freshly prepared drugs
sometimes differed considerably from that of older preparations.[106]

In limiting himself largely to preparations that could be tested by
chemical means, Remer reflected the advance of analytical chemistry

and also the use of such sources as Richter, Fourcroy, and Crell. When he dealt with an animal substance, such as castoreum, however, he was forced to admit that chemistry did not enlighten him much on this subject.[107]

He fared best with a class of non-chemical products, such as the volatile oils, for which empirical methods provided a fairly reliable means of detecting common adulterants. The test methods described for volatile oils had already appeared in Vanden Sande and probably did not originate with him either.[108]

A. P. Favre: De la sophistication des substances médicamenteuses. —The last work to be examined in this brief survey of the period before 1820, A. P. Favre's *De la sophistication des substances médicamenteuses* (Paris, 1812), evolved at least in part because its author questioned whether Vanden Sande's work had fulfilled his stated purposes.[109]

Favre's lack of modesty provides us with a detailed account of his experiences, mainly in Anvers and Holland, that points to the extent and complexity of the problem of drug adulteration.[110] "There isn't a city in the world," Favre commented of Marseilles, "where adulteration is practised more adroitly; there, not only is nothing lost, but everything doubles in weight, and a month after a boat arrives loaded with drugs, its contents have at least tripled." [111] Non-pharmacist dealers in drugs were consistently blamed for the adulteration practices described, and in extreme cases pharmacists were cautioned not to trust the preparations of these dealers, but to prepare them themselves.[112]

To combat this *piraterie pharmaceutique*, as Favre termed it, he envisaged the interference of a wise government in a number of respects, including inspection, by experienced persons, of all drug imports, first upon their entrance to the country and then before local distribution; severe fines levied on guilty non-pharmacist dealers in drugs for a first offense, followed by the closing of their shops for a second; control of the sale of drugs and medicines by spicers and herbalists; limitation of the number of pharmacies; and comprehensive examination of all pharmacists, regardless of whether they intended to practice in Paris or in the country.[113]

In spite of his good intentions, Favre fell short of his avowed intentions, just as Vanden Sande did. These authors and their contemporaries faced insurmountable difficulties in trying to deal with the non-chemical drugs as precisely as the chemical. Favre was repeatedly forced to admit that certain adulterations of animal and vegetable products were difficult, sometimes impossible, to detect;

and like his predecessors he had to fall back upon largely organoleptic distinctions.[114]

Sixty years passed after the publication of Favre's treatise before the first comprehensive English legislation was adopted, in 1872, to deal with the adulteration of drugs, as well as of foods. A comparable act did not come in the United States until 1906.

It had been nearly two thousand years since the ancient world learned of adulteration problems from Dioscorides, Pliny, and Galen. Since then, few advances had occurred either in control or in methods of detection up to the nineteenth century, a pivotal century for everyone interested in the control of drug adulteration.

PART II

THE DETECTION
OF ADULTERATION
THROUGH SCIENCE
AND TECHNOLOGY

2.

AN OVERVIEW

Why did the techniques of detecting adulteration remain relatively empirical until this late period? Why did better means of detection evolve only in the last decades of the eighteenth century and the early part of the nineteenth century? The answers lie largely in the history of science and technology. Analytical chemistry and analytical scientific instruments did not, to be sure, suddenly arise, for antecedents of particular techniques or instruments trace back to Greco-Roman antiquity. But not until the theory and application of science developed far enough to permit extensive, accurate, and reproducible analytical techniques could they be significant in the detection of adulteration. Just before and during the years that the French Revolution and the Napoleonic Wars upset most of Europe, the Industrial Revolution swept England and the Continent, and equally startling changes took place in technology and science. For just at this time analytical chemistry was maturing, and a number of scientific instruments ceased to be merely curious toys. Refinement and systematization of techniques continued through the century, but when Fredrick Accum startled the world with his *Treatise on Adulterations* in 1820 he had at his disposal—if he wished to use them—many means of detecting adulteration.

In general, a number of analytical techniques and instruments were then available, although few persons were qualified to apply them and still fewer realized their special application to problems of adulteration. Spot tests had been systematized and used since the time of Boyle, as had specific gravity. The analytical balance first approached adequate precision as the result of the requirements of

Black, Cavendish, and Lavoisier and was being manufactured on a commercial scale in England by about 1823. By 1820, microscopes corrected for chromatic and spherical aberration were becoming available; the thermometer had been practicable for almost a century; the blowpipe's analytical use had been recognized for almost half that length of time; and the refractometer had been available for two decades. Marggraf, Boerhaave, Neumann, Scheele, Bergman, Gay-Lussac, Thenard, Lavoisier, Berzelius, and others had laid the foundations of organic analysis. Some of these men, and others, like Klaproth, had similarly founded the qualitative and quantitative analysis of inorganic substances. Decroizilles and Vauquelin had used empirical volumetric analysis. These techniques and others were known in 1820.

Continental physicists and chemists—with pharmacists such as Marggraf, Scheele, Klaproth, and Vauquelin prominent among them —had been and were capable of using these techniques. In England, pharmacists played a minor role before 1820, mainly because the confused development of the health professions there gave little basis for scientific work. English apothecaries practiced medicine to the neglect of pharmacy, and the emerging pharmacy class, the chemists and druggists, largely lacked the requisite scientific qualifications. Besides, there were few English analytical chemists. Until later in the century, the development of analytical techniques, including those associated with food and drug analysis, remained almost solely in the hands of workers in Continental Europe, particularly France and Germany. In England, food and drug analysis developed little until after 1874, when the Society of Public Analysts devoted itself to the field. A few members of the Pharmaceutical Society played a significant role in the Society of Public Analysts and in the development of analytical methods applied to food and drugs. These were mainly those who were also members of the British Pharmaceutical Conference, the organization (founded in 1863) of British pharmacy devoted to scientific pursuits.

The general lack of real literature on the subject in English, prior to 1875, underlies the problems of early public analysts and reflects the relative lack of attention paid the subject before the last quarter of the nineteenth century.[1] The only work in their own language which English public analysts could apply comprehensively to their special problems was the Outlines of Proximate Organic Analysis (1875), by the American physician, chemist, and pharmaceutical educator, Albert Benjamin Prescott, of the University of Michigan.[2] Two British analysts, Alexander Wynter Blyth (1844–1921) and

Alfred Henry Allen (1847–1904), helped fill the gap soon after, in 1879.[3]

Few of the analytical test methods existing before 1820 seem to have found wide application. This is especially true of England, but also of France and Germany, where that special class of literature dealing with adulteration—continuing in the tradition of Richter, Vanden Sande, and Favre—assumed an ever more scientific character that reflected the growing maturity of science itself. But the continuing preponderance of vegetable drugs, throughout the nineteenth century, makes it no anachronism that organoleptic means of detecting adulteration remained predominate. In second place stood physical identification tests, notably specific gravity and solubility. Other simple physical constants, such as melting point, boiling point, and congealing point, apparently found little application, even in connection with existing chemical drugs. Chemical tests remained largely qualitative, though quantitative methods were not lacking. Neither the microscope nor the refractometer seems to have been applied, but the 1809 translation of the *Pharmacopoeia Londinensis* did direct the use of a magnifying glass.

Not until the last quarter of the nineteenth century, in England largely as a result of the work of the Society of Public Analysts, did science and technology begin to find systematic application to the detection of adulteration. This was partly because many of these techniques, particularly organic and instrumental methods of analysis, were not really refined and systematized until the end of the century. Equally important, few persons in England qualified for such specialized work; and indeed it was not until after food and drug legislation that need for such specialized knowledge was felt.

In England the detection of adulteration in drugs was complicated by two additional factors. Organized British pharmacy, in its modern sense, emerged only in 1841 with the formation of the Pharmaceutical Society of Great Britain. In spite of its efforts to correct adulteration problems by raising the level of British pharmacy, especially through education, the Pharmaceutical Society had no jurisdiction over a compulsory curriculum until 1908. Furthermore, not until 1933 did the Society achieve real control over the practice of pharmacy in England. Therefore, while the Pharmaceutical Society's school stressed a scientific curriculum that enabled its graduates to do analytical work, the average practicing pharmacist had not availed himself of the educational opportunity. Moreover, the membership and activities of the scientific British Pharmaceutical Conference remained on a modest scale.

The absence of recognized scientific standards for drugs seriously hampered systematic detection of adulteration by pharmacists, or others, throughout the nineteenth century. The first *British Pharmacopoeia* (1864) appeared to obviate some of the confusion existing from the use of three pharmacopeias in the British Isles—those of London, Edinburgh, and Dublin. But during most of the period up to 1906, the *British Pharmacopoeia* had no real legal status under the Adulteration Acts, although out of necessity it gradually acquired some status from the courts and practicing public analysts. At the end of the century, however, British pharmacists and others questioned not only the legal status but also the scientific stature of the *Pharmacopoeia*. Discussion centered about the necessity of improving drastically the standards set forth in the *Pharmacopoeia*—and the *United States Pharmacopeia* was held up as a model to be emulated—or of discarding the *British Pharmacopoeia* entirely.[4]

For convenience of discussion we shall examine by topical categories the various means of detecting adulteration that evolved during the period from 1820 to 1906. In many respects the topical division also represents a chronological progression, as we move from a consideration of the earlier organoleptic tests to the later biological tests.

Our selection of certain organoleptic, physical, optical, chemical, and biological tests from among the many tests that came to be applied to detecting drug adulteration in Great Britain may seem rather arbitrary; yet, discussion of them intensifies and clarifies our awareness of the relative importance of emergent scientific and technological means for the control of adulteration at just this period. Although many tools were already available for this purpose in 1820, they were not applied in a significant way until half a century later. (The microscope was one of the few exceptions.)

Scientific and technological techniques in the hands of a few dedicated persons provided both the proof that adulteration was a problem, and the certainty that it could be detected and so controlled. Effective groups of individuals in society first had to come to a full realization of the significance of the problem, however, before any meaningful control could be achieved, as we shall see in Part III.

3.

ORGANOLEPTIC TESTS

Unaided by artificial devices for detecting adulteration, man instinctively turns to his natural senses. This remains true for the present electronic age as for earliest times. Faced with the problem of identifying a sample of crude drug, such as opium, the British pharmacist of 1820 depended upon the visual appearance of the sample, and perhaps its taste, its smell, or other characteristics that might be determined by manual manipulation. If he was not familiar with crude opium, most of the descriptions in books of the period, including the *Pharmacopoeia* would have provided him with little discrimination, unless he had a pure sample for comparison. If he were dealing with powdered crude opium, even comparison with a pure sample would not have guided him. Had he known some elementary chemistry, he might have detected such crude adulterants as starch by the blue color of the iodine test, or carbonaceous material by its effervescence with acids. Had he been exceptionally well informed and skilled, he might have determined the percentage of morphine in his opium. The microscope was at his disposal, but—if he had one within reach, or was willing to master its use—he would have been remarkable indeed to use it almost a quarter-century before this instrument found serious application to the problem.

Had this hypothetical British pharmacist of 1820 turned to Fredrick Accum's *Treatise on Adulterations,* just published, he might have suspected the worst in Accum's statement that "nine tenths of the most potent drugs and chemical preparations used in pharmacy are vended in a sophisticated state." [1] Yet Accum gave no definite tests for most of the non-chemical drugs he discussed. Thus, commenting upon the adulteration of volatile oils one with another, he noted that smell and taste were the only certain tests of purity and that it was only from use and habit, or comparisons with specimens of known quality, that one could "judge of the goodness, either of the drugs themselves, or of their oils." [2]

Elsewhere in his *Treatise,* Accum observed that berries other than buckthorn were sometimes used to prepare syrup of buckthorn. He directed the identification of buckthorn berries by the number of seeds they contained and the green stain they produced if crushed on white paper, yet in a later edition he admitted there was "no method of detecting the genuineness of buckthorn syrup." [3] In this later edition, Accum also admitted there were no "ready" means to detect the adulteration of "Peruvian bark" (cinchona, source of quinine and other alkaloids), or of ipecacuanha powder (an emetic).[4]

A startling contrast to Accum's *Treatise* in terms of scientific awareness is the *Histoire abrégée des drogues simples,* published in 1820, by the French pharmacist N. J. B. G. Guibourt.[5] Guibourt's superiority over Accum reflects his wide erudition in materia medica, an impressive example of the more advanced state of Continental activity in this field generally.

Like Accum's *Treatise,* the translation of the *Pharmacopoeia Londinensis* (1809) current in 1820 stressed reliance upon organoleptic methods. This was especially evident in the caution to apothecaries against having their drugs ground, "since when those external qualities, by which the goodness of drugs is chiefly estimated are lost, it is very difficult indeed, if not impossible, to identify them." [6]

In spite of reforms that the pharmacist Richard Phillips introduced into later editions of the *Pharmacopoeia Londinensis,*[7] these concerned mainly chemical preparations. The tests for detecting impurities and adulterations ("Notes") incorporated into the 1836 *Pharmacopoeia,*[8] applied mainly to chemical preparations. A brief introductory paragraph explained that it was "less necessary" and at the same time "more difficult" to apply such tests to vegetable and animal substances. It pointed out that books of botany and zoology adequately described the characteristics of plant and animal drugs, but extracts or other preparations could not be distinguished "by any certain sign, or be briefly described," because of their greatly altered taste, color, and smell.[9]

Even though the British *Pharmacopoeia,* like those elsewhere, became ever more scientific during the nineteenth and twentieth centuries, organoleptic tests remained in *Pharmacopoeial* monographs, even to the present day. But until the *British Pharmacopoeia* of 1914 (after the period covered by this study), macroscopic descriptions dominated the criteria for vegetable drugs.[10]

The activities of the Pharmaceutical Society's members also reflected continued stress upon organoleptic test methods for crude drugs. Key members of the Society, such as its vice-president, Charles James Payne, considered a thorough knowledge of the "sensible properties of drugs"—particularly of those drugs that were then (in 1842) difficult to procure—one of the primary requisites of sound pharmaceutical education. He felt the Society's museum answered an important part of this need through its collection of "specimens of drugs and chemicals of every kind and quality, some of them very curious and rare, some of them in the state in which they ought ordinarily to be found in the shops, and some of such a deteriorated character, as by contrast with the good, [might] guide the judgement in distinguishing what ought to be selected and what rejected and destroyed." [11]

When students and members of the Society heard lectures on materia medica by such authorities as Jonathan Pereira, they also had an opportunity to examine specimens of the drugs being described.[12] In these lectures, especially those dealing with crude drugs, as in the papers that appeared in the *Pharmaceutical Journal,* organoleptic tests remained in evidence throughout the century,[13] and played an important part in the materia medica examinations set by the Society.[14]

At the same time some members of the Society realized that "the purity of many articles [of medicine could not] be estimated by their obvious or sensible qualities"; and that conventionally accepted external characters had little meaning in some cases, in which "beauty or delicacy of appearance, [gave] conventional worth, which has no reference to medicinal properties." [15]

In the introductory section to *Commercial Organic Analysis*—one of the most important works in English to appear at the end of the nineteenth century—Alfred Henry Allen referred to color, taste, and odor, among those characteristics that might provide useful information about the composition of an organic substance, in the process of a "judicious preliminary examination." [16] Allen included color reactions resulting from the addition of acids or alkalis, as well as absorption spectra of colored organic substances. He considered the odor of organic compounds, particularly neutral alcoholic derivatives, highly characteristic.[17] Allen not only recognized the distinctive odors of essential oils, but went beyond Accum by differentiating one oil from another through their physical and chemical characteristics.

Color, more than any other sense-perception, of course plays a great part in the interpretation of many physical and chemical tests, as in colorimetry, spectroscopy, flame tests, spot tests, and color reactions. Moreover, such tests remained limited by errors of human observation until the development of electrophotometric instruments. In other test methods, the observation of particular odors has always played a part, particularly in chemical tests. The important difference in reliance upon the senses after the middle of the nineteenth century, as compared to earlier times, is essentially one of degree: they were demoted from a dominant to a supplemental role in assuring the quality of drugs.

4.

PHYSICS AND
INCREASING CERTAINTY

As physics matured somewhat earlier than chemistry as a science, so physical methods for detecting adulteration appeared earlier and had wider application than chemical methods. A considerable part of the history of physical test methods ties to the evolution of precision instruments of analysis and these will be discussed wherever it seems appropriate.[1]

Some physical properties of matter—such as solubility, diffusibility, flammability, fusibility, volatility, viscosity, and ponderosity—could be and were observed empirically from early times. Only much later did the idea of physical constants become associated with some of these properties, and later still did physical-chemical theories evolve to explain them. Before the development of instruments to measure these constants, physical tests for adulteration possessed little more certainty than organoleptic tests. Even in the case of specific gravity, precise scientific constants could not be derived until the analytical balance approached its modern form at the beginning of the nineteenth century.

WEIGHT AND THE BALANCE

Probably no analytical device has had so long a history, nor undergone such little basic change, as the balance, which was used even by Egyptian and other ancient cultures.[2] Yet not until the end of the eighteenth and the early nineteenth century did the first precision balances appear. Necessity has often dictated developments in technology before satisfactory theories existed to explain the phenomena.

35

So the development of precision balances seems to have taken place to satisfy the needs of chemists, such as Cavendish and Lavoisier, before the quantitative approach to chemistry was firmly established upon the basis of theories of conservation of matter.

The analytical balances constructed for these founders of quantitative chemistry were custom-made and often took two years for delivery. The manufacture of precision balances on a commercial scale—and using for the first time the triangular perforated beam and the agate knife-edge—came first in 1823; knife-edges and accompanying friction were eliminated in 1882 with the development of the torsion balance.

The history of weights accompanies that of the balance; but while the balance remained largely unchanged in general principle and form, weights (like measures) differed—until the nineteenth century—from one culture to another, and even from one locality to another, based as they were upon natural units, such as seed grains.[3] One of the first systems of metrology based upon precisely defined standards was the Metric System (first integrated decimal system), which became legal for France in 1795, a year after Lavoisier's death.

Weights and balances are important here because of their wide application in chemical and physical tests for adulteration, and because of the relatively late development of the degree of precision that was a prerequisite for some of the tests most important to modern control of drug adulteration. Among the earliest applications of the balance to adulteration was specific gravity.

SPECIFIC GRAVITY

Aside from solubility, and temperature, few physical properties found such wide application before 1820 as did specific gravity.[4] The application of specific gravity to adulterated drugs dates from at least the time of Boyle,[5] but could probably be traced back much further.

Each of the three or four methods used to make specific gravity determinations—the balance, hydrometer, pycnometer, and Lovi's beads—was known long before 1820. Archimedes used a balance, and the balance (hydrostatical balance) continues in use to the present time for this purpose, with notable modern modifications in 1848 by the German pharmacist Karl Friedrich Mohr (1806–1879), and further modifications by the mathematician Westphal. While the balance method was recognized already by Boyle and others as more accurate than the hydrometer, the hydrometer remained popular for certain purposes. The hydrometer (like the balance, and perhaps the blowpipe) is one of the oldest instruments to come down to the present almost unchanged. Although invented about the end of the third century, the hydrometer remained little used until the sixteenth century, then found considerable use by the end of the eighteenth century. Of more recent history, the invention (1121–22) of the pycnometer or specific-gravity bottle is attributed to the Persian author al-Khāzinī, who also made early and accurate specific gravity determinations with the hydrometer and hydrostatic balance.

While Boyle made some of the earliest known applications of specific gravity to detect adulteration in drugs, a century passed before wide application of the technique. Specific gravity stands out among the physical properties cited in some of Accum's early (1798–1800) printed papers [6]—mainly because of the minor use at this time of other physical constants or properties.

A glance at the *Pharmacopoeia Londinensis, 1809* (still being used in 1820), and the Powell translation, reveals much the same stress upon specific gravity as that given by Accum.[7] As Accum had already pointed out in Nicholson's journal, and as Phillips repeated, many of the specific gravities given in the *Pharmacopoeia* (and Powell's translation) did not correspond to those of its preparations, if these preparations were made according to *Pharmacopoeial* direction.[8] While no indication was given of how these specific gravities were to be determined, it was directed that they be made at 55°F.[9] A definition of specific gravity did not appear until the *British Pharmacopoeia, 1914*, and while no method was mentioned, the pycnometer seemed indicated.[10]

Specific gravity as a test for purity became less predominant in relation to other methods as the nineteenth century progressed. However, it remained important throughout the century, indeed to the present time, and became more widely applied. Yet both Accum (*Treatise on Adulterations, 1820*), and his most notable successor in exploiting the "death" theme genre of adulteration literature (anonymous author of *Deadly Adulteration, 1830* [?]) appear to have missed the important application of specific gravity as a test of purity (for essential oils, for instance).[11] This application must have been generally realized by this time, because *The Domestic Chemist*, another popular work on adulteration, mentioned it; at the same time the author conceded this might be an unreliable test,[12] a conclusion expressed long before by the German pharmacist Kaspar Neumann.[13]

A remarkable contrast to these works were some of those appearing about the same time on the European Continent. The pharmacist Guibourt's *Histoire abregée des drogues simples* (1820) devoted as

many pages to a general discussion of specific gravity and the hydrostatic balance as it did to organoleptic tests.[14] And a contemporary,
the German pharmacist E. F. Aschoff, included in his *Anweisung zur
Prüfung der Arzneymittel* both the hydrometer and alcoholometer as
equipment essential to the pharmacy.[15]

Members of the Pharmaceutical Society also paid attention to the
applications of specific gravity. An early contributor to the *Pharmaceutical Journal* tabulated, from many sources, the readings of alcoholic solutions of different strengths according to their specific gravity at 60°F and the scales of four different hydrometers then used
in Europe; [16] Theophilus Redwood, lecturer to the Society and editor
of its journal, discussed various methods of determining specific
gravity and a variety of different hydrometers, with their specific
applications; [17] and a correspondent was advised of the value of
specific gravity for detecting the adulteration of essential oil with
fixed oils.[18] Society members were informed by the chemist Andrew
Ure of the value of specific gravity to differentiate between various
types of sugars—in solutions of the same percentage strength.[19] They
were also treated to a lively controversy, involving Ure, H. C. Jennings, and others, concerning the value of "Jennings' saccharometer"
and its use for customs purposes.[20] And half a century later, W.
Whippel Gadd was suggesting specific gravity as one of several
physical properties that might serve as standards for pharmaceutical
preparations where chemical standards were not available.[21]

Outside the Society, different British and foreign authors paid
varying degrees of attention (depending largely upon their purposes)
to the application of specific gravity.[22] Almost the only English books
devoted especially to the detection of adulteration to appear during
the first three-quarters of the nineteenth century, and favorably
comparable to the work of scientists in continental Europe, were
those of Arthur Hill Hassall. Hassall, the great English pioneer
against adulteration, dealt briefly with a few of the more important
vegetable drugs in the second of his books, *Adulterations Detected*
(1857). Hassall here stressed microscopic methods of detection, as
he did in all his work. In the introduction he discussed methods of
analysis and analytical apparatus, including that applicable to specific gravity determinations, namely, "a good balance . . . a specific
gravity bottle . . . densimeters, as a saccharometer, galactometer
and urinometer." [23] But the only reference Hassall made to specific
gravity in connection with drugs was the value cited for oil of cloves
by his near-contemporary, Pereira, taken partly by him in turn from

the Frenchman Bonastre.[24] Hassall gave the most complete account of various methods of specific gravity determination in his discussion about estimating the quantity of alcohol in spirituous liquors.[25]

Of particular interest are two American publications, Frank Wigglesworth Clarke's great compilation of specific gravities (along with other physical constants) and Prescott's *Outlines of Proximate Organic Analysis.*[26] Both works appeared in 1875, within a year of the founding of the Society of Public Analysts, before the first appearance of Blyth's *Manual of Practical Chemistry* (1879) and Allen's monumental *Commercial Organic Analysis* (1879) and long before the founding of the British National Physical Laboratory (1891).[27]

Blyth made ample use of specific gravity constants in his *Manual* (1879) to indicate the strength of alcohol and to correlate strength and specific gravity to the scale of Sykes' hydrometer, and to identify different fixed and essential oils.[28] Aside from these instances, Blyth used specific gravity to determine purity or adulteration only on one more occasion of interest to us—in his *Foods* (1882). Here he cautioned that specific gravity gave conclusive proof of the adulteration of olive oil only when the specific gravity of the adulterants varied considerably from the oil itself, but he considered determination of specific gravity a matter of course, since it might confirm other tests.[29]

Allen used specific gravity repeatedly in his *Commercial Organic Analysis*, considering it "a valuable criterion of . . . identity or purity," an accurate method for estimating the quantity of a substance in solution or admixture, and a method for differentiating between isomers of the same percentage composition. Blyth described in detail various methods of determining specific gravity—pycnometer, Sprengel tube, Mohr's hydrostatic balance, and hydrometer—but pointed out the inaccuracies of hydrometers and seemed to prefer the pycnometer method.[30]

Aside from an elaborate table giving the specific gravities of various mixtures of alcohol with water, in relation to the percentage of absolute alcohol by weight, and the percentage of proof spirit by measure,[31] Allen made wide use of specific gravity as a criterion of purity or adulteration. For instance, he referred to its use in connection with fixed oils and fats, with appropriate corrections according to the coefficients of expansion of individual oils; in connection with essential oils, though pointing out considerable variations with age; and in connection with Peruvian balsam.[32]

Application of specific gravity, among the earliest physical properties of matter applied to the detection of adulteration, was widespread and relatively easy for nineteenth-century chemists, physicists, and the Department of Inland Revenue to use.

SOLUBILITY

Aside from specific gravity, solubility and temperature were the physical properties most widely used for detection of adulteration in the first quarter of the nineteenth century. Although today it is difficult to dissociate the idea of specific solubility from a specific temperature, this link developed relatively late. For long before the development of the thermometer to any useful accuracy, the relative solubility of different substances had been observed in the same or different solvents, or merely by their dissolving or not dissolving in the mouth. Early solubility tests developed from such rudimentary empirical observations.

Powell in his translation of the *Pharmacopoeia Londinensis, 1809* (still official in 1820) expressed solubility in a variety of different ways, but usually in terms of parts.[33] Thus for citric acid, he noted that water at 212°F dissolved twice its weight of citric acid, whereas 75 parts of cold water dissolved 100 parts. Similarly, benzoic acid was soluble in alcohol, or in twenty-four times its weight of boiling water, but as the water cooled, nineteen-twentieths of what was previously in solution precipitated out.[34]

Before 1820, and for some time after that, the most common solvents appear to have been water and alcohol ("spirit of wine"). Gradually other solvents became more readily available in reasonably pure form—such as chloroform, ether, various acids and alkalis—and were more widely used.[35]

Solubility served to detect adulteration in a variety of ways. In popular treatises, adulteration tests remained extremely empirical;[36] for instance, the common test for the purity of whole pepper was its insolubility in water—the same test given by Galen. Valuable tests that probably originated empirically were the ready solubility of castor oil in absolute alcohol, the only fixed oil (aside from croton oil) known to behave in this way; and the solubility of volatile oils, unlike most fixed oils, in alcohol. Both tests were cited frequently before and after 1820.[37] Only later did it become apparent to some scientists, that it was quite misleading to rely upon solubility alone in the case of castor oil, for instance.[38]

While solubility provided one tool for discerning adulteration, it offered another to facilitate adulteration. Thus easy solubility of essential oils in alcohol provided sufficient temptation for the wide use of alcohol as an adulterant of these oils. This in turn could be detected by a solubility test of another sort, for the presence of alcohol became apparent from the milky appearance resulting from the addition of water and the diminution in volume of the oil.[39]

Various extraction procedures that depended, wholly or partially, upon solubility served at the same time to separate pure drugs from their adulterants. The simple separatory funnel is one example of an extractive procedure depending upon variable solubilities in different solvents.

Solubility also came to play an important part in expressing the purity of drugs, as the nineteenth century progressed. This followed the isolation of more and more constituents of plant and animal drugs and the fuller establishment of the quantitative approach to analytical chemistry. A common expression of the value of vegetable drugs particularly came to be made in terms of water-soluble and acid-soluble ash, and alcohol-soluble and water-soluble extractive. Such an approach to determining the purity of drugs could and did of course come before any real understanding of the nature of the active constituents of drugs developed.

Just as solubility might aid the extraction of active constituents, it also served to separate or distinguish desired drugs from adulterants; [40] and helped to distinguish between substances—such as quinine, cinchonine, and quinidine—which had a common origin, were similar in many of their properties, and consequently might serve as adulterants one for the other.[41] A variation of the latter procedure took advantage of the wide range of solubility at different temperatures.

Another phase of solubility or insolubility is that which results in the coagulation or precipitation of insoluble material, due to changes in solvent, temperature, or chemical reactions. Accum, for instance, suggested that one test for the adulteration of spirit of hartshorn (diluted ammonium hydroxide solution) with liquid caustic ammonia was the addition of spirit of wine, "for, if no considerable coagulation ensues, the adulteration is proved." [42] He also considered magnesia (magnesium oxide) free of lime (calcium oxide) if a solution of the magnesia remained clear when dissolved in a dilute solution of sulfuric acid, or after the addition of ammonium subcarbonate to a solution of magnesia in muriatic acid (crude hydrochloric acid).[43]

Solubility, the choice of appropriate solvents and the concentration of solutions, also became an important consideration for the effective completion of chemical reactions that formed part of adulteration tests. And solubility was important for establishing the best conditions for observing certain analytical tests, for example, meaningful microspectroscopic observations.[44]

Solubility tests formed an important part of the adulteration literature ranging from the popular treatises that still depended upon Dioscorides and Pliny to the most scientific manuals of pharmacy and chemistry, and official pharmacopeias.[45]

However, the fullest application depended upon many factors, including the availability of a variety of pure solvents, a system of standardized weights and measures, and standard methods of expressing solubility. But equally important for the evolution of accurate statements of solubility was the relation of solubility to temperature.

TEMPERATURE, HEAT, AND CHANGES OF STATE

When were melting points, boiling points, and congealing points— which are among the most easily applied physical constants—first applied to adulteration? When were variable solubilities at wide ranges of temperature first applied? Volatility, sublimation, distillation? The answers in some cases are as difficult to determine as those concerning the application of solubility, for somewhat the same reasons.

The meaningful application of all these methods to truly scientific ends depended upon the evolution of theories of heat and temperature and, of course, upon the development of the thermometer.[46] The tortuous history of this instrument meant it could not become a practical analytical tool until the eighteenth century. For not until then did a blending of technology and scientific theory combine the various elements needed for a scientific analytical tool: a suitable medium—mercury; the purification of mercury to ensure consistent composition; glass tubing of uniform, reproducible bore; two fixed reference points; the development of theories of temperature and heat.

Just as empirical observations concerning solubility were possible long before solubility assumed the status of an accurate physical constant, so observations concerning temperature, heat, and changes of state were possible before the development of precision thermometers or modern theories of heat and temperature.

The Dutch physician-chemist Hermann Boerhaave (1668–1738) is generally credited with introducing the use of the thermometer into chemistry.[47] But application was slow, not only application of the instrument, but also of constants (such as boiling points, melting points, congealing points). An explanation, as far as chemical compounds were concerned, may be that chemical theory had to develop, especially acceptance of the idea of chemical identity. Besides, such constants meant little until processes grew up for making pure chemicals. Moreover, such constants as boiling points and melting points had little meaningful application for detecting adulteration in the bulk of the vegetable and animal materia medica until the active constituents of these drugs were isolated during the nineteenth century.[48]

The foregoing may partially explain why Accum in his first papers on adulteration gave only one boiling point, that of sulfuric acid.[49] More than twenty years later, in his *Treatise on Adulterations* (1820), Accum still made little apparent use of temperature, or processes involving heat, for uncovering adulteration in drugs. The only temperature he gave was the congealing point of olive oil, as a means of revealing its adulteration with poppy seed.[50] The only other adulteration tests involving heat applied by Accum were boiling temperature applied to test the purity of calomel, gentle heat applied to a paper dipped in volatile oil to reveal turpentine adulterant by odor, and volatility of essential oils at the heat of boiling water.[51] With the exception of the congealing point of olive oil, all the other tests Accum presented were empirical in nature,[52] not original with him, and in some cases no advance over methods used by Dioscorides and Pliny. The small number of chemical preparations included in Accum's *Treatise* may explain his apparent disregard of the thermometer, then in practicable form for almost a century.

What use did the current (in 1820) *Pharmacopoeia Londinensis* (1809) and its translation, make of constants involving temperature, or changes of state involving heat? The only piece of apparatus mentioned in the introductory remarks of the *Pharmacopoeia* is a Fahrenheit thermometer. This suggests that this instrument was considered indispensable for intelligent use of the *Pharmacopoeia*, but it may merely have been intended to point to the official temperature scale. In his 1809 translation, Richard Powell used temperature readings mainly in connection with solubility, or specific gravity, statements and only rarely as a constant to indicate purity (e.g., alcohol, b.p., 176°F, and S. G. 0.815).[53]

Later editions and translations of the *Pharmacopoeia Londinensis* showed an increasingly scientific approach under the direction of the pharmacist-chemist Richard Phillips—an approach at least partially evident in Phillips' increased use of physical constants involving temperature. For instance, he gave both the boiling point and freezing point of dilute sulfuric acid, the approximate temperature at which glacial acetic acid solidifies and crystallizes, and the boiling point of creosote.[54] Among processes involving heat, Powell mentioned volatilization, sublimation, and loss of weight on heating (as the result of the loss of water of crystallization, or chemical reaction). Notable additions to the list of pharmaceutical-chemical equipment in the 1836 *Pharmacopoeia* were the water-bath, the sand-bath, and the crucible.

With the appearance of the *British Pharmacopoeia* in 1864, and throughout the rest of the nineteenth century, there was a gradual increase in the number of *Pharmacopoeial* preparations for which constants were given. The 1867 *Pharmacopoeia* mentioned the steam-bath among other equipment; the *Pharmacopoeia* of 1898 gave temperature readings in both the Centigrade and Fahrenheit scales, specified both the temperatures at which Metric and Imperial measuring and volumetric vessels were to be graduated, and indicated the temperature at which Metric capacity units were to be defined; the *British Pharmacopoeia, 1914* was the first to give directions for determining melting points and boiling points, the latter by distillation methods.[55]

Looking now beyond the *Pharmacopoeia* to see what application was being made of temperature and heat for detecting adulteration, we find that Arthur Hill Hassall made scant use of melting point, or other constants, in his *Adulterations Detected* (1857), because of his stress upon microscopical observations. Yet Hassall did mention desiccation, evaporation, distillation, and incineration—distillation methods to determine the purity of cinnamon and cloves, by estimating their essential oil content, and incineration to detect the adulterant chalk in scammony and ipecac.[56]

Some of the best examples of the application of physical properties involving heat were in the *Outlines of Proximate Organic Analysis* (1875) by the American Albert Prescott, who made wide and almost universal use of constants such as melting point, boiling point, and congealing point, and referred frequently to the temperature at which solution, sublimation, vaporization, efflorescence, or distillation occurred.[57] Like Prescott, his countryman Frank W. Clarke made contributions useful for revealing adulteration, by including boiling points and melting points among the physical constants he reported (1873 and subsequently).[58]

About the same time, the newly founded Society of Public Analysts began to pay attention to the applications of temperature and heat to the detection of adulteration. Various members of the Society dealt with the melting point of fats, the use of the thermo-oleometer to test fats and oils, the bromine thermal value as an indication of the degree of unsaturation of fats and oils, the application of fractional distillation methods to the analysis of fats, and distillation methods for the determination of pentosans.[59]

One of the famous members of the Society, A. H. Allen, made extensive use of temperature and heat in his *Commercial Organic Analysis* (1879). Allen devoted several introductory pages to a discussion of "Observations of Changes of Physical State," in which he described methods for determining and applying melting point and solidifying point, subliming point, and boiling point (including distillation procedures).[60] In his discussion of fixed oils and fats, he detailed various methods of determining melting point and boiling point, with particular attention to the method of the Association of Official Agricultural Chemists (an American organization, founded in 1884). Allen also noted the co-efficient of expansion of various fats and oils (to allow the significant determination of specific gravity at different temperatures) and the characteristic rise in temperature (thermal value) upon the addition of nitric or sulfuric acid (Maumené), or bromine.[61] As we would expect, Allen found much value in fractional distillation methods for rough proximate analysis and for the detection of specific adulteration, and as an adjunct to test methods involving optical activity.[62]

Test procedures concerning changes of physical state found a prominent place in the special literature of food and drug analysis contemporary with Allen and Prescott. Blyth, another prominent public analyst, devoted special attention in his *Manual of Practical Chemistry* (1879) to sublimation as a means of identifying alkaloids and used other constants and procedures where applicable.[63]

It seems reasonable to suppose that the application of the thermometer and also of solubility for determining purity found fairly wide use among chemists, pharmacists, and others, because they were relatively easy to apply and required minimal training. The meaningful application was necessarily limited to more or less pure chemical compounds, inorganic and organic. Such processes as distillation and sublimation, because of the additional equipment and techniques involved, were probably not applied by the average British pharmacist;[64] on the Continent such equipment was required.[65] In Great Britain, the public analyst—usually a chemist, but sometimes a well-trained pharmacist—was most likely to possess the knowledge and have the occasion to apply such tests.

VISCOSITY AND SURFACE TENSION

Viscosity is another physical property of matter that could be observed empirically before there were methods to measure it accurately, or scientific theories to explain it.[66] An empirical description is provided by the German author of a nineteenth-century work on adulteration tests (almond oil as an adulterant in castor oil).[67]

Even simple tests for viscosity seem to have been developed and applied rather late.[68] Perhaps this can be related to the great activity centering about fats and oils in the last decades of the nineteenth century. Neither Prescott nor Blyth referred to viscosimetry in connection with oils, until Blyth touched the subject in a discussion of "oils" in his *Dictionary of Hygiene and Public Health* . . . (1876).[69] He mentioned specifically the work of his countryman, J. J. Coleman, who extended the earlier observations of Schubler and Ure.[70] The need for a standard (defined and constant) viscosimeter, allowing regulation of temperature and reproducible results, gave rise to many adaptations of apparatus like Coleman's as it became apparent that temperature bore an important relationship to viscosity. Many of these viscosimeters, such as one designed by Boverton Redwood, found wide and continued use.[71] (See Figure 4.)

Allen referred to viscosity as a "useful physical test for oils" and discussed the simpler rate-of-flow type of apparatus. He stressed the relationship between temperature and viscosity and the desirability of comparing test samples with others of known quality and origin, using the same instrument. Allen also published tables showing the viscosity of the more common fixed oils and the variation in viscosity encountered between different samples of the same oil.[72]

While the phenomenon of surface tension, like that of viscosity, was empirically evident—for instance, a needle floating upon water —probably no significant application resulted from this observation until the theories of molecular action involved were better understood. One surface-tension phenomenon that found application was the "cohesion-figure" test for the identification of certain oils during the nineteenth century. As carried out by Charles Tomlinson, lecturer on physical science at King's College School in London, a drop of oil was allowed to come in contact with the surface of "chemically clean water, in a chemically clean glass." Tomlinson felt each liquid developed its own characteristic figures or patterns, and explained the phenomenon in this way:

The drop [of oil] flattens down by its gravity upon the surface of the water. The adhesion of the liquid surface tends to spread out the drop into a film, the cohesive force of the particles of the drop strives to prevent the extension, and the resultant of these two forces is a figure which we believe to be definite for every independent liquid.[73]

Tomlinson questioned the usefulness of an extension of his method called the "oleograph." [74]

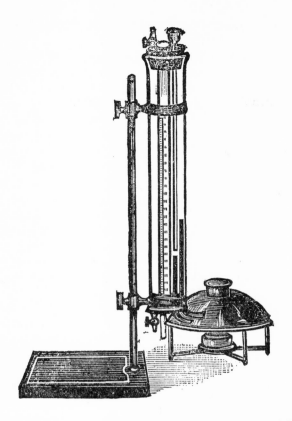

Figure 4. Sacker Viscosimeter. An early viscosimeter of the rate-of-flow type, the Sacker instrument consisted essentially of a burette surrounded by a constant-temperature bath. Reproduced from Alfred Henry Allen, *Commercial Organic Analysis*, 2 (American ed.; Philadelphia, 1882), 142, fig. 5. (University of Wisconsin Memorial Library.)

In spite of the apparent delicacy of the cohesion-figure method, the difficulty of performing it, and the problem of recording it for comparative purposes, many treatises on food and drug analysis in subsequent decades recognized it and Tomlinson's contributions. Prescott characterized fixed and volatile oils by this method; Blyth extended it (in 1880) to solid fats (melted) and compared pure samples with adulterated ones; Allen admitted that "the surface tension of [fixed] oils [that he illustrates by cohesion figures] is a property which in certain cases is capable of useful application, though its value has been much exaggerated." [75] The cohesion-figure method survived into the twentieth century [76] although other precise chemical and physical methods gradually made this particular test less useful.[77]

As far as we know, the modern tensiometer [78] did not come into use before the end of the period under consideration here (1820–

1906), though other methods seem to have been known and used. These involved the height to which liquid rose in a capillary tube and the number of drops delivered by a measured volume of a liquid from a tube of known diameter ("stalagmometer").[79]

By the end of the nineteenth century, a variety of instruments and methods for determining viscosity and surface tension were available to pharmacists who wished to use them. Many procedures had been worked out by continental workers,[80] but in England, Redwood and Allen played an important part, and in the United States, Saybolt and Doolittle. In England, public analysts—chemists, including some pharmacists—probably made greatest use of these procedures in their application to adulteration problems. The average pharmacist could easily have measured viscosity roughly, using a simple pipette, and he might have tried his hand at Tomlinson's cohesion figures, fruitless as these proved, to measure surface tension, but it appears doubtful that he often did so.

CRYSTALLOGRAPHY

Gross variations in crystal form between different mineral salts must have been familiar to chemists—alchemists, mineralogists, pharmacists—from an early period.[81] But a systematic approach to crystallography did not come until the nineteenth century, no doubt related to Wollaston's development (1809) of the reflecting goniometer, an instrument for measuring solid angles such as those of crystals.[82] To a few of those who realized the peculiarities of individual crystal structure this suggested at least one means of identifying substances, including drugs.

By 1820, descriptions of the crystalline nature of mineral substances formed part of the identification of drugs where applicable. Accum, for instance, noted the specific crystalline form of boric acid in his early publications on adulteration; Powell, in his translation of the 1809 *Pharmacopoeia Londinensis*, observed that citric acid consisted of rhomboidal crystals, whose sides inclined at 120° and 60° angles; and Phillips, in his translation of the 1836 *Pharmacopoeia*, brought illustrations of the crystals of citric and tartaric acid showing the plane of the angles measured in degrees and minutes.[83]

The work of Guibourt on the Continent well illustrates the extent to which crystallography was pushed in the nineteenth century. Not only did Guibourt discuss crystalline form among the geometric characters of minerals,[84] but he based his whole chemical classification of mineral drugs upon the elaborate crystallographic system of René Just Haüy (1743–1822).[85]

In spite of the importance crystallography had for the development of chemical theory during the nineteenth century,[86] it (and goniometry) apparently never gained full favor as a test for purity or adulteration. The reason probably lies in the growing availability of other chemical and physical tests, more precise and more easily applied. Allen seemed to sum up the applicability of tests involving crystalline form by his comments that "this character [was] rarely a test of their purity [for] in the great majority of cases the crystals [were] too small or indistinct to admit of any goniometric determination, though the action of polarised light [might] frequently be observed."[87] He went on to point out the usefulness of crystalline form as a means of identifying cholesterin, salicylic acid, tartaric acid, and some alkaloids and their salts. The application of this means of identification for the alkaloids was also apparent in the works of his contemporaries, Prescott and Blyth.[88]

The observation of crystals by means of the microscope remained of some importance and constituted a valuable combination of physical and chemical forms of analysis.[89] However, the use of another physical-optical instrument, the goniometer, probably remained largely in the hands of chemists and physicists. On the other hand, pharmacists were able to apply general descriptions of the crystalline nature of substances as one means for gauging the approximate purity of their drugs by macroscopic or organoleptic means.

In discussing selected physical tests applied to the detection of adulteration, the space devoted to a particular method reflects the amount of material available as well as the test's importance; and estimates of the manner and extent of application often rest upon examples that may or may not be typical of common practice; hence deeper specialized investigations might yet modify the picture. Probably only a few English pharmacists had sufficient qualifications and time to apply newly developed physical techniques to the detection of adulteration. Some members of the Pharmaceutical Society, especially those who also became active in the British Pharmaceutical Conference after 1863, showed such qualification and interest. Such individuals also played an important role in the Society of Public Analysts, founded in 1874 to devote special attention to adulteration problems.

The use of more certain physical methods by practicing pharmacists became less necessary towards the end of the nineteenth century as manufacturing pharmacists assumed greater responsibilities for the purity of the drug supply. It was always desirable of course that all pharmacists have a basic understanding of the different analytical procedures involved, but it became requisite for a relatively small minority actually to apply this knowledge.

The detection of adulteration assumed a truly scientific character by the last quarter of the nineteenth century, much stimulated by special efforts of the new Society of Public Analysts in Great Britain and some of its outstanding members, such as A. H. Allen. More fundamentally, the stimulus drew upon new resources of better analytical instruments and techniques, chemical as well as physical, but not yet physical-optical methods, with the possible exception of microscopy.

5.

THE ADDED DIMENSION
OF OPTICS

Almost every form of physical test for adulteration that we have considered so far was applied at least crudely by Dioscorides and Pliny, and by their medieval and early modern counterparts. This is not true of various optical methods and their requisite instruments, which were developed mainly in the nineteenth century.

It became possible during the nineteenth century, for the first time in the case of many drugs of vegetable and animal origin, to detect with certainty the nature as well as the extent of adulteration. Moreover, substances could thereafter often be examined without in any way destroying their original form, and it became possible to detect adulteration in powdered drugs and preparations that no longer bore any resemblance to the original crude drug.

The analyst still used his eyes and his other senses, but he increased his perception immeasurably with the extra pair of eyes provided by such instruments as the microscope, refractometer, and the polariscope. The uncertainties of human perception, which were still a problem in reading instrumental results, even gave way in time to precise, impersonal, photo-electric perceptors.

The application of the microscope probably carried greater significance for the winning fight against adulteration than did any other single instrument. Yet, each optical technique permitted a further step toward certainty in detecting even the most clever sophistications. Because these often are complexly intertwined innovations, no attempt will be made below to discuss the different optical methods in any exact sequence of development or application.

51

COLORIMETRY, FLUORIMETRY, AND TURBIDIMETRY

Colorimetry, fluorimetry, and turbidimetry offered, in their most elementary form, simple optical methods of analysis. For example, identical tubes containing solutions of known and unknown concentration were compared against a white background; or the unknown sample was compared with a graduated series of standard solutions to find the solution it most closely resembled. Such observations were made long before the development of the colorimeter.[1] The French instrument maker Jules Duboscq first designed and manufactured (1854) the colorimeter, which still bears his name.[2] (See Figures 5 and 6.)

If we ignore visual color tests (sample darker or lighter than a genuine sample) and ignore color-reaction tests, then the application of colorimetric methods to adulteration appears relatively late, despite the simplicity of the colorimetric method. The same holds true for fluorimetric and turbidimetric techniques involving more than the observation of fluorescence or turbidity.

Alphonse Normandy used colorimetric tests for indigo, madder, and saffron (crocus), in his *Commercial Hand-Book of Chemical Analysis* (1805),[3] while Soubeiran, on the Continent, used a colorimetric method in 1874 to evaluate a sample of indigo.[4] And British pharmacists read in their journal, on the one hand, that the fluorescent test for the adulterant quinidine in quinine sulfate was too difficult; on the other, that adulteration of such substances as mustard and saffron might easily be detected by fluorescent means, when the adulterants, such as turmeric, were fluorescent.[5] Various members of the Society of Public Analysts, about this time and later, applied colorimetric tests for different purposes.[6]

Figure 5 (*facing page*). Rousseau Diagometer, Labillardière Colorimeter, LeFebvre Oleometer, Gobley Elaimeter, Gay-Lussac Chlorometer, and different kinds of Nitrogen Determination Apparatus. In this plate (V) reproduced from J. B. Alphonse Chevallier's *Dictionnaire des altérations et falsifications*, 1 (Paris, 1850), we see a variety of different instruments then in use for determining the purity of drugs. The Rousseau diagometer (fig. 27 in this plate) measured the purity of olive oil (in cup C) by the rate of electrical conductance indicated by the arc through which a delicately pivoted needle (E) swung. The Labillardière colorimeter (fig. 25) shown here is a simple apparatus for comparing solutions of known and unknown concentration, in tubes tt, when viewed from aperture o through apertures aa; the depth of color of the two samples was equalized by adding solution of known concentration. (Compare with Figure 6 on p. 54.) The LeFebvre oleometer (fig. 26) and Gobley elaimeter (fig. 28) were specially designed hydrometers used for testing the specific gravity of oils. The Gay-Lussac chlorometer (fig. 29) was one of the forerunners of the modern burette. Figs. 21, 22, 23, and 24, represent various forms of apparatus for the determination of nitrogen. (University of Wisconsin Memorial Library.)

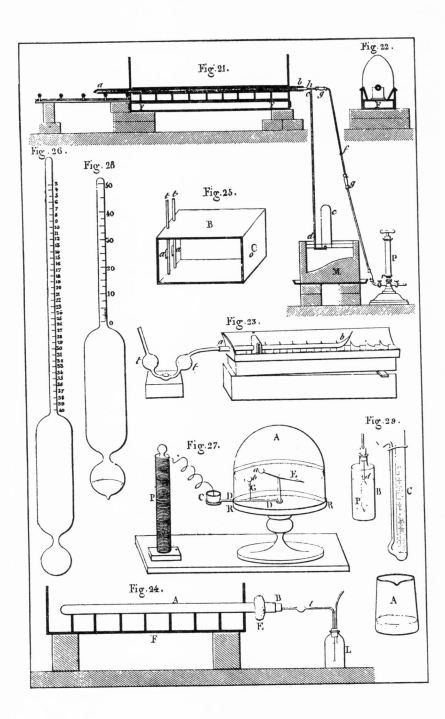

Fig. 22.

Fig. 21.

Fig. 26.

Fig. 28.

Fig. 25.

Fig. 23.

Fig. 29.

Fig. 27.

Fig. 24.

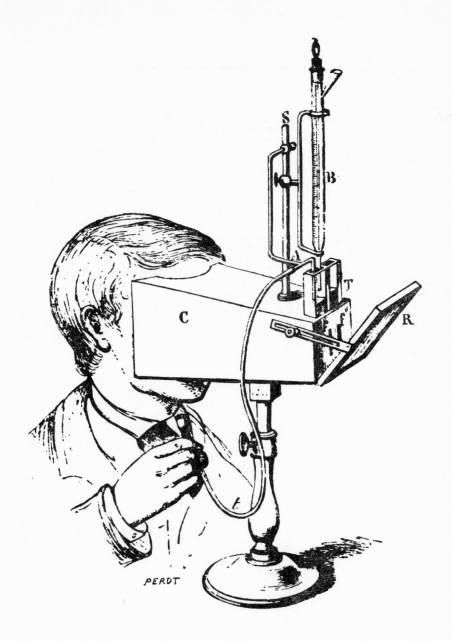

PEROT

Figure 6. Colorimeter by Houton de Labillardière, the operation of which depended upon the equalization of the color intensity between solutions of known and unknown concentration, by drawing additional solution (of known concentration) from a burette (*B*). In Figure 5, on p. 53, fig. 25 shows an earlier form of this instrument by the same inventor. Reproduced from J. Léon Soubeiran, *Nouveau Dictionnaire des falsification et altérations* (Paris, 1874), fig. 94. (National Library of Medicine.)

Blyth and Allen are two noted public analysts whose work throws light on the state of colorimetric and fluorimetric assay procedures. Blyth appears not to have presented colorimetric tests in the early editions of his *Foods,* though he applied spectroscopy widely to colored substances and used a variety of methods to detect such substances. Blyth may have recognized fluorimetry to detect turmeric (strongly fluorescent) in mustard (non-fluorescent), and he described the detection of the same adulterant in alcoholic solution.[7] Of course if Blyth only observed fluorescence, then we cannot consider this fluorimetry, any more than we can consider some of the color tests colorimetry.

In the 1885 edition of *Commercial Organic Analysis* Allen did not mention colorimetry among physical tests for organic substances, although in the same volume he referred to a simple colorimetric method for determining the strength of alcohol.[8] Allen did mention fluorescence among physical properties of organic substances, but he too stopped short of giving a fluorimetric method. In addition to the usual viewing of fluorescence by holding a tube against a dark background, Allen suggested viewing it in an improvised tube through a microscope. If no fluorescent substance was present, he reasoned, the field would be black, because there would be no reflection of light.[9] Allen was on the verge of a fluorimetric method, but did not push quite far enough. He described essentially the same technique for detecting certain coloring matters—such as cosins, magdala-red, purpurin, turmeric, resorcin-blue—by their fluorescence, but again went no further.[10]

In the same volume, Allen described colorimetric methods of assay for indigo and saffron. In a variation of the tests for detecting dyes in wine (in which samples of cloth were dyed), cotton and wool cloths dipped in solutions of indigo, under controlled conditions were compared with cloths dyed in the same manner with pure indigotin or standard indigo. He also mentioned a colorimetric test, including its limitations, based on the depth of tint of a sulphindigotic solution.[11] Allen referred to a procedure for assaying saffron colorimetrically, by comparing a test sample with a solution of potassium bichromate, but unlike Soubeiran, who used a colorimeter, these tests apparently were conducted by Allen in the simplest comparative manner.[12]

Although these scattered references to colorimetric and perhaps fluorimetric analysis were found, not a single reference to turbidimetry was discovered in the period under discussion. Where turbidity was mentioned, it usually entailed solubility tests at particular temperatures, rather than assay procedures.

In general, we conclude that colorimetry did not find wide application for the detection of adulteration during the nineteenth century. Colorimeters seem to have been little used; and, in most cases, absorption-spectroscopy was apparently preferred to colorimetry. And while fluorescence played a part in detecting adulteration, fluorimetry as well as turbidimetry, as such, were absent from the sources examined.

Why did these relatively simple analytical techniques remain largely unused? Perhaps simple comparative methods involving the observation of color, fluorescence, and even turbidity, were applied to a greater extent than our retrospective view can discern. The application would have been limited of course to that relatively small number of drugs whose characteristic color or fluorescent properties would provide a reliable test method.

In any of these cases, more accurate and reliable physical and chemical tests were probably already available; and these must have seemed considerably more reliable than colorimetric tests then in use. Perhaps a true understanding of the principles underlying these optical methods of analysis came only with a greater understanding of the theory of solutions, developed toward the end of the century by Arrhenius, Ostwald, Nernst, and others.

SPECTROSCOPY

Application of spectroscopy to adulteration came quickly following the availability of the spectroscope. Like other instruments we have discussed, the spectroscope depended upon the observations of many individuals (notably of the German physicist Fraunhofer) over a long period. But the association of the German chemist Robert William Bunsen (1811–1899) with the physicist Gustav Kirchhoff (1824–1887) first brought all these observations to a significant fruition, in 1859, by their invention of a practical spectroscope and development of spectrum analysis.[13]

Scarcely a decade afterwards, spectroscopy was being applied to food and drug preparations, amid some controversy as to its real value. The members of the Pharmaceutical Society first read about the detection of various adulterants by means of spectroscopy in 1869, but the work of H. C. Sorby, one of the authors on the subject, preceded this by at least two years.[14] The value of spectroscopy depended upon the characteristic absorption bands shown by a particular adulterant, which Sorby used to detect analine dyes or cochineal when these were used to improve the appearance of certain syrups or tinctures.[15]

About the same time, another writer in the *Pharmaceutical Journal* listed the typical spectra of a number of *British Pharmacopoeia* preparations, including infusions, tinctures, extracts, decoctions, solutions, syrups, and wines.[16] Stoddart considered the "extreme delicacy of spectral testing . . . almost incredible"; he summed up the value of the technique with his statement that "microspectroscopic observations [promised] well to detect adulteration and substitution, for hardly ever [did] the spectra of any two articles appear exactly the same, [and] . . . the smallest discrepancy was immediately seen when the spectra [were] placed side by side by means of the additional prism." [17] At the same time, Stoddart pointed out that only in a few cases was it actually possible to determine all the constituents in a mixture by means of their spectral characteristics.

In spite of some opinions on the unimportance of the spectroscope to pharmacy, test methods that depended upon spectroscopy in one way or another became increasingly popular for a large group of substances. Notices on absorption spectra as tests of purity—for oils and alkaloids, as well as for coloring matter per se—continued to appear frequently in the *Pharmaceutical Journal* and other scientific journals during the rest of the century.[18]

Books on food and drug analysis and some on microscopy, on both sides of the Atlantic, devoted attention to spectroscopy and its special applications to adulteration. Hogg included Sorby's work on spectro-microscopy in *The Microscope* (6th ed.; 1867); while Blyth, in his *Manual* (1879), gave the spectrum of boracic acid, phosphine, and barium chloride, and considered the spectroscope "indispensable" for detecting certain dyes in wine.[19] Blyth devoted considerably more attention to spectroscopy in his *Foods* (1882). He discussed in detail the spectroscope, particularly the microspectroscope, and the special work of Sorby in applying it. He saw its use primarily for the detection of colored materials and reported (diagramatically) more than forty absorption spectra of colored substances.[20] Blyth's comments suggest that quantitative spectroscopy was still insufficiently developed at that time to be of practical value.[21]

An impression of the subsequent development of absorption spectroscopy is gained by comparing the first edition of *Foods* (1882) with the sixth edition that appeared at the end of the period (1909) here considered. Not only was more space in the latter devoted to a discussion of the spectroscope, but quantitative spectroscopy had gained acceptance. The exact wave-lengths at which absorption took place were reported, instead of a vague indication of the color band of the spectrum.[22]

As for colorimetry, so for spectroscopy the more or less general application to the detection of adulteration can be traced by examining successive editions of Allen's *Commercial Organic Analysis*.[23] He introduced the subject of absorption spectroscopy in 1885 by noting that it "occasionally [furnished] information not to be obtained in any other way." [24] The only applications he mentioned here were in connection with colored substances. Taking note of recent work upon ultra-violet and infra-red absorption spectra, he remarked succinctly: "No practical application of these interesting and suggestive facts has hitherto been made." [25]

Allen did devote special attention to absorption spectra of coloring materials in a later volume of this same edition,[26] but in the next edition he extended the application to fixed oils as "valuable indications of their purity." [27] Allen considered the chief value of absorption spectra applied to oils was the means they afforded of detecting vegetable-oil adulterants (by reason of their chlorophyll absorption bands) in animal oils. The non-absorption of castor and almond oils, among vegetable oils, offered a ready means of determining their adulteration.[28]

With Allen, as with Blyth and the other authors discussed, the first wide application of spectroscopy to adulteration appears to have come only in the last decades of the nineteenth century. Spectroscopy did not, so far as we are aware, enter any *British Pharmacopoeia* monographs during this period (1820–1906).

In the United States, Prescott mentioned (1875) absorption spectra as one means of differentiating between volatile oils, but gave no values.[29] Battershall, a little later (1887), appeared to make no use of this technique.[30]

The relative difficulty and practicality of the technique remained an open question in the decade following initial reactions. It is difficult, for example, to reconcile the apparently conflicting opinions expressed on different occasions by one author, William Gilmour. He concluded his discussion of the detection of adulterants (rape oil and linseed oil in other oils, such as olive, sesame, castor, almond, and cod liver) by means of the positioning of absorption bands, as well as characteristic spectra, by expressing the opinion that anyone would be able "with even little experience to detect adulteration, where such exists, and this with an ease and precision hitherto unknown in this department of pharmacy." [31] Yet in a series of articles the following year, while lamenting the fact that the spectroscope had found no great application, Gilmour said that the spectroscope failed to give any indication of purity, or a more certain indication of the nature of a particular substance than could be obtained by other methods.[32]

The microscopist Henry Pocklington raised with Gilmour just this point of practicality concerning the application of the spectroscope in pharmacy, as well as the difficulties of the technique.[33] Gilmour considered that the differences between his own and Pocklington's results depended upon Pocklington's use of the microspectroscope.[34]

However one might account for the differing opinions of Gilmour, it seems clear that, regardless of the form of the instrument used, spectroscopy remained too difficult a technique for the average pharmacist to use, especially since other satisfactory analytical test methods existed.

As with other test methods mentioned, it seems unlikely that the average pharmacist used spectroscopical methods to determine the purity of his drugs. The technique probably remained in the hands of those few members of the Pharmaceutical Society and British Pharmaceutical Conference who were also members of the Society of Public Analysts, or who otherwise had a special knowledge of food and drug analysis.

REFRACTOMETRY

William Wollaston [35] is associated with the development of both the refractometer and the goniometer.[36] The refractometer found its greatest application in the identification of fats, oils, and essences for which no ready chemical means of detection existed, the goniometer in the identification of crystalline substances possessing very similar chemical properties (see pages 48–49).

The refractometer offers one of the few examples of the development of an analytical technique that was immediately applied to the detection of adulteration. Usually, as we have seen, considerable time elapsed between the stage when a particular test, or instrument, was ready for use and the point when it was actually applied to detecting adulteration. Such a lapse of time in fact subsequently took place after the first applications (in 1802) by Wollaston, its inventor, of the critical-angle (total-reflection) refractometer. More immediate general application in Britain of this discovery made there might have been expected when it is compared with most of the other inventions we have described which were made on the Continent and first announced in foreign publications.

Long before 1802 and Wollaston's discovery, studies of the refraction of light had progressed, and crude refractometers were used in the seventeenth century by Hooke and Bartholinus, but credit usually

goes to Wollaston for inventing the first modern, critical-angle refractometer, giving results correct to four significant figures.[37] Improvements upon the Wollaston instrument appeared during the nineteenth century, following the growth of theories of physical optics,
the perfection of optical glass, and closer association between skilled
technologists and physical theorists.[38] The lasting importance of Wollaston's work lies in his determination of the refractive indices of
opaque substances and the application of the refractometer to the
detection of adulteration in oils.[39]

Almost twenty years after Wollaston's discovery, Accum apparently remained unaware of the analytical possibilities inherent in the
refractometer, for he did not mention refractive indices in connection with either volatile or fixed oils. Accum, as we have seen,
restricted himself to physical methods involving solubility and temperature, and to the simplest organoleptic tests.[40] And while the
popular nature of the *Treatise* perhaps explains this omission, might
he not have mentioned the potential of the refractometer if he had
been aware of it?

No indication of the use of refractive indices could be found in
either the *Pharmacopoeia Londinensis* (including its translations),
or the *British Pharmacopoeia*, during the whole period 1820–1906.
Directions for determining refractive indices, and inclusion of such
indices in *Pharmacopoeial* monographs, apparently appeared for the
first time in the *British Pharmacopoeia*, 1914. In his *Digest of Researches and Criticisms* [1899–1902] *bearing on the Revision of the
British Pharmacopoeia, 1898*, William Chattaway again and again
presented suggestions, from various sources, concerning the desirability of incorporating refractive indices, as well as other physical and
optical constants, into the monographs dealing with oils.[41]

Just as we could find no sign that refractive indices had found any
place in the London or British *Pharmacopoeias* between 1820 and
1906, so evidence was lacking of application of the refractometer, or
refractive indices, in any of the special literature dealing with adulteration during the first three quarters of the nineteenth century.
This holds true whether we speak of Great Britain or Continental
Europe. It holds equally true of the handbooks of drug analysis we
examined.

In the United States, the subject was similarly ignored by both
Lewis C. Beck, in his *Adulterations of Various Substances Used in
Medicine and the Arts* . . . (1846),[42] and Charles Henry Peirce, in
*Examination of Drugs, Medicines, Chemicals, Etc. as to their Purity
and Adulterations* (1852).[43] Although many outstanding contri-

butions were made, as we have seen, by the American Prescott in his
Outlines of Proximate Organic Analysis (1875), he did not discuss
refractive indices for oils to the same extent he discussed specific
gravities and congealing points. Yet Prescott was aware of the importance of this constant, because he mentioned refractive indices
among various constants for volatile oils.[44]

A turning point in the realization of the value of refractive indices
for discerning adulteration is represented by Prescott. Why general
application of the refractometer was so long delayed after 1802,
when Wollaston first reported its use, can only by surmised. Wollaston's interest lay in fields other than adulteration, even though he
was perhaps the first to realize this particular application of refractometry. The interests of other physicists concerned with refractometry
also lay elsewhere. Isolated reference to its use for detecting adulteration may have passed unnoticed, especially in Great Britain, where
Accum's *Treatise on Adulterations* (1820) stirred the first real interest in adulteration problems. We have seen that Accum himself may
have been unaware of Wollaston's publication and its significance,
although Accum's own interest in adulteration stemmed from the
period just prior to 1802.

The year 1874 marks the appearance of the Abbe refractometer
and of the Society of Public Analysts. Certainly Wollaston's refractometer was already capable of giving accurate readings, but Abbe's
was unquestionably better and, besides, found a group of specialized
individuals ready and eager to apply it.

Even so, there seems to have been a delay of yet another ten or
fifteen years. Beginning about 1885, and especially in the 1890's,
various members of the Society of Public Analysts paid increasing
attention to systematic investigation of the analysis of fats and oils;
refractive indices were among the many test methods they tried and
recommended.[45] The pages of the *Pharmaceutical Journal*, the *Yearbook of Pharmacy*, and the *Chemist and Druggist*—representing all
branches of pharmacy, professional, scientific, and commercial—
bore ample proof by about 1900 of this interest,[46] an interest subsequently reflected in the *British Pharmacopoeia, 1914*. Special books
on food and drug analysis, such as those of Parry and Blyth, also gave
increased attention to this method at the end of the period in which
we are interested (1820–1906).[47]

Curiously, Blyth did not mention refractive indices in either his
Manual of Practical Chemistry (1879) or *Foods* (1882),[48] but he did
allude to the subject in a single sentence in an earlier work, *A
Dictionary of Hygiene and Public Health* . . . (1876): "The index

of refraction in a single drop of oil is also useful, as suggested by Dr. Wollaston." [49]

Certainly in the great work of Allen, we are close to first general application of refractive indices. Referring to the study by J. H. Gladstone and others concerning specific refraction of many organic compounds, Allen concluded that "no practical application has been made of their observations." [50] Refractive indices seem to have first appeared in the discussion of fixed oils in part I, volume 2, of the third edition (1899) of Allen's publication, in which increased activity in fat and oil research was much in evidence.[51] Allen supported his view of the value of refractive indices in determining the purity of fats and oils by several pages of charts giving the refractive indices of commercial and purified samples of more than thirty oils, determined by different workers.[52] He also included a detailed account of the use of the Abbe refractometer (taken from the American Association of Official Agricultural Chemists' [A.O.A.C.] bulletin), discussed the oleofractometer of the French scientists Amagat and Jean, and mentioned the Zeiss butyro-refractometer and the Pulfrich refractometer.[53]

Refractive indices also received considerable attention for their application to essential oils, when the third part of this same volume appeared (3rd ed.; 1907).[54] And while Allen qualified the value of this method for cases in which the indices of a pure oil and its adulterants overlapped, he found many cases of important application, such as those in which the specific gravity and optical rotation of an oil and its adulterants lay close together. He also pointed to the sharper and more definite results obtained by examining the fractions of a complex oil obtained by distillation and the value this has for the detection of adulteration. The contribution of Ernest J. Parry to this application and to the essential oils in general, Allen freely acknowledged.[55]

Despite this attention in Allen's *Commercial Organic Analysis,* the 1907 edition probably still stood just at the beginning of wide application of refractive indices. This opinion is based, aside from what has already been said, upon the statement by Allen in the discussion of essential oils that "other useful applications of the determination of refractive indices [would] be made when its value [was] more generally recognized." [56]

Thus, although Wollaston had already applied his refractometer to the detection of adulteration in 1802, general adoption did not come until the end of the nineteenth century, when analysts were turning their attention to the analysis of fats and oils. Considering the expense and techniques involved, it seems that the average British pharmacist did not use the refractometer, even though better educated pharmacists—in special laboratories, such as those of the Pharmaceutical Society—unquestionably did. Besides, by the end of the nineteenth century, the testing of drugs by elaborate chemical and physical means became more and more the responsibility of the manufacturing branch of pharmacy. This holds true also for the next optical instrument we will consider, the polarimeter.

POLARIMETRY

Specific optical rotation, like refractive index, specific gravity, or melting point, is a valuable physical constant, though primarily for organic compounds.[57] Consequently, the history of the polarization of light and the polarimeter have been intimately associated with the development of organic chemistry. At the same time, and for the same reason, this property served as a valuable aid for the detection of adulteration in a large group of compounds for which chemical, or simple physical, tests proved inapplicable. Jean Baptiste Biot (1774–1862), French physicist and crystallographer, used the polarimeter for this purpose soon after he constructed the first instruments in 1840. He might well have realized this application of optical rotation twenty-five years earlier, when he first observed the optical activity of oil of turpentine and other organic compounds.[58] Although Biot was able to discover certain basic laws governing optical activity by means of his simple polarimeter, improvements upon his instrument were made in quick succession throughout the century.[59]

Just when Biot first realized that his polarimeter might be used to detect adulteration cannot be reported; but in 1842, two years after its invention, he used optical means to detect fraudulent manna (which was potato-sugar).[60] He may have been aware of the potential of differences in optical rotation much earlier, for when Biot first (in 1818) stumbled upon the optical activity of oil of turpentine, he noted the difference in rotation between the commercial oil and that purified by several distillations.[61]

The members of the Pharmaceutical Society of Great Britain heard of the most recent applications of polarized light for detecting adulteration in the spring of 1843, in a series of special lectures by the noted physician Jonathan Pereira.[62] Considering the scientific level of pharmacy in Britain at this time (the Pharmaceutical Society had just come into being in 1841), Pereira's lectures were on a high technical and scientific plane. Whether or not many of his listeners could follow these lectures without extreme difficulty, we may be confident that they questioned the practical value of their high theoretical content. As if in anticipation of criticism, Pereira in his very first lecture commented at length:

> If I can show them [utilitarian members of the Pharmaceutical Society] that this agent furnishes us with a more intimate knowledge of the nature and properties of those substances, by the commerce in which most of the Members of this Society gain their bread; if I can demonstrate its *applicability to the detection of adulteration of foods, drugs, and chemicals;* if I can point out its applications to the determination of the commercial value of saccharine juices; if I show how it has been applied to determine the nature of the changes which occur in certain chemical and vital processes, in which ordinary chemical analysis completely fails us . . . I trust even the utilitarians will admit that the study of polarized light is both advantageous and profitable, and that the time of this Society has not been unprofitably occupied by these lectures.[63]

Pereira did not go back on his word to provide his utilitarian-minded audience with some practical pharmaceutical and medical uses of polarized light, but for the most part the lectures were theoretical.

Pereira repeatedly acknowledged Biot in the preface and in the text of this lecture, and referred specifically to Biot's application of polarized light in pharmacy to detect the adulteration of manna,[64] as an outgrowth of its general use in sugar work.[65] Pereira also reproduced the degree and direction of optical rotation reported by Biot (1835) for a number of essential oils. In an almost offhand way, Pereira concluded his remarks upon essential oils by commenting that, "in some cases, perhaps, this fact might be available to the pharmaceutical chemist in detecting mixtures of one oil with another, as the adulteration of oil of peppermint with oil of rosemary." [66]

Members of the Pharmaceutical Society periodically throughout the rest of the nineteenth century heard, or read, reports upon the application of the polariscope.[67] But most of them either had little occasion or knowledge to use the instrument; for, more than twenty years after Pereira suggested its possible use in connection with adulterated essential oils, H. Sugden Evans still (in 1865) made a point of recommending the polariscope for detecting the admixture of essential oils with turpentine.[68] Regardless of the value of the polariscope, and this was questioned, few British pharmacists probably owned or used the instrument. It appears, from the remarks of one German author, that the same situation existed on the Continent.[69] Apparently some individuals considered polarimetry too complex for wide application in pharmacy, for one author considered the polariscope test for quinidine too difficult and one that required too much study; another suggested that "in the examination of syrups, where the polarimeter [was] of the highest value, it [would] be of little use to pharmacists, who [would] find ordinary chemical tests quite equal to their requirements." [70]

Perhaps similar reasons explain why optical rotation found no place in the *British Pharmacopoeia* throughout the period 1820–1906. As far as we could determine, tests involving optical activity appear for the first time in the *British Pharmacopoeia, 1914,* that remarkable edition of many "firsts" as far as scientific tests of quality and adulteration were concerned. Recommendations for their inclusion form a prominent part of the *Digest of Researches and Criticisms* (1899–1902) of the *British Pharmacopoeia, 1898,* edited by William Chattaway.[71]

Observations concerning the optical activity of various organic drug substances appeared from the time Biot first observed the activity of oil of turpentine in 1818.[72] But the general application of polarimetry to adulteration does not seem to have come before the last quarter of the nineteenth century. Earlier the instrument appears to have widest use as a saccharimeter. This seems equally true in Britain and Europe. As in the case of the refractometer, the reasons are not readily apparent. Certainly more modern instruments did not begin to appear until then, and again a great part of the interest centered about the essential oils. As late as 1879, one could read in Flückiger and Hanbury's famous *Pharmacographia* that the optical properties of olive oil "demand further investigation." [73]

In his *Adulterations Detected* (1859), Hassall mentioned the "optical saccharometer of M. Biot" to test the purity of honey and to determine the amount of sugar in various wines.[74] Oddly, Hassall did not realize its full application, for he referred to the adulteration of honey with glucose as one "which, so far as we are aware, it is scarcely possible in many cases to detect . . . since this possesses the same chemical properties as the sugar of honey." [75]

Across the Atlantic, Prescott, in his *Outlines of Proximate Organic Analysis,* neither mentioned nor used polarimetry, as far as we could determine. That same year Soubeiran, in France, referred to the polarimeter in his *Dictionnaire des falsifications,* for its special applications to sugar analysis (Soleil saccharimeter—see Figure 7); and later (1887) Battershall described in detail the use of the Ventzke-Scheibler saccharimeter.[76] By the time Parry brought out his *Food and Drugs,* in 1911, optical rotation had achieved sufficient recognition as a valuable constant to be mentioned frequently.[77]

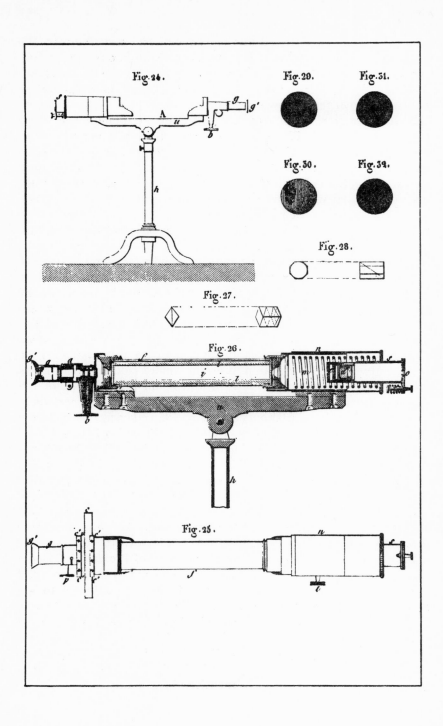

Fig. 24.

Fig. 29.

Fig. 31.

Fig. 30.

Fig. 32.

Fig. 28.

Fig. 27.

Fig. 26.

Fig. 25.

The publications of Blyth and Allen perhaps best illustrate the growing awareness of optical activity as an aid to analysis during the last quarter of the nineteenth century. Considering the narrower scope of Blyth's work in his *Manual of Practical Chemistry,* it should not be surprising that he dealt most extensively with various types of polariscopes in their application to sugar analysis. But Blyth knew the value of this technique for testing the purity of oils, because he mentioned that pure oil of juniper polarized to the left; reported that the micropolariscope (along with the microscope) could "detect most organic adulterations of volatile oil of mustard"; and gave the specific rotation of amygdaline, the active glucoside in oil of almonds.[78] No significant changes between this work and the first edition of Blyth's *Foods* (1882) could be found. Optical activity appears to have been used only incidentally, aside from sugar analysis, and to have been stated mainly in general terms rather than in terms of specific rotation.

Allen, about the same time, seems already to have found a much broader application for the polarimeter. In his introductory comments on optical properties of organic substances, he devoted almost four and a half times as much space to optical rotation as to all other physical-optical properties combined.[79] He reported the specific rotation of some organic substances at the same time, but held back detailed information on the carbohydrates and alkaloids for the appropriate sections of the work.

Allen discussed in detail the application of specific rotatory power to the sugars and produced numerous charts listing this physical property.[80] He also reported the optical activity of starch and its isomers, of tartaric acid, and of other substances.[81]

"One of the most valuable factors in its examination for purity" was Allen's opinion of the application of optical activity to essential oils, their fractions obtained by distillation, and their constituents.[82] He supported this opinion by including values of optical rotation in numerous tables.[83] This great emphasis undoubtedly reflects "the enormous amount of successful research carried out in recent years on the chemistry of the *resins* and the *essential oils.*" [84]

Figure 7 (*facing page*). Soleil Saccharimeter, one of the more popular varieties of this specialized form of polarimeter applied to testing the purity of syrups and sugar. Figures 29, 30, 31, and 32 of this plate (IV) from J. B. Alphonse Chevallier, *Dictionnaire des altérations et falsifications,* 2 (Paris, 1852), show various colors that might be encountered in using the instrument, with an explanation of their significance. Fig. 28 is a detail of the analyser (*a* in fig. 26); and fig. 27, a detail of the polarizer (*d* in fig. 26). (University of Wisconsin Memorial Library.)

Thus, the full realization of the use of optical rotation, like that of refractive indices, for the detection of adulteration does not appear to have come until the last quarter of the nineteenth century. This seems remarkable because (again as in the case of refractive indices) polarimetry had been used for this purpose almost as soon as it was discovered. The explanations for the delay may be similar in both cases—namely, better instruments came only late in the century; special investigations of essential oils (such as those of Parry in England) and the significant development of organic chemical analysis, particularly applied to foods and drugs, came relatively late; and the Society of Public Analysts (founded in 1874) directed its concerted efforts to determining better and more systematic tests for adulteration during the last quarter of the century.

MICROSCOPY

Microscopy, more than any other analytical method we have discussed, brought adulteration practices into the open. For the first time it was possible to detect adulteration in many organic substances for which chemical tests remained unavailable. The certainty that the microscope [85] gave to detection, regardless of the processes to which crude products had been subjected, provided powerful ammunition in the hands of a few zealous crusaders for pure foods and drugs. The storm raised by revelations with the microscope of extensive adulterations of almost every necessity of life forced the British government to make concrete efforts to curb existing practices. The first British Adulteration Act (1860) resulted and, though it proved inoperative, a beginning had been made.

The compound microscope appeared first at the end of the sixteenth century; became practicable, as the result of the correction of spherical and chromatic aberrations, in the first quarter of the nineteenth century; and became a modern precision instrument in the last quarter of the nineteenth century. Many persons representing many fields of technology, in association with others developing scientific theory, contributed to the evolution of the microscope.

Yet the name of a single person, the English physician Arthur Hill Hassall, stands out as the first to realize the significant, systematic, and comprehensive *application* of the microscope to the detection of adulteration. Hassall's first paper on detecting adulteration by means of the microscope appeared in 1850.

But instruments suitable for this purpose had been available twenty-five or thirty years previously. Did no one before Hassall realize this application? The German pharmacist Andreas Sigismund Marggraf (1709–1782) usually receives credit for introducing the microscope into chemistry, as the result of his use in 1747 of the instrument to examine sugar from the sugar beet and other plants.[86] But none of the early microscopists seems to have realized any application of the microscope beyond observing details invisible to the unaided eye for purely descriptive purposes.

The simple hand lens may have been used to detect adulteration before 1820. For Powell, in his 1809 translation of the *Pharmacopoeia Londinensis,* directs the use of a magnifying glass to detect metallic globules of mercury as a sign of insufficient trituration in a preparation calling for equal parts of sulphur and mercury.[87] The *Domestic Chemist* (1831) makes what may be one of the first references in English to the application of either of these optical instruments to detecting adulteration. The anonymous author of this little work used the magnifying glass to distinguish arrowroot from other kinds of starch. In addition, he used the microscope to detect "sharp whites" and "stuff" (mixtures containing alum and salt) in ground potatoes, and insects in flour.[88] "Microscope" in these passages may signify nothing more than a magnifying glass, because advertisements late in the century still use the term in this sense. (See also Figure 8.) Although the author did not specify, possibly he also used a hand lens to distinguish potato starch from wheat starch by its "very sensible crystalline appearance." [89]

The same year the *Domestic Chemist* appeared, the German pharmacist Johann Friedrich Niemann brought out the third edition of his *Anleitung zur Visitation der Apotheken* and in it mentioned the microscopic appearance of calomel.[90] But he pushed the matter no further and may also have intended a hand lens rather than a microscope. Niemann's countryman, E. F. Aschoff, referred specifically to a good magnifying glass among the equipment he considered important to a well-run pharmacy.[91]

These references all remain isolated examples of the realization of the application of the microscope, simple or compound, to detecting adulteration. One explanation, of course, is that a certain time had to elapse before microscopes with properly corrected lenses became generally available and before the discouragement over inadequacies of the old, uncorrected compound microscopes was overcome. However, probably the most important reason is that few technically trained individuals in England were seriously interested in the problem of adulteration, in spite of Accum's work and that of his successor, and probably fewer still were adept microscopists.

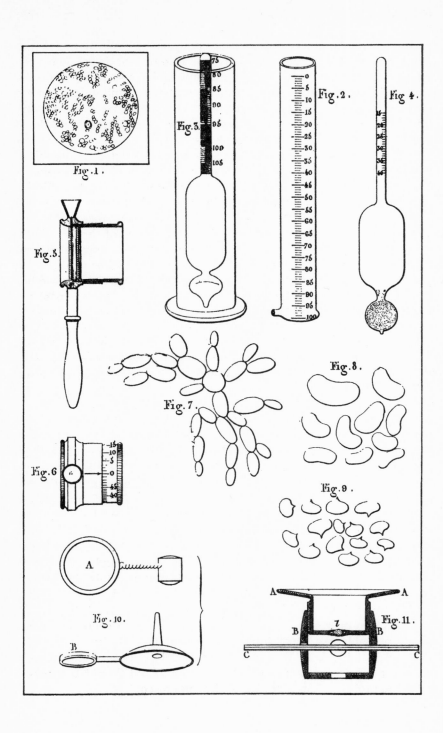

In the 1840's references to microscopy applied to detecting adulteration became more and more frequent, though at first most attention seems to have centered about differentiating various types of starches. The Pharmaceutical Society's eminent lecturer in materia medica, Jonathan Pereira, pointed this out to members of the newly founded society in his introductory lecture; [92] and during the first decade of the Society's existence others noted similar applications, probably because the size and shape of starch grains made them so readily distinguishable one from another.[93] Chemical tests could detect starch as an adulterant, but could not distinguish between starches of different origin used to adulterate one another. Probably no special credit should be given, as Blyth and Blyth do, to Alphonse Normandy —in connection with his *Commercial Hand-book of Chemical Analysis* (1850)—as "one of the first who recommended the use of the microscope for the detection and discrimination of starches." [94]

During this early period, Pereira and others directed the searching eye of the microscope against other common and gross forms of adulteration, such as those of coffee, tea, and pepper, which had all largely defied detection by chemical means.[95] Therefore, when Hassall read his famous paper on the discovery of the adulteration of coffee by means of the microscope,[96] he made no startlingly new revelations; and neither Hassall himself, nor his greatest admirers ever made such a claim.

Why should Hassall receive special credit? Why and how did he succeed where others had failed? We shall explore the answers to these significant questions when we discuss Hassall in detail (in Chapter 13), rather than digress at length here. At this point it is enough to say that Hassall deserves particular recognition for the *comprehensive* and *systematic* application of microscopy as a means of discerning adulteration.

We digress briefly to suggest that the application of microscopy and subsequent legislation might more logically have been expected on the Continent than in England, since the microscope and other instruments were largely Continental developments, and since the special literature dealing with adulteration developed vigorously on

Figure 8 (*facing page*). Stanhope and Gaudin Microscopes. The Stanhope (fig. 10) and Gaudin (fig. 11) instruments shown in this plate (I) from J. B. Alphonse Chevallier, *Dictionnaire des altérations et falsifications*, 2 (Paris, 1852), represent simple microscopes in use about 1850, the same year in which Arthur Hill Hassall began his famous investigations of adulteration using the microscope as a means of detection. The cross section of fig. 11 shows the eyepiece *AA*, with lens *l*, and object slide *CC*. (University of Wisconsin Memorial Library.)

the Continent, in marked contrast to that in England. Moveover, pharmacy in England was still in its infancy as an organized profession and only much later, if indeed ever, did it achieve the scientific and social status it had in Europe. The names of Scheele, Klaproth, Baumé, and Pelletier are but a few of the many European pharmacists who made significant contributions to science in general. Besides, there was greater acceptance of government interference in social and professional matters in Continental Europe.

Hassall's greatest contribution to microscopy was his application of it to food analysis, but he also realized some of its earliest applications to drugs. In his *Lancet* reports between 1851 and 1854, he reported upon isinglass, ginger, cinnamon, cassia, nutmegs, mace, cloves, turmeric, opium, scammony, jalap, and ipecacuanha.[97] Aside from those drugs, which may also be considered condiments, Hassall included no drugs in his *Food and Its Adulterations* (1855), although he referred to the subject of adulterated drugs in the introduction and promised to deal with them in a future work.[98] That work, *Adulterations Detected . . . in Food and Medicine* (1857), included only a few more drugs than were contained in the *Lancet* series, namely: colocynth, rhubarb, squill, "compound scammony powder" (scammony, jalap, and ginger), "aromatic confection" (cinnamon, cloves, nutmegs, cardamoms, saffron, prepared chalk, and sugar), and liquorice.[99] Hassall claimed lack of space prevented him from extending his discussion on drugs and instead gave a list of drugs, together with their adulterations, and authorities for this information; but added that his list might have been greatly extended, especially by reference to Pereira's *Materia Medica* and the *Pharmaceutical Journal*.[100]

As might be expected, Hassall relied heavily upon microscopical test methods and gave a brief introduction "On the Application of the Microscope to the Detection of Adulteration." [101] At the same time, he discussed the application of chemistry to the detection of adulteration and acknowledged the relative value of microscopical and chemical analysis.[102] The chemical portions of the book are drawn from other authors, many Continental, though all are freely acknowledged.

Hassall's last book, *Food: Its Adulterations and Methods of Their Detection* (1876), was largely limited in scope to food, as its title suggests. In it he discussed only a few drugs, those that also found use in foods.[103]

Hassall's microscopy appears completely qualitative, which explains the need for 225 engravings in about three times as many pages of text in his *Adulterations Detected*. He did, it is true, refer to a "micrometer eye-glass" to show the value of each space with reference to different object-glasses he described, but he seems not to have realized its applications even in the most obvious cases, such as the size of starch grains.[104]

Hassall's part in the application of microscopy to adulteration deserves to be told in some detail here—although further details will be discussed as part of his biography—because of its significance for the evolution of legislative controls of adulteration, not only in Britain, but elsewhere. Without minimizing the part played by others— such as Wakley, Postgate, and Scholefield—one can say that Hassall provided the scientific ammunition needed to bring the adulteration issue to more than a mere storm, which might have quickly subsided into an unproductive calm.

How soon did others realize the full potential of Hassall's methods? Almost immediately; in fact, so quickly that others soon claimed precedence, though without real justification. Readers of the *Pharmaceutical Journal* were frequently reminded of the value of microscopy for the detection of adulteration. Besides, numerous articles told them of applications to specific adulterations, just as they had before Hassall made clear the hitherto unrecognized extent to which such applications might be pushed.[105]

Specific reference to the use of the microscope in any edition of the *British Pharmacopoeia* before that of 1914 could not be confirmed. Detailed descriptions of the appearance of wheat, maize, and rice starch imply that either a hand lens, or microscope of low power, may have been used for tests specified in the *British Pharmacopoeia*, *1898*.[106]

The microscope as a test for adulteration was mentioned in several works of different scope and intent that appeared in England about the same time as Hassall's books. Griffith and Henfrey, in their *Micrographic Dictionary* (1856), mentioned this application without referring to Hassall; while the anonymous *Tricks of Trade . . .* (1859) obviously depended heavily upon Hassall, and acknowledged it.[107]

On the Continent, Hassall's work was quickly assimilated. Hermann Klencke, a German physician and surgeon, used Hassall and Chevallier, along with some of his own observations, for his *Verfälschung der Nahrungsmittel und Getränke* (1856–1858).[108] Chevallier in France also recognized the value of Hassall's investigations and microscopy for detecting adulteration, as Soubeiran did later.[109]

Microscopy had a tremendous impact upon the growing science of pharmacognosy in the last half of the nineteenth century. The developing literature on this subject always touched upon the identification of pure drugs and adulterants.[110]

By the end of the nineteenth century the microscope had come into such wide general use that the Division of Microscopy of the U.S. Department of Agriculture was abolished (1895) as "an absurdity." [111]

Did British pharmacists make wide use of this instrument to test the genuineness of their drugs and preparations? Beginning at least as early as 1852, the *Pharmaceutical Journal* made a point of informing its readers about microscopy and its applications to pharmacy, particularly to the detection of adulteration. The reviewer of the new *Quarterly Journal of Microscopical Science* commented:

> Among our readers we have reason to believe there are a large number of microscopists, and we have not unfrequently endeavoured to augment the number of such by directing attention to the microscope as affording the best means of detecting many of the adulterations of drugs. The value and importance of this instrument in the hands of the Pharmaceutist who knows how to use it is unquestionable.[112]

The author of this review was perhaps unduly optimistic both as to the number of British pharmacist-microscopists and those who would apply this weapon against adulteration. For, five years later, another writer on the subject complained of the "lack of earnestness in observers" and challenged British "pharmaceutists" to catch up with their "continental and even transatlantic brethren." [113] Still, in 1864, pharmacists attending the Bath meeting of the newly formed British Pharmaceutical Conference were told that the applications of microscopy to research had been "but little followed out, at any rate with reference to pharmacy." [114] And about the same time, one writer acknowledged the neglect of microscopy by British pharmacists, in contrast to the German and French.[115] Another asked how the dispensing "chemist" without the microscope would "be able to tell that his wholesale brother had been putting bean-flour with his fenugreek, or lignum vitae with his jalap." [116]

We can in fact trace remarks of this sort to the end of the century. The accomplished pharmacist-microscopist Henry Pocklington considered the microscope "yet in its infancy" as late as 1872; and a few years later, the English pharmacist was still being compared unfavorably in use of the microscope with his German and American counterparts, though contemporary comment in American publications suggest that on closer view no widespread use of the microscope among practicing pharmacists could be perceived there either.[117]

The evidence suggests that wide application of microscopy to the detection of adulteration, under the given circumstances, played a greater role in the nineteenth-century control of adulteration than did any other test method. (The significance of this circumstance increased as polarimetry and spectroscopy were integrated with microscopy.) There are several reasons for the importance attached to microscopy, aside from the publicity it received. The certainty of scientific and technological methods of detecting adulteration was thus extended to almost the entire organic materia medica. This occurred before either organic chemical analysis, in general, or other instrumental methods of analysis were developed fully or found significant application to food and drug analysis. It also came at a time before any group of individuals arose in England to make such special applications. But perhaps as important as any consideration, microscopy offered a relatively simple test method, easily and widely applicable, in the hands of many classes of operators. It often provided (and continues to provide) a quick test of purity, following macroscopic observations and preceding chemical analysis.

6.

THE APPLICATION
OF CHEMICAL ANALYSIS

Analysis, or the art of determining the constituents of which every compound is composed, constitutes the essence of chemistry; it was therefore attempted as soon as the science put on anything like a systematic form.[1]

The development of chemical tests will be examined here in terms of broad groups of tests (such as qualitative and quantitative, inorganic and organic) and subgroups. This discussion will be less comprehensive than the preceding one for several reasons: inorganic chemical analysis remained far more highly developed than organic analysis through the greater part of the nineteenth century, although plant and animal drugs greatly outnumbered mineral and chemical drugs. Moreover, British chemists worked somewhat in the shadow of their Continental counterparts, and, similarly, British pharmacists made fewer major scientific contributions. An important handicap in tracing the application of analytical techniques is that the attention paid to the history of the techniques themselves and to analytical chemistry in general by modern historians of chemistry has been minimal.[2]

As in physical methods of detecting adulteration, so in chemical methods the development of techniques came first, then the theories of analytical chemistry. After a lapse of time, came the application of these techniques to adulteration problems by chemists, physicians, and pharmacists.

The first chemical tests for adulteration were empirical tests known already to Dioscorides and Pliny. Gradually, as alchemy, then metallurgy, contributed to practical chemical knowledge, modern analytical chemistry grew. Chemical analysis became more sophisticated as chemical theory changed, particularly with Lavoisier at the end of the eighteenth century and with Berzelius and others early in the nineteenth century. Boyle, Black, Cavendish, and especially Lavoisier introduced into chemistry the quantitative approach that became firmly established in the nineteenth century. Organic analysis had its beginnings towards the end of the eighteenth century and early in the nineteenth, furthered by Marggraf, Boerhaave, Scheele, Bergman, Gay-Lussac, Lavoisier, Berzelius, and others.

Frederick A. Filby believed (in 1934) that "all that really counts in analytical chemistry owes its rise to that period 1780 to 1830." [3] This oversimplifies the case. The systematization of qualitative and quantitative analytical tests came first with Fresenius in the 1840's. Volumetric analysis began with Gay-Lussac in the 1820's, but became popular only after 1855, when the German pharmacist-chemist Karl Friedrich Mohr (1806–1879) published his *Lehrbuch der chemisch —analytischen Titrirmethode*. The systematic analysis of fats and oils did not come until the end of the nineteenth century. From this period we may trace our modern saponification value, iodine value, and so on. Kjeldahl nitrogen determinations likewise came late in the century, and the technique of proximate analysis developed during the last half of the century.

Agreement upon atomic weights came after the famous Karlsruhe conference in 1860, where Lothar Meyer recognized the significance of Cannizzaro's suggestions, following upon Avogadro's work. The first official atomic-weight tables appeared in 1893—prepared at the request of the American Chemical Society by the American chemist Frank Wiggelsworth Clarke—and were followed in 1898 by those of the Deutsche Chemische Gesellschaft and in 1903 by those of the International Committee on Atomic Weights. The important questions of the combining ratios of hydrogen and oxygen and which one should be used for atomic weight comparisons were also relatively late in being settled.[4]

Equally important to meaningful chemical analysis was the development of special equipment and apparatus to expedite new analytical techniques. The late nineteenth century was an especially fertile period, particularly in equipment for organic analysis.[5] The general standardization of glassware, equipment, and analytical procedures was largely a twentieth-century development.

Filby and others have pointed out that many analytical methods developed before 1820, but large-scale application to adulteration problems came only after the later extensive systematization of chemical analysis. Hassall's application of microscopy in the middle of the century had provided for the first time a certain test method for the greater part of the animal and vegetable materia medica. This in itself indicates the wide area then still untouched by organic chemical analysis; and we have referred repeatedly to the extent that a gap was filled by Prescott's *Outlines of Proximate Organic Analysis* (1875) and Allen's *Commercial Organic Analysis* (1879).

It seems clear that a turning point was reached in food and drug analysis about 1875 on the Continent as well as in England. Only then did chemical and physical methods of analysis begin to find wide and systematic application; only then did many techniques begin to become readily available; and only then did a special group come into being in England to apply these techniques. Until late in the century chemical analysis, including food and drug analysis, remained almost entirely in the hands of Continental workers. The founding of the Society of Public Analysts (1874) and the British Pharmaceutical Conference (1863) provided the stimulus in England for concentrated attention to analytical chemistry applied to adulteration problems.

The standardization of drugs was pursued broadly only at the end of the nineteenth century; and indeed for most of the organic drugs, it could not have been pursued significantly before that time. Standardization of analytical methods and equipment was an even later development. The *British Pharmacopoeia* began to assume a modern form in 1898, but perhaps genuinely achieved it only in 1914. These changes are graphically illustrated by such publications as C. G. Moor's *Suggested Standards of Purity for Foods and Drugs* (1902) and Chattaway's *Digest of Researches and Criticisms . . . on the British Pharmacopoeia, 1898* [1899 to 1902] (1903).[6]

For convenience, we shall discuss the application of analytical chemistry to drug adulteration under the heads of inorganic qualitative, inorganic quantitative (volumetric and gravimetric), and organic analysis (qualitative and quantitative).[7]

INORGANIC QUALITATIVE ANALYSIS

Here we shall consider such qualitative tests for adulteration as the use of test papers, acid-base reaction, the use of the blowpipe, and flame, spot, ring, and color-reaction tests. Without exception these test methods had their origin before 1820. Some trace back to empirical tests of the Greeks and Romans. A number were first brought to systematic use by Boyle in the seventeenth century and became refined during the century following. A significant modern ordering of qualitative analytical methods came in 1841 when Fresenius published his *Anleitung zur qualitativen chemischen Analyse,* which was already in its second German edition when the first English translation appeared in 1843.[8]

By 1820, when Accum published his *Treatise on Adulterations,* the following inorganic qualitative tests or techniques had been developed and could have been mentioned by him, had he chosen to do so: flame tests, indicators, test papers, spot tests, color reactions (other than with indicators), acid-base reactions, oxidation-calcination type reactions, burning tests, blowpipe analysis. That Accum knew many of these test methods is clear from an examination of his first publications on drug adulteration, which appeared twenty years before his famous *Treatise.*[9]

We have been unable to find that Accum mentioned either the blowpipe or the flame test in his *Treatise,* but he did mention a wide variety of other qualitative tests. For instance, in a test to detect lime in magnesia, he described the precipitate that occurs upon adding a solution of ammonium subcarbonate to a solution of magnesia in muriatic acid. And to test the purity of calcined magnesia, Accum described the non-effervescence of the sample upon the addition of dilute sulphuric acid and the non-precipitation upon the addition of ammonium oxalate to a sulfuric acid solution. According to Accum, calomel was considered pure if no precipitation followed the addition of potassium carbonate to a filtered aqueous solution of calomel, containing a trace of ammonium chloride. Accum determined the contamination of olive oil with lead by means of the well-known black precipitate produced with hydrogen sulfide.[10] We have here then a wide variety of qualitative tests, depending upon acid-alkali reactions, color reactions, and precipitation reactions. These are tests that even an inept amateur chemist could perform.

When Accum's *Treatise* appeared in 1820, the English pharmacopeia in current use, the *Pharmacopoeia Londinensis* (1809), was essentially a list of drugs and preparations, offering few means for determining purity. It did require a specified specific gravity for some acids and some quasi-quantitative chemical tests for at least two of these acids. For instance, the *Pharmacopoeia* directed immersing a lump of limestone in muriatic and nitric acid and specified the amount that should dissolve,[11] which involves little more than an acid-alkali reaction. There was no reference to effervescence, as there was in the test to determine, by the addition of dilute acid, whether potassium hydroxide solution is free of carbonate.

Beyond such isolated and simple tests, even qualitative chemical directives were notably lacking from the *Pharmacopoeia* until the guiding influence of the pharmacist Richard Phillips made itself felt. Before this time, and even with Phillips, chemical tests found association with the *Pharmacopoeia Londinensis* largely in the notes added in the English translation.[12]

In the case of organic compounds, satisfactory chemical tests were still largely lacking. This seems implicit in the statement by the College of Physicians, which issued the 1809 *Pharmacopoeia*, that it "looked chiefly to uniformity of strength, and consequent precision in the effects of medicine, rather than to that degree of purity which would be required in the preparation of chemical tests." [13] The rapid transition the *Pharmacopoeias* underwent is evident from the preface of almost every one of the early nineteenth-century editions. For example, in this same 1809 edition, the College felt impelled to apologize for introducing the new chemical nomenclature, but considered it "proper, for the sake of uniformity and consistency, to adopt also its language." [14]

Richard Phillips introduced the chemical symbolism of Berzelius (along with that of Brande), as well as special tests of purity in his translation of the 1836 *Pharmacopoeia Londinensis*. The concession to the chemical symbolism of Brande is a reflection of the transition through which chemistry was passing at this time, as was Phillips' rather candid remark: "I have also added the symbols of most chemical compounds, not that I would be understood as admitting their utility, but in compliance with the practice of some of the most eminent chemists of the present day." [15]

The purity tests Phillips gave applied almost exclusively to inorganic chemical compounds. Phillips considered this an important feature because "the College no longer [insisted] that the medicines they [directed], should be prepared exactly in the mode prescribed, provided they [would] stand the trials of their purity, to which it [was] proposed they [should] be submitted." [16]

The College of Physicians incorporated Phillips' "Notes" or purity tests into the 1836 edition of the *Pharmacopoeia*, as a separate section preceding the preparations, but following the materia medica; [17] Phillips, in turn, added further chemical notes in his translation. And when the first *British Pharmacopoeia* appeared in 1864, brief chemical tests for impurities and adulterations formed a regular part of the monographs, as they still do.

Phillips' translation of the 1836 *Pharmacopoeia* had a strikingly modern character, aside from the separate "Notes" on impurities and tests. He divided his notes after each monograph, topically, and, depending upon the monograph, into approximately the following main sections: Process, Properties, Qualities, Composition, Symbol, Impurities and Tests (referring to "Notes"), Adulteration (this appeared only seldom, but pertinent information on purity did appear under "Notes"), Incompatibles, Pharmacopoeia Preparations, Pharmacopoeia Uses, and Medicinal Uses (including dose).[18]

Already, in his published (1811) criticisms of the 1809 *Pharmacopoeia* and the Powell translation, Phillips had dwelt mainly upon improvements in the chemical character of the work. Typical of the qualitative tests used by him, are those he mentioned to test the so-called alkaline solution of iron, obtained from Apothecaries' Hall. Powell noticed the effect upon turmeric paper and litmus paper, precipitation upon the addition of nitric acid or water, and the absence of a precipitate upon the addition of potassium subcarbonate.[19]

The "Notes" or tests of purity that appeared in the 1836 *Pharmacopoeia* also indicate Phillips' heavy reliance upon qualitative tests. He noted the typical green flame of borax, a litmus paper test for the admixture of some other acid with dilute hydrocyanic acid, turmeric paper to test the neutrality of potassium iodide and bromide, the blue precipitate from iron sesquioxide with potassium ferrocyanide, and the white precipitate from zinc preparations with potassium ferrocyanide.[20]

When the Pharmaceutical Society came into being in 1841, pharmacists had at their disposal a fair variety of qualitative tests, at least for the chemical preparations of their materia medica. But apparently some members of the Society, like Robert Howard, considered these insufficient in "detail to enable a person of the average degree of acquaintance with Chemistry, and with ordinary care, to avoid erroneous conclusions." [21] At the same time, Howard recognized that these notes were "the most valuable collection of information on the subject, to which [he could] turn for assistance"; the Society recognized this by recommending Phillips' translation for those individuals preparing for its examinations.[22] Howard's chief concern with the brevity of Phillips' notes constituted part of his general concern over other tests for adulteration appearing regularly in the pages of the *Pharmaceutical Journal*. This concern included: condemnation of a pure article as adulterated, failure to observe gross adulterations as the result of preoccupation with unimportant impurities, and the unsuitability of some substances in a perfect state of purity. Howard illustrated his points with examples of qualitative tests.

These comments by Howard reveal the little chemical training that most pharmacists possessed before and immediately following the founding of the Society and the serious absence of textbooks in English on pharmaceutical subjects. Both problems were gradually solved by the Society and some of its more prominent members. What opportunity did members of the Society have to learn analytical tests for adulteration? Aside from lectures, regular and special, the pages of the *Pharmaceutical Journal* presented many opportunities to learn tests for particular adulterations from the experience of the best British and Continental scientists.

One of the most comprehensive series of reports on *Pharmacopoeial* preparations, incorporating adulteration tests, to appear in the early volumes of the *Pharmaceutical Journal* was by Richard Phillips, the editor and translator of the *Pharmacopoeia*.[23] For the most part, Phillips dealt with chemical preparations of the *Pharmacopoeia*— mineral acids, solutions, and salts—that could readily be tested by physical and chemical methods then in common use.[24] He determined impurities in *Liquor Potassae* by the use of nitric acid, barium chloride, and silver nitrate; potassium hydrate by its effect upon turmeric paper; and distilled water by its non-reaction with oxalic acid or ammonium oxalate, lime water, silver nitrate, and barium chloride.[25]

Aside from Phillips' contributions, pharmacists found numerous other articles upon analytical tests for drug adulteration in the pages of the *Pharmaceutical Journal,* and these continued throughout the century. Pharmacists read, for instance, that calcium carbonate as an adulterant of zinc oxide might be detected by its effervescence with sulfuric or muriatic acid; that the adulteration of silver nitrate by lead nitrate could be remedied by precipitating the silver salt with excess hydrochloric acid, leaving the lead in solution; and that calcium carbonate in magnesia preparations could be detected by adding an excess of ammonium hydrochlorate and potassium carbonate to a solution of the test substance in hydrochloric acid, followed by gentle heating.[26] Particularly after the founding of the British Pharmaceutical Conference in 1864, the dependence upon foreign sources seemed to decline.

A knowledge in chemistry was expected of examinees for both the society's minor and major examinations.[27] Soon after it opened its school, the Society added a laboratory (in 1844), which was enlarged within a few years. The stress placed upon practical chemistry—including analytical, qualitative, and quantitative—in the Society's curriculum is obvious from the comments of the director of its laboratory, John Attfield, himself an English chemist of note, and from the complaints of some of the Society's examinees that this part of the curriculum was overly stressed.[28] The case for training pharmacists in chemistry as an aid in the detection of drug adulteration was stated eloquently by the vice-president of the Society, Charles James Payne:

Without some knowledge of Chemistry a man is working in the dark, he can know nothing correctly of the results of, or the reasons for the operations he constantly performs—he can never properly judge the accuracy and quality of his preparations, he can neither detect any error that may occur nor rectify any untoward circumstance that may arise—he has no established data to reason upon—no fixed principles to guide him; but is like a mariner without a compass, exposed to endless confusion and mishap.[29]

Improvements in qualitative analytical techniques continued to be made throughout the rest of the century after Fresenius. The German chemist Bunsen carried out experiments on flame colors, using colored glass or solutions to distinguish between similar flames;[30] Bunsen's English student, R. Cartmell, worked in England to systematize flame tests; and the blowpipe continued in use in Attfield's *Chemistry* later in the century, as it had earlier in Aschoff's *Anweisung*.[31] The Pharmaceutical Society's professor of practical chemistry and secretary of the British Pharmaceutical Conference, Attfield, provides a good example of the development of qualitative analysis during the nineteenth century. In an appendix to his *Chemistry*, Attfield listed the official tests for impurities in preparations of the *Pharmacopoeia* and throughout the work he gave analytical charts for the analysis of various classes of substances.[32]

The growing stress upon chemical tests for purity is also apparent in the *British Pharmacopoeia*, beginning with the first edition of 1864. Besides giving purity tests in the monographs of the materia medica section, the 1864 edition incorporated several appendices: A) "Articles Employed in the Preparation of Medicines," each with its own purity tests, where applicable; B–I) "Articles Employed in Chemical Analysis," again with tests; B–II) "Test Solutions for Volumetric Analysis; C) Symbols and equivalent weights of elements. It was possible, for the first time, to see almost at a glance the nature of the analytical tests employed in the *Pharmacopoeia* by examining appendix B.[33]

No change appears to have taken place in the appendices for the 1867 *Pharmacopoeia* except for the deletion of appendix A, but a significant step toward a modern compendium was taken by integrating the previously artificial divisions of materia medica and of preparations and compounds. In the preface to the 1867 edition, we read:

Pains [have been] taken to make the descriptions of all the substances in the work sufficiently comprehensive and minute to afford a clear indication of what the medicines of the Pharmacopoeia are intended to be, and to enable those who are engaged in their administration to determine the identity and test the purity of such as are met with in commerce.[34]

The editions of 1885 and 1898 remained structurally unchanged, but the 1898 *Pharmacopoeia* added an appendix, "Tests for Substances Mentioned in the Text of the Pharmacopoeia." This new appendix included qualitative tests for metallic ions and chemical radicals. The *British Pharmacopoeia, 1914,* added quantitative limit tests for lead and arsenic and brought tables of proportions relating to the preparation of diluted alcohols from 90 per cent alcohol.

Without pretending to read any quantitative significance into these various appendices of the *Pharmacopoeia,* we have tabulated the number of entries under each of the main divisions of the appendices for the *Pharmacopoeias* from 1864 to 1914, inclusive (see Table 1).

TABLE 1

Chemical References in Appendices of the *British Pharmacopoeia*

	1864	1867	1885	1898	1914
Articles Employed in Chemical Analysis	26	28	27	95	122
Test Solutions for Qualitative Analysis	30	29	30	74	77
Test Solutions for Volumetric Analysis	6	6	6	6	12
Tests for Substances Mentioned in the Text	0	0	0	41	40

A change in complexity occurred with the 1898 edition, compared to preceding editions, which remain remarkably alike. Perhaps part of this change may be attributed to the increased participation of pharmacists in the preparation of the *Pharmacopoeia* and to the editor John Attfield.[35] The change also reflects a greater appreciation of the chemical character of active constituents of organic substances, which was widely felt by this time. A general appreciation of the increased analytical chemical activity in the organic area, as well as of the increasing refinements of inorganic analytical techniques during the late nineteenth century and the early twentieth century is apparent in important publications of the time which touched upon drug standards.[36]

Between Accum's time and the end of the nineteenth century, a great change had taken place in the complexity, the scope of application, and the systematization of qualitative analytical tests. During the greater part of that time, the application of such tests to detecting the adulteration of drugs lay in the hands of a small group of chemists, a few pharmacists, and a few physicians.

INORGANIC QUANTITATIVE ANALYSIS

Gravimetric and Volumetric.—Before there could be any significant quantitative approach to chemical analysis, there had to be a refinement of technology that permitted precision weights, balances, and analytical equipment. We saw that probably the first precision balances were constructed for Cavendish and Lavoisier at the end of the eighteenth century, which helps to explain why their attempts at analysis were more successful than those of Boyle and Black.[37]

The credit for establishing the quantitative approach usually goes to Lavoisier, though Meyer qualified this by noting that "Lavoisier . . . introduced no original methods for the quantitative analysis of inorganic bodies and their separation from one another." [38] Meyer, like Thomson, pointed to the work of Bergman, but more especially to that of Klaproth.[39] The French pharmacist Vauquelin ranks high, along with Klaproth, for the development of quantitative analysis.[40] A quantitative approach was also made in the analysis of salts by Carl Friedrich Wenzel (1740–1793) and Jeremias Benjamin Richter (1762–1807).

In England the contributions of Wollaston are noteworthy, but Thomson complained (in 1831) of the real dearth of English analytical chemists during the first decades of the nineteenth century. He lay some of the blame upon the English economic system and upon the government.[41]

The law of constant proportions, enunciated (in 1799) by the French chemist Joseph Louis Proust (1754–1826) and John Dalton's (1766–1844) atomic theory (1805) provided basic concepts without which analytical chemistry could not proceed far.[42] The greatest contributions thus far had come from Berzelius; more would come from his talented students and successors.[43] In 1846 Fresenius was to bring his genius for organizing to quantitative analysis just as he had to qualitative analysis a few years previously.[44]

In briefly highlighting developments in quantitative analytical chemistry before 1820, we could do little more than mention some important contributors and even had to ignore completely some who deserve a prominent place in the history of analytical chemistry. Here the aim has been mainly to indicate the character and range of analytic tools that had become available to individuals, like Accum, who wished to apply the most scientific means to the detection of drug adulteration. It now became possible to state with some certainty not only the nature of the adulterant but also the extent of adulteration. This was to be extremely important in convincing the public's representatives in Parliament and the public itself that adulteration constituted a serious problem requiring strict measures of control.

What use did Accum make of quantitative procedures in his work on drug adulteration? Considering the popular tone of Accum's *Treatise*, it should be no surprise that the approach was almost entirely qualitative. Besides, precision analytical balances were not manufactured in England until a few years later (1823), although Accum himself is said to have supplied Dalton's balance.[45] Such balances undoubtedly remained expensive, and would have been used principally by chemists or physicists conducting research that required accuracy. The average pharmacist, especially in Great Britain, probably still used a more or less crude apothecary's balance, even for any quantitative analyses he might have carried out.

The few quantitative indications Accum gave are crude. To test the purity of calcined magnesia (from carbonate), he added dilute sulfuric acid, "and, if the magnesia and acid be put together into one scale of a balance, no diminution of weight should ensue on mixing them together." [46] To test the purity of calomel, Accum directed the preparation of a solution of one part calomel, one thirty-second part ammonium chloride, in ten parts of distilled water; but the test itself is a qualitative one.[47] Considering Accum's reputation as a chemist, he must have used quantitative methods. This is suggested in other parts of the *Treatise*, notably in connection with the alcoholic content of various alcoholic beverages and in the detailed directions for determining the quantities of "earthy and saline matter" contained in water.[48]

The *Pharmacopoeia Londinensis* (1809) in use at this time presented a picture similar to that of Accum's *Treatise*. Powell added analogous directives in his notes to the *Pharmacopoeia* and in the case of nitric acid, for instance, showed the quantity of marble that should be dissolved by acids prepared by different processes.[49] The importance of the quantitative approach in the 1809 edition and the notes of its translator are perhaps more apparent in the procedures than in the tests themselves.

The tests of purity incorporated by Phillips into later editions of the *Pharmacopoeia* showed a slight advance in their use of the quantitative approach. He still referred routinely to the amount (in grains) of calcium carbonate required to neutralize ("saturate") 100 grains of acid.[50] He also mentioned the weight of certain reactants or precipitates as a sign of the purity or impurity of pharmacopeial preparations and noted the change in weight—from a variety of causes, including loss of water of crystallization, oxidation—that resulted from heating certain preparations.[51]

By the time the first *British Pharmacopoeia* appeared in 1864, as we have seen, there was an increased emphasis upon analytical tests of purity. For the *Pharmacopoeia* included special indices devoted to test substances and test solutions, for qualitative and volumetric analysis. This partially reflected a change that had been taking place in chemical analysis itself, from about Accum's time on. We refer to the growing importance of volumetric analysis (another of the "wet" methods), a form of quantitative chemistry distinct from gravimetric analysis.

Aside from the rather empirical procedures devised by the French pharmacist-chemists F. A. H. Decroizilles and L. N. Vauquelin, volumetric analysis really had its beginnings with Joseph Louis Gay-Lussac (1778–1850). In 1824, four years after the first appearance of Accum's *Treatise*, Gay-Lussac worked out his methods of chlorimetry, followed by alkalimetry (in 1828), and the determination of chlorine and silver (in 1832).

In spite of the advantages of the system, many problems—not the least of which were appropriate indicators and equipment—prevented its real acceptance until the last half of the nineteenth century. Improvements were made by E. Margueritte, who introduced (in 1846) the use of potassium permanganate for the estimation of iron; and by Bunsen, (in 1853) iodine and sulfurous acid for the estimation of copper and other substances.

But the most significant contributions came from the German pharmacist Karl Friedrich Mohr (1806–1879), who had helped to popularize the technique when he published his textbook on the subject in 1855. His importance lies not only in the new methods he devised and the new indicators he introduced, but also in the special equipment he designed.[52]

Numerous refinements continued to be made in volumetric analysis through the rest of the century, such as that of J. Volhard, who introduced (in 1874) the ammonium sulfocyanide method of determining silver. The striking contributions to volumetric methods by chemists on the Continent, particularly Germans, stand in marked contrast to those made in Britain.[53]

Volumetric analysis quickly became one of the most widely applied methods for testing the purity of drugs,[54] yet it took forty years from the time of Gay-Lussac's first work, in 1824, until its entry into the *Pharmacopoeia* of 1864. We have already seen the reasons for the delay of general acceptance of the technique for analytical chemistry, until past the middle of the century (1855). A new edition of the *Pharmacopoeia* did not appear between 1851 and 1864, when volumetric analysis apparently came to be more widely applied.

Fresenius, in the first English edition of his *Instruction in Chemical Analysis (Quantitative)*, referred briefly to alkalimetry—the methods of Decroizilles and Gay-Lussac, and those of himself and Will—and chlorimetry—the methods of Marozeau, Gay-Lussac, and Otto.[55] In the United States, Beck mentioned the alkalimeter in connection with potassium carbonate, but remarked that the "instrument may be advantageously employed in ordinary cases, but in accurate analytical investigations it cannot be relied on."[56] For the most part, the purity tests given by Beck were qualitative, and in the few cases in which he did make quantitative distinctions they resembled those of the *Pharmacopoeia Londinensis*, to which we have already referred. The chlorometer, alkalimeter, and acetimeter were all used in the well-known *Dictionnaire des altérations et falsifications* by the pharmacist J. B. Alphonse Chevallier.[57] (See Figure 9.)

Among books on chemistry likely to be used by pharmacists during the century, William Thomas Brande's *Manual of Chemistry* evidently did not mention volumetric methods, though it appeared sev-

---

Figure 9 (*facing page*). Gay-Lussac Alkalimeter, Pesier Natrometer, Henry Potassimeter. The Gay-Lussac alkalimeter shown in this plate (III) from J. B. Alphonse Chevallier, *Dictionnaire des altérations et falsifications*, 2 (Paris, 1852), is essentially the same apparatus, an early form of burette, as the Gay-Lussac chlorometer in Figure 5 on p. 53. The Pesier natrometer (figs. 21, 22) was a special form of hydrometer used to determine the purity of potassium salts, in terms of sodium salt adulterants. The Henry potassimeter (fig. 23) was an early form of burette, like the Gay-Lussac instruments. (University of Wisconsin Memorial Library.)

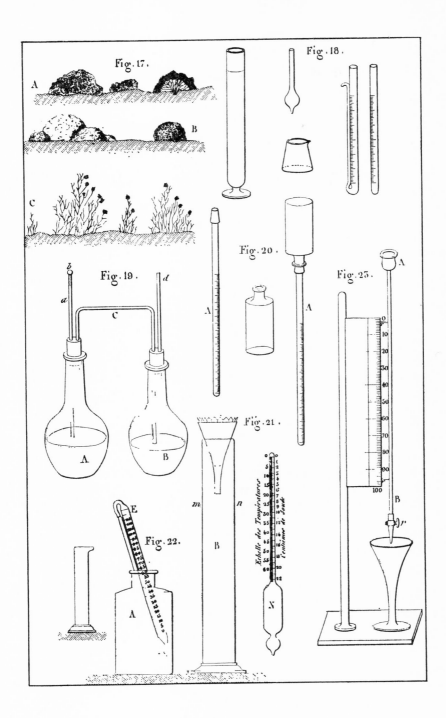

eral years after their promotion by Gay-Lussac.[58] By the time of the
1843 edition of Graham's *Element of Chemistry*, both chlorimetry
and alkalimetry seem to have been sufficiently recognized to be
included. But the end point of the assay was still observed by remov-
ing drops of the solution at various stages of neutralization and
testing externally with test paper or solution. The analyst also apparently still calibrated his own cylindrical vessels at this time, and
although the "French alkalimeter . . . [was] a more convenient instrument to pour from . . . it [was] too fragile for common use." [59]
Graham also instructed his readers in the preparation of "delicate"
test papers, requisite for alkalimetry, by "dipping good letter-paper
several times in a filtered infusion of litmus" or other dye until the
appropriate shade was obtained.[60]

Considerable refinement in the techniques of volumetric, as well as
gravimetric, analysis took place between this time and the appearance of the 1871 edition of John Attfield's *Chemistry*. Attfield referred to volumetric flasks and graduated burettes ("the best form
. . . is Mohr's"), which continued in use to the present day for
volumetric analysis, and to several standard solutions.[61] By the turn
of the century, the increased number and use of gravimetric methods
and even more so of volumetric methods of analysis was striking.[62]

ORGANIC ANALYSIS

Writing at the end of the nineteenth century, the German chemist
and historian Meyer remarked:

While the elementary constituents of organic compounds are thus easily
arrived at, the detection of the compounds alongside of one another can
only be carried out in a few cases; only small beginnings have as yet been
made at a systematic course of qualitative organic analysis, in the sense in
which we apply the term to inorganic. In many instances one has to
depend upon isolated characteristic reactions of organic substances, e.g.,
in the investigation of colouring matters, alkaloids, etc.[63]

Filby traced the beginnings of organic analysis before 1830, finding significance in the early work on plants by members of the
French Academy of Sciences (in 1667), of Bourdelin, Homberg
(1692), and especially the analyses of the French pharmacist Lemery (the younger).[64] Among the most important early contributions
to organic chemistry touching drugs was the work of the pharmacists Andreas Sigismund Marggraf, Kaspar Neumann, and Carl Wil-
helm Scheele.[65] Lavoisier was perhaps the first to realize that organic
compounds consisted usually of carbon, hydrogen, oxygen, and sometimes nitrogen, and to work out methods for the quantitative estima-

tion of carbon, hydrogen, and oxygen.[66] Dalton, Theodore de Saussure, Thenard, Gay-Lussac, Berzelius, and Liebig all attacked the same problem during the first decades of the nineteenth century, with perhaps the greatest contributions coming from the last three named and particularly from Liebig.

Jean Baptiste Dumas proposed (in 1830) the first satisfactory method for nitrogen determination, while Heinrich Will and Franz Varrentrapp (in 1841) developed a more widely applicable method in general use until Johann G. C. T. Kjeldahl developed (in 1883) the process, subsequently improved by others, and still called by his name.

Organic chemical analysis profited greatly from the refinement of techniques developed for inorganic analysis, from the invention and perfection of certain instruments such as the polarimeter, and from the designing of special apparatus. But no significant application occurred in use of organic analysis for food and drug analysis and particularly for the detection of adulteration, until at least the last half of the nineteenth century and probably not until the last quarter of the century.

We have mentioned some reasons for this, but a brief résumé, specifically for organic analysis, may be useful. The central importance of the Society of Public Analysts, founded in 1874, is unquestionable; and equally important was the growing scientific status of pharmacy in Great Britain, as a result of the efforts of the Pharmaceutical Society and the British Pharmaceutical Conference (founded 1863). The refinement and application of physical-optical instruments such as the refractometer, polarimeter, and spectroscope came to fruition only during the last quarter of the century, although the microscope found earlier use. Proximate analysis, as contrasted with ultimate analysis, came to be appreciated and utilized fully only after 1850, and the first books in English on the subject did not come before 1875.[67] Analysis for functional groups—ethyl, methyl, methoxyl, ethoxyl, carboxyl—achieved importance only during the last decades of the century, as did the special investigation of proteins, carbohydrates, and the large class of fats and oils.[68] The great increase in the number and meaningful characterization of active constituents of plant and animal drugs—the alkaloids and glycosides, for instance—permitted a broad chemical approach to much of the organic materia medica late in the century. We have seen how the increased activity in investigation of the fats and oils and of the alkaloids was reflected in a work such as Allen's.

In spite of the late application of organic analysis to testing the purity of drugs, qualitative and quantitative tests of a sort had long been in use. In some cases these tests were necessarily empirical, because they came before the isolation of the basic constituents themselves. It was possible, for instance, to determine the percentage of certain components in vegetable drugs by extraction or distillation procedures before the principles themselves could be chemically characterized. It was also possible to determine the moisture content of drugs and the quantity of ash resulting upon incineration before the full significance of this was understood, or before appropriate procedures for accurate determinations became available.

Redi and Boyle in the seventeenth century, for instance, reported the ash content of a number of drugs and plants, while Vanden Sande at the end of the eighteenth century reported the weight of extracts obtained from various vegetable drugs by different processes. It soon became apparent to pharmacists and others who dealt extensively in drugs, as did Guibourt in France, that the percentage of gum or resin in a drug such as scammony might indicate its purity. In the same way, it became apparent that a fairly accurate way to gauge the purity of opium was to determine the morphine content of an unknown sample.

At the same time, some workers realized that in certain cases the percentage of gum, or resin, or morphine, could vary significantly from one sample to another, even if these were perfectly pure. They also realized that certain tests of purity, qualitative as well as quantitative, were meaningless if the characteristics of the adulterant resembled too closely those of the active constituent.

Writing in 1820, Accum reported no means for detecting the extensive adulteration of cinchona, rhubarb powder, or ipecacuanha powder.[69] Accum gave a tenuous type of quantitative test in his observation that "one ounce, by measure [of distilled vinegar], should dissolve at least thirteen grains of white marble [calcium carbonate]." [70] Accum had in fact used crude quantitative methods twenty years earlier in his publications on drug adulteration in Nicholson's journal.[71]

Accum's contemporary, the eminent French pharmacist Guibourt, published a consciously more scientific work that same year. He referred to the latest researches of his contemporaries Fourcroy, Vauquelin, Séguin, Serturner, and Robiquet.[72]

Accum of course was writing for a chemically uninitiated public, Guibourt, for his scientifically informed peers. Accum concerned himself primarily with foods, only slightly with drugs, Guibourt, entirely with drugs. And yet, the difference seems to go deeper, for an examination of the *Pharmacopoeia Londinensis, 1809* in current use in 1820 reveals little of the scientific character of Guibourt's *Histoire*. Powell, in his translation of the 1809 *Pharmacopoeia Londinensis*, referred pharmacy students to Fourcroy and Vauquelin for further information on the chemical properties of cinchona and other barks and reported that cinchona extract and powder differed in their efficacy weight for weight, but gave no further information. He referred to the narcotic principle reported by Derosne in opium, but noted that "the whole subject [would] bear further elucidation." He realized that the activity of opium varied with climate and considered the activity of the extract to be six times less than that of opium itself.[73] Powell referred to a quantitative test, citing Proust as his authority, in the preparation of citric acid; namely, that "7½ parts of citrate of lime [required] 20 parts of sulphuric acid of a sp. gr. [specific gravity] 1.15 for this purpose." [74]

Phillips added little in his criticisms (1811) of the 1809 *Pharmacopoeia,* although he determined the quantity of opium in tincture of opium by evaporating a fluid ounce on a water bath and, in the manner of the time, referred to the weight (in grains) of calcium carbonate "decomposed" by various fractions of distilled vinegar (all of different specific gravity).[75]

Phillips gave purity tests for a few substances of organic origin in the "Notes" to the 1836 edition of the *Pharmacopoeia,* but these were much in the minority compared to tests for inorganic chemical substances. The *Pharmacopoeia* directed that sulfate impurity precipitated from vinegar and its barium salt "not exceed 1.14 grain"; and 100 grains of dilute hydrocyanic acid yield 10 grains of silver cyanide on the addition of silver nitrate, the precipitate being soluble in boiling nitric acid, unlike any possible hydrochloric acid contaminant. The *Pharmacopoeial* tests for alkaloids—morphine, aconitine, quinine, strychnine and veratrine—were almost entirely qualitative. Aconitine burned without leaving a residue; morphine was alkaline to turmeric, gave a red, then a yellow, color with nitric acid, a blue color with iron sesquichloride, was precipitated by potassium hydroxide, and its salts turned brown with chlorine and ammonia; and quinine affected turmeric.[76]

The only tests that might be considered quantitative were those given for quinine disulfate. The *Pharmacopoeia* noted that 100 parts of the salt lost 8 to 10 parts of water with gentle heat; Phillips added that 100 grains in aqueous solution, acidulated with hydrochloric acid, yielded "26.6 grains of ignited sulphate of barytes on the addition of a solution of chloride of barium." [77] The tests given for animal charcoal were intended to detect inorganic adulterants or impurities, while honey was tested with potassium iodide to uncover starch adulterant, and lard was merely directed to be well washed.[78] A change toward more precise and more quantitative tests came in the 1864 *British Pharmacopoeia*.

Glancing through early volumes of the *Pharmaceutical Journal* gives an impression much like that gained from the *Pharmacopoeia*. Pereira, writing on the adulteration of scammony, instructed his readers to detect starch adulteration by the familiar iodine test (except in preparations containing ginger powder, which gave the starch test) and guaiacum adulterant by the blue color that developed when a paper moistened in an alcoholic or ethereal tincture of scammony was exposed to nitrous fumes. He added that scammony should yield 75 to 80 per cent of resin, distinguished from jalap resin by its solubility, and that on incineration, it should yield only 3 per cent ash, though the proportion might be as high as 40 per cent, if sand were present.[79] Andrew Ure described the detection of potato sugar as an adulterant in other sugar by means of the color changes of a slightly alkaline solution of copper sulfate. The application seemed principally designed to guard pharmacists against the frauds perpetrated by grocers, but it is interesting that he apparently anticipated Fehling (1848), who used this test to detect sugar in diabetic urine, by at least six years, though Ure did not apply it to urine.[80] And Theophilus Redwood, discussing some of the false tests currently in use to detect adulterated balsam of copaiba, concluded that the only method that appeared "at all satisfactory" for estimating its purity was "first to resolve it into its proximate constituents, and then to examine these separately, with reference to their physical and chemical characters." [81] During this time, the *Pharmaceutical Journal* also kept its readers abreast of the most important research by Continental European scientists.[82]

Fresenius devoted only a small portion of the 1846 English edition of his *Instruction in Chemical Analysis* (*Qualitative*) to the better known alkaloids, and this in an appendix, although he did discuss the organic acids.[83] In the companion work on quantitative analysis appearing the same year, he gave over a portion to organic elementary analysis and a few pages of a special section to the analysis of the ashes of plants.[84] This certainly seems to support Meyer's comments forty years later concerning the state of organic analysis. (See p. 90.)

Arthur Hill Hassall naturally stressed the microscopic detection of adulteration in the few drugs that he discussed in his *Adulterations*

Detected (1857). However, he did report in detail the analyses made by various Continental workers concerning the constituents of opium, jalap, ipecacuanha, and liquorice. In the case of opium, he recommended determining the alkaloidal content, and in that of scammony he mentioned the same tests given by Pereira. But, with respect to ipecacuanha, Hassall saw little value in depending upon the percentage of the extractive as an indication of purity, because of the variation even among pure samples, and for liquorice he depended upon the microscope.[85] Hassall mentioned an alkalimeter for the detection of acetic acid in vinegar, but used a gravimetric method to determine sulfuric acid in the same substance.[86]

As late as 1871, in his *Chemistry: General, Medical, and Pharmaceutical*, John Attfield paid comparatively little attention to the "Chemistry of Certain Substances of Vegetable and Animal Origin." [87] It appears that the tests he cited were entirely qualitative. Attfield mentioned a few organic substances in a short section on "Chemical Toxicology" and in his discussion of quantitative analysis, volumetric and gravimetric.[88]

A month after the Society of Public Analysts held its first general meeting and called for suggested limits or standards (among other things), Prescott, at the University of Michigan, wrote:

> Proximate organic analysis is not altogether impracticable, and organic chemistry is not solely a science of synthetical operations even at present. It is true, as the chief analytical chemists have repeatedly pointed out, that in the rapid accumulation of organic compounds the means of identification and separation have been left in comparative neglect. It is true, also, that the field is limitless; but this is not a reason for doing nothing in it. Fifty years ago, the workers in inorganic analysis were unprovided with a comprehensive system, but they went on exploring the mineral kingdom and using their scanty means to gain valuable results.
>
> That this compilation is a fragmentary and very brief exponent of this part of analytical science as it exists at present, the author is fully aware, but he hopes that, as a beginning, it may prove to be worth enough to afford an opportunity for its improvement hereafter.[89]

Prescott, we see, was fully conscious of the need he was filling in this publication of fewer than two hundred pages.[90]

Allen followed closely behind Prescott in time and subject, fully acknowledging his debt to Prescott in proximate analysis. He brought out volume after volume, of increasing size with each succeeding revision, and in keeping with the burgeoning investigation of organic substances in the last decades of the nineteenth century. The fact that Allen was himself a public analyst and a lecturer in chemistry lends weight to his conviction, echoing Prescott, that:

While the libraries of chemists are replete with manuals and treatises on Inorganic Analysis, and the number of works is being increased almost monthly, books on Organic Analysis are chiefly conspicuous by their absence; and the unfortunate chemist who requires to make an assay or analysis of a commercial organic product, is driven to seek for various items of information—often contradictory or unreliable—in the pages of one or two very imperfect works, and of a few English and foreign scientific periodicals.

It is a lamentable fact, that while our young chemists are taught to execute ultimate organic analyses, and to ring the changes on the everlasting chloro- bromo- and nitro-derivatives of bodies of the aromatic series, the course of instruction in many of our leading laboratories does not include even qualitative tests for such everyday substances as alcohol, chloroform, glycerin, carbolic acid, and quinine. As a natural consequence of this neglect, the methods for the proximate analysis of organic mixtures, and for the assay of commercial organic products, are in a far more backward state than is justified by the great inherent difficulties of this branch of analysis.[91]

We saw previously how the application of various physical, and particularly physical-optical, techniques to adulteration was reflected in different editions of Allen's work. The same sense of great activity and progress, within a short period of twenty or twenty-five years, pervades his writings on organic chemical analysis in its application to certain classes of organic drugs. We refer to a few areas, by way of example.

In his discussion (in 1882) of fats and oils, in the first American edition of *Commercial Organic Analysis*, Allen reported Koettstorfer's saponification ("saturation") equivalents, announced three years earlier (in 1879); and mentioned the elaidin test, various color reactions, and the elevation of temperature upon the addition of concentrated sulfuric acid (the Maumené test). The entire section on fixed oils and fats occupied 140 pages, including a lengthy description of the special characteristics of fourteen common fats, oils, and waxes.[92] When the third edition of the same volume appeared in 1899, the same material occupied an entire volume of almost 400 pages, and the editor (the American chemist and physician Henry Leffmann) felt called upon, in his preface, to point to the special important additions to this volume.[93]

In addition to more detailed listings of saponification equivalents, the volume now described the determination of Reichert's number (the amount of potassium hydroxide required to neutralize the volatile fatty acids), bromine absorption, iodine absorption (Hübl's iodine number), acetyl value, and bromine thermal value (announced by the English public analysts Hehner and Mitchell, in 1895, as

1. Testing Drugs by Taste. This decorative initial letter taken from a fifteenth-century manuscript of Galen pictures the application of a simple organoleptic test method in use since at least the time of Galen himself and continuing, for many drugs, until more scientific methods developed in the nineteenth century. The figure in the long ermine-trimmed robe to the left is thought to be the physician Galen, in a representation contemporary to the artist. (The manuscript containing the original was destroyed during World War II. Here reproduced, with permission, from the version [redrawn?] in *Chemist and Druggist,* 106[1927]: facing p. 808. See also p. 11, 53.264r, with explanation, p. xxvii, in the magnificent folio edition by Evert Cornelius van Leersum and W. Martin, *Miniaturen der lateinischen Galenos-Handschrift der kgl. Oeffentl. Bibliothek in Dresden Db. 92–93 in phototypischen Reproduktion* [Leiden, 1910].)

II. Punishment of a Dealer in Fraudulent Goods. The *muḥtasib*, overseer of the market place of medieval Islam, watches (from the right of center, rear) as corporal punishment is inflicted upon the dishonest dealer. (Reproduced, with permission, from *Ciba Zeitschrift*, 8[No. 85, Sept. 1942, Basel ed.]: 2991; also reprinted in *Ciba Symposia*, 6[Nos. 5 & 6, 1944]: 1872. Noted as being from a seventeenth-century Persian manuscript, but otherwise unidentified.)

III. Testing the Purity of Roll-Sulfur. In this reproduction of a woodcut of the medieval Latin West, we see a figure (on the right) testing the purity of roll-sulfur by holding a sample to his ear. When sulfur of great purity is warmed by the hand, a crackling sound may be heard. (From the Bayerische Staatsbibliothek, Munich, Germany, Codex Monacens germ. 600, fol. 9r.)

IV. Pharmacy Inspection. The scene pictured here—the inspection of a pharmacy by a group of physicians, perhaps accompanied by pharmacists—was common in England before the nineteenth century, and had its origin with the medieval guilds. (From Johann Michaelis, *Ordo visitandi officinas*, in *Opera Medicochirurgica* [Nürnberg, 1688]. National Library of Medicine.)

V. John Postgate, F.R.C.S., from a portrait by Vivian Crome, in the Town Hall at Scarborough, England. Note the mortar and pestle and the small discs which may be "nux vomica" buttons; the conical graduate Postgate holds may contain tincture of nux vomica, or strychnine. (Photo by Walkers Studios Ltd., Scarborough, courtesy of Councillor W. C. Wilkinson, Mayor of Scarborough.)

VI. Richard Phillips, pharmacist-chemist. (Royal College of Surgeons of England, London.)

VII. Thomas Wakley, from an engraving by W. H. Egleton, after a painting by K. Meadows. (National Library of Medicine.)

VIII. Arthur Hill Hassall, with his microscope, books, and a statuette presented to him at a public testimonial in May, 1865, which symbolized the overcoming of fraud (the toad) by the spear of science. (Royal College of Surgeons of England, London.)

IX. Fredrick Accum about 1820. This engraving by J. Thomson, from the *European Magazine* (77[1820]: facing p. 483), is supposedly after an oil portrait by S. Drummond, but differs somewhat, as Charles Albert Browne showed (*Chymia,* 1[1948]: 88, and portrait facing p. 8). (University of Wisconsin Memorial Library.)

X. "Death's Register," a caricature by the British painter and engraver Richard Dagley, illustrated a satirical poem, "Death (A Dealer) to his London Correspondent," which referred to various ingredients for adulterating food and drink; adulterated drugs were not mentioned. But note the large demijohn labelled "Spirits Apothecary Hall." Elsewhere may be seen a barrel of cocculus indicus (used to adulterate beer and ale), a basket labelled "Sal Saturn" (lead acetate, used to adulterate certain wines), and a bag containing plaster of paris and burnt bones (to be mixed with flour). The inscription "Columbia" on the shovel may allude to the practice of sending substandard drugs to the United States. "Accum's List" suggests the lists of adulterants in Accum's *Treatise on Adulterations*. (From *Death's Doings* [London, 1826], p. 296; National Library of Medicine. William H. Helfland of Philadelphia drew this caricature to our attention.)

superior to the Maumené test).[94] Quite marked here, as in other areas of organic chemical research, were the independent contributions being made now by English public analysts, in addition to their critical evaluations of Continental methods.[95] Allen himself was one of the most important research workers in the field.

Work on essential oils was equally great. In Allen's first edition (1882), volatile oils occupied 5 pages as a somewhat minor division under terpenes; by the time of the third edition (1907), more than 300 pages were devoted to them.[96] Equally remarkable is the development of alkaloidal analysis during a ten-year period between the first and second editions, resulting in a four-fold increase in the amount of space devoted to the subject (not including the less important alkaloids in the second edition).[97] In the second edition, Allen expanded his discussion of general precipitants of alkaloids and brought new material on color reactions, on isolation and purification, and on constitution and synthesis.[98] On the subject of opium alkaloids alone, twice as many individual alkaloids were mentioned in this later edition. The 1882 edition considered only the opium, cinchona, and nux vomica alkaloids among the more important alkaloids deserving extensive discussion.

During the preceding glance at Prescott and Allen, little has been said concerning specific tests for adulteration. It goes without saying that the increased chemical knowledge provided concerning these organic substances permitted precise and accurate detection of adulteration that had been largely impossible before.

A glance at the work of the members of the Society of Public Analysts, as reflected in the *Analyst,* reveals an equally great increase in research on alkaloids, and fixed and volatile oils.[99] Equally instructive is an examination of C. G. Moor's *Suggested Standards of Purity for Foods and Drugs* (1902), and Chattaway's *Digest of Researches and Criticisms bearing on the British Pharmacopoeia, 1898* (1903). The gradual improvement in analytical chemical tests given in the *Pharmacopoeia* (especially in the 1898 edition) was reinforced from books such as those by Moor, Chattaway, and Allen, which undoubtedly contributed to the still more marked change that took place in the 1914 *British Pharmacopoeia.*[100]

7.

THE BEGINNING
OF BIOLOGICAL
STANDARDIZATION

We gain some idea of the minor extent to which the biological testing of drugs was accepted during the period that interests us here (1820–1906) from the proud advertising of a Philadelphia company of chemists, H. K. Mulford. In 1909, under the bold banner "Drug Standardization: U.S.P. Anticipated," the Mulford advertisement boasted:

> The H. K. Mulford Company standardizes *one hundred and twenty-one more vegetable drugs and preparations* than is required by the United States Pharmacopeia.
>
> The U.S.P. requires the chemical standardization of 56.
> The H. K. Mulford Company standardizes 177.
> The U.S.P. does not require physiological testing of drugs.
> The H. K. Mulford Company physiologically tests 50 pharmaceutical and biological preparations.
> In addition to this, we make a bacteriological or clinical test of 38 of our preparations.
> This four-fold testing and standardization is practicable only in specially-equipped laboratories and where large quantities are manufactured.[1]

Biological testing was clearly new enough in industrial application in 1909 to make valuable such stress upon the technique in advertising.

More subdued though equally proud attention was paid to physiological testing, about the same time, by the English company of Evans Sons Lescher & Webb Limited, "Wholesale and Export Druggists, and Manufacturing Chemists," of Liverpool, London, and New York.[2] This company apparently met the problem of finding "spe-

98

cially-equipped laboratories" referred to by the Mulford Company by submitting its drugs to the physiological laboratories of the University of Liverpool.[3] Evans evidently saw some advantage in this arrangement of "scientific physiological testing by specialists working independently of the manufacturing departments."[4] Those specialists mentioned confirming the activity of preparations of "those imperfectly understood drugs," digitalis, squill, and strophanthus by means of the isolated mammalian heart method and of ergot by testing on the isolated rabbit uterus.[5] Anticipating criticism of their methods, the author of this short article explained:

> Among the chief objections to all forms of physiological testing is the probability of variations in susceptibility of the animals or animal organs employed. Our scientific advisers on the University staff assure us that, by a suitable system of repeat tests, as great, if not greater, confidence may be placed upon the results reported by them than upon those obtained by any other method.[6]

At the end of the period in which we are most interested here (1906), certain English pharmacists questioned the value of physiological testing. The issue seemed to hinge mainly upon factors quite aside from the reliability of animal testing. Perhaps most important was a feeling that the method required such special techniques that the manufacture of galenicals would fall more and more into the hands of manufacturing or wholesale pharmacy, thus diminishing the role of the community pharmacy. Besides, it was feared that the community pharmacist would no longer be able to guarantee the galenical preparations he purchased as he could those of his own production—an argument that ignored the circumstance that facilities now required would have precluded testing by the practicing pharmacist.[7] One proponent of physiological standardization not only considered this argument fallacious, but said he would sooner trust the accuracy of a firm than an individual.[8]

One opponent of physiological standardization, E. M. Holmes, a noted English pharmacist and public analyst, admitted the possible usefulness of the method for certain preparations (digitalis, ergot, strophanthus), but felt that if pharmacists took care to buy drugs of highest quality and subsequently attended to the best storage and preservation of those drugs, pharmacists would have a source of drugs of high and uniform quality. Holmes put forth two additional arguments against physiological standardization: one concerned the necessity of agreement among manufacturers upon the proper standard (he mentioned wide divergence among manufacturers); the other, the remaining possibility of variation on standing.[9]

An editorial in the *Pharmaceutical Journal* opposing physiological standards and tests admitted the usefulness of the method in cases where galenicals were difficult to make uniform. The editorial suggested such tests be made by some national laboratory rather than by a wholesaler, retailer, or ordinary manufacturer, who probably would not have the means.[10] The average pharmacist, who perhaps did not even possess a hydrometer, certainly had neither the equipment nor knowledge to apply such tests; and some manufacturers, as we saw in the case of the Evans Company, found it both practical and profitable to have their products tested by an independent agency— in this case a university laboratory. "It may be fair to demand, because possible to ensure," stated this same editorial,

that a galenical should conform with a fixed standard of alkaloidal content or even of the much-despised "extractive." But it is not fair to insist— because it is impossible to ensure—that a galenical shall conform with a fixed standard based upon the average effect produced upon the system of a rabbit or frog. The adoption of physiological standards to which drugs *must* approximate is therefore quite impossible, and when that is recognised, further discussion on the subject is unnecessary.[11]

One pharmaceutical chemist suggested that the "difficulties surrounding the application of physiological methods are so patent and numerous that it can hardly be conceived that much would be heard of them except for the purpose of advertisement." [12] This same correspondent to the *Pharmaceutical Journal* suggested that specific gravity, alcoholic strength, and amount of solid extractive provided a good basis for official standards, presumably as an alternative to physiological assay wherever possible.[13] This suggestion was, in fact, followed wherever feasible, for example, in the American lead toward drug standardization taken by Parke, Davis and Company, beginning in 1879 with their "Liquor Ergotae Purificatus" and continuing with many new preparations after 1883.[14]

The advantages of biological testing did not seem to have entered any of the recommendations concerning proposed revision of the *British Pharmacopoeia, 1898*,[15] even for those preparations for which opponents of the method admitted some usefulness. C. G. Moor, the English chemist, public analyst, and prolific writer on food and drug analysis and standards, referred to only one physiological method of testing (for ergot) in his *Suggested Standards of Purity for Foods and Drugs* (1902).[16]

No clear-cut reference to biological or physiological assay is to be found in either of the early works of Blyth or Allen. Blyth recognized the pharmacologic action of ergot and digitalis and suggested a method for determining the presence of digitalis by comparing the effects upon two frogs of an unknown sample and of commercial digitaline.[17]

Allen appeared to make no reference to physiological testing in connection with alkaloids in the first edition of *Commercial Organic Analysis,* but he did devote a few pages to pharmacologic tests in a later edition.[18] Allen discussed the use of various animals, including man, for testing alkaloids pharmacologically and noted in detail the special effect upon the pupil of the eye.[19] However, he gave no indication of using these tests for more than the identification of a particular group of alkaloids.

A curious reference to physiological tests was made by the chemist Wippell Gadd, who wrote frequently on the importance of standardized drug preparations, especially those of the *British Pharmacopoeia.* Gadd recognized physiological tests, along with physical tests, in cases where chemical standards and assay procedures were not possible, yet he recognized that physiological tests were applicable only under special conditions in special laboratories that seemed almost prohibitive for manufacturers in England. "With truly British generosity, however," continued Gadd, "the physiologically tested drugs of other lands are admitted freely, and, in so far as they are used as medicines for patients, so far are they poisonous to home industries." [20]

As late as 1905, two authors writing in the *Pharmaceutical Journal* were urging the necessity of adopting some sort of biological methods of standardization for digitalis, squill, and strophanthus. Their suggested method was based upon the minimal lethal dose for frogs.[21]

Biological methods of testing and standardization thus were making their first appearance toward the end of the nineteenth and early in the twentieth century. Although at least a few pharmaceutical manufacturers used such test methods about this time, only later did they enter the official compendia of Great Britain and the United States.[22]

PART III

THE EVOLUTION

OF SOCIAL CONTROLS

8.

THE BACKGROUND

In the existing state of society do you think that caveat emptor *should be changed into* caveat venditor?—*Yes.*[1]

The words, the speaker, the occasion are significant. In the dramatic simplicity of his reply, the central figure in the English movement for pure foods and drugs signalized a revolutionary change in social philosophy. This unequivocal assertion was Arthur Hill Hassall's, in testimony to the closing session of the Parliamentary Select Committee on Adulterations of Food, Etc., before which he had appeared as first, last, and chief witness during the two years of proceedings—1855–1856.[2] A change from *caveat emptor* to *caveat venditor* was indeed revolutionary.

Did no one before 1856 seek such a change to protect the consumer from adulteration, a protection we take for granted today? Certainly many persons in Britain, and elsewhere, had long realized the problem of adulteration and the necessity of protecting the public from abuses against which they had no defense. German-born and German-trained Fredrick (Friedrich Christian) Accum (1769–1838) had expressed such opinions in England more than half a century before (1798). Yet, when he voiced his convictions more publicly twenty years later (1820), the time still was not right for general acceptance of a change.

In spite of his personal popularity, the scientific underpinning he gave to his cause, and the support he received from some quarters, Accum—who had been reared in a climate that accepted government

105

protection—misjudged the viability of the British spirit of laissez faire. Prevailing conditions still made it "safer to be a felon than a reformer," as Trevelyan pointed out.[3] The problem of protecting the British public by controlling adulteration formed part of the broader problem of social, economic, and political reform; only thus viewed is the movement for adulteration control seen in proper perspective.

Thus we must examine the prevailing socio-political climate during the three decades between Accum's *Treatise on Adulterations* (1820) and significant awakening to the abuses of rampant adulterations, even though the nature of the present work precludes a full discussion of the social, political, or economic background to the scientific events with which we are primarily concerned.[4]

During the Middle Ages some control had been exercised over adulteration practices in England by the craft guilds, whose chief concern was the prevention of unfair competition between guild masters by setting standards of quality, inspecting shops, confiscating substandard goods, and punishing offenders. A partial check on the guilds was maintained by town officials through the "assizes" of the throne, which still took seriously its function as protector of the poor.

The Renaissance witnessed a marked increase in trade and commerce, which paralleled a revived culture. The rise of a new monied class and the concomitant readjustment of social values brought a gradual change in the nature of royal protection, which more and more encouraged commerce, often through the granting of monopolies, special privileges, or letters patent. More and more also there developed a certain dichotomy between protection of the economic rights of all classes to some degree and encouragement of the emerging middle classes, who could best fill the royal coffers. This dichotomy sharpened with sixteenth- and seventeenth-century absolutism, which embraced a significant shift from a medieval society which had made a real effort to guarantee to all classes certain economic rights and protections to a society which tended to favor the economic rights of one or more classes over those of some others, coupled with and encouraged by increasing disregard for long-standing laws and traditions.

The late eighteenth and early nineteenth centuries brought to a head in England serious social and economic problems which had long been developing. Increasing industrialization, coupled with progressive enclosure of large tracts of land, snatched from the majority of the small land-holders both their "cottage" industries and land and destroyed many of the old village trades. Moreover, controls exercised under the old system of guilds and apprenticeship were breaking down, accompanied by the demise of regulated trade. Many small productive units failed and their operators joined those ejected from the land. Thus, several disruptive forces converged, and within fifty years converted what had been before 1750 primarily a rural agrarian society into an increasingly urban and industrial society.

The insecurity of trade, both during and after the Napoleonic Wars, the high taxation, and the corn laws all added to the economic turmoil. Perhaps an even greater effect stemmed from the growth of strong anti-Jacobin feeling, leading to a general government policy of repression of all types of reform. This spirit began to wane only after 1820.

Out of the philosophies of individualism propounded by Adam Smith, Thomas Malthus, Jeremy Bentham, and, later, Herbert Spencer, grew a pronounced government policy of laissez faire, encouraging to the growing middle class. This official attitude hampered not only the passage of British food and drug laws but also their effective operation until the end of the nineteenth century, because it hindered the development of public responsibility through government action. This was to some extent true also of public health, of public education, of public assistance to the indigent, sick, and aged, and of factory reform.

THE PUBLIC HEALTH MOVEMENT IN BRITAIN

The gradual growth of awareness and concern for public health on the part of the British public and eventually its legislators paralleled in many ways this process as it touched adulteration of foods and drugs. The latter phenomenon mainly concerns us here, but we should recall briefly the wider framework of the emergent public health movement.[5]

Although the first half of the nineteenth century was characterized by a number of humanitarian reforms, such as the abolition of the slave trade, only slowly was general concern shown for the deplorable social conditions fostered by industrialization. These conditions were aggravated by the problems of over-population, low wages, a high rate of illiteracy, low morals, the lack of police (in London, until 1829), and disregard for the dignity of life. The growing use of the press to air public grievances helped to break down old practices of repression, but reform did not proceed with much speed until after the Reform Bill of 1832. For many citizens the lack of political franchise, or the newness of its acquisition, limited the effectiveness of the pressure of public opinion.

Public health questions were tied closely to those of poverty and the Poor Laws, of occupational health and the Factory and Mine Acts, of overcrowding and Urban Improvements and Housing Acts. Most of these problems sprang from the evils attendant upon the Industrial Revolution, and as George Rosen pointed out, "modern public health took its origin in England because it was the first modern industrial country." [6]

First serious attempts to deal with these interrelated problems in Britain began in the 1830's, after the Reform Act of 1832, usually with statistical surveys or "sanitary commissions," either governmental or private, followed by public agitation and legislation. Most of the early legislation was permissive in nature, but it represented a beginning of government concern for public health that sharpened by mid-century and matured during the last quarter of the century. During this period there also took place a gradual change from temporary to permanent, and from individual, local action to co-ordinated central (that is national) organization.

In the area of child and woman labor, the first effective Factory Act, that of 1833, applied primarily to textile factories, but it did prohibit employment of children under 9 years and specified the maximum hours of work for those from 9 to 16 (e.g., 9 hours per day, or 48 hours per week, for those in the 9-to-13 age group) and provided for inspection. Mines came under the scrutiny of a commission in 1840, and its disturbing report led to the 1842 Mines and Collieries Act that prohibited underground employment of women and of boys under 10 years of age and set other controls. By 1848 a 58-hour week was set as the maximum for women and for children 13 to 18, and the 1850 Factory Act further regulated work hours of women and children. The consolidating Coal Mines Act of 1860 provided further restrictions, as did the Factory Acts of 1864 and 1867.

Problems of overcrowding and sanitation, compounded by poverty, were inseparable in industrial centers like Manchester, where 2500 cellars served as dwelling places, with 3 to 5 persons sharing one bed; where in one district 2 privies served 250 people and in another 33 "necessaries" (tubs for toilet purposes) served 7000 people; where communal cesspools and dunghills blighted every court and alley; and where not a single public park existed before 1845. Such conditions led to Urban Improvements Acts such as the Liverpool Sanitary Act of 1846, and in the same year the Nuisances Removal and Diseases Prevention Act and the Baths and Washhouses Act, and the 1847 Towns Improvement Clauses Act—all before the first British Public Health Act. These conditions also prompted the first Housing

Acts of 1851, the Laboring Classes Lodging House Act and the Common Lodging Houses Act.

A major turning point in such social and public-health oriented reform and one of the earliest results of the Reform Act of 1832 was the noteworthy Poor Law Amendment Act of 1834, for it provided administrative means to ferret out the problems of the burgeoning cities and nation. The first sanitary commission appointed by the Poor Law Board in 1838 to investigate an epidemic in London's East End drew sharp attention to the city's frightful water-supply and drainage system; and a year later there began a searching investigation climaxed by the monumental *Report on the Sanitary Condition of the Labouring Population of Great Britain* (1842), described by Rosen as the "fundamental document of modern public health." [7] Aside from the disturbing facts it presented in detail, the *Report* was important for several reasons: namely, for its author's (Sir Edwin Chadwick) recommendation that district medical officers be appointed, for its wide distribution to the public (10,000 copies), and finally for Chadwick's idea ("sanitary idea") that much disease was preventable and that health was markedly influenced by the environment, physical and social. It has been suggested that perhaps the full realization of the effect this latter idea, as expressed by Chadwick and others, could have upon the cost of public assistance and upon industrial profits, through its beneficial effect upon the labor force, prompted sanitary commissions and legislative reform in an otherwise predominantly laissez faire society.

This *Report* led almost immediately to a Royal Commission for Inquiry into the State of Large Towns and Populous Districts, with two comprehensive reports (1844 and 1845), prepared largely by Chadwick, proposing that the central government assume responsibility for public health by establishing an official government department. Chadwick's report was bolstered by the vigorous campaign of public education conducted by an early voluntary health association, the Health of Towns Association (founded 1844), and notably by its *Address to the Working Classes of the United Kingdom on their Duty in the Present State of the Sanitary Question* (1847), as well as by the several Urban Improvement Acts mentioned. But the deciding factor for the passage of the Public Health Act in 1848 probably came in the form of a natural phenomenon—a dread cholera epidemic raging across Europe toward Britain in 1848; for as Rosen has commented, "in the history of public health, epidemics occupy a prominent place among the situations that precipitated action in the interest of the community's health." [8]

The Act was a milestone that created the first General (i.e., national) Board of Health to help co-ordinate activities of local authorities on sanitary matters, to promote the appointment of local medical officers of health, and to help establish adequate sewage systems and necessary clean water supplies. While the Act did provide for the appointment of local boards of health, officers of health, inspectors of nuisances, etc., and gave them control over such things as sewage, water supply, control of offensive trades, provision and regulation of cemeteries, the Act was permissive in that it did not require such appointments and did not extend to London. Nevertheless, it was a beginning, and the General Board of Health, under the vigorous leadership of Chadwick and with the help of Dr. Southwood Smith (founder of the Health of Towns Association), accomplished much during the short period of its existence (1848–1854).

The needs of London were met by a newly created Metropolitan Local Management Board, also speeded by the cholera epidemic, and to a lesser extent by an 1847 commission of inquiry into the sanitary state of London. Sir John Simon, a great pioneer (along with Chadwick and, to a lesser degree, Smith) of the British public health movement, served as the first medical officer of health for London. His classic annual reports (1848–1855) did much to attract public attention to numerous, serious health problems of London and among other things accomplished the abolition of cesspools in London in 1855.

Simon's prominence during this period led to his appointment as medical officer to a new Board of Health created in 1855 to replace the first General Board, abandoned after growing apprehension in some circles over Chadwick's crusading activities. In his new post, Simon continued his policy of public education on health problems, including a comprehensive report on vaccination (1857), and a *Report on the Sanitary State of the People of England* (1858) that led to the Public Health Act of 1858 and the absorption, in 1859, of the Board of Health into the Privy Council, with Simon as medical officer to the Council (until 1876).

Simon's work as medical officer is amply recorded in the reports of the Privy Council from 1859 to 1872 and includes an inquiry (1862) into the dangers to health associated with certain industries using lead, mercury, phosphorus, arsenic, etc., a survey of British hospitals (1863), and a survey of housing for the poor in town and country (1864). Simon's official position changed again under the Local Government Act of 1871, when the medical department of the Privy Council amalgamated (over his objections) with the old Poor Law

Board and the Local Government Act Office, following the recommendations of a Royal Sanitary Commission appointed to investigate the administration of sanitary laws and the formation of local sanitary areas. Simon resigned his post in 1876 when, as he feared, the medical department became lost within the new Local Government Board. A further consequence of the Sanitary Commission's report of 1871 (and probably also a reflection of the Reform Act of 1867) was the Public Health Act of 1875 that consolidated existing public health legislation, made uniform local health agencies, and made mandatory the appointment of medical officers of health in each district (previously compulsory only for London under its Metropolis Management Act of 1855).

With the Public Health Act of 1875 (not replaced until 1936) came the end of a period of evolution that saw a gradual change in attack upon public health problems, beginning with temporary boards of health, or fever committees, which were still in existence as late as the 1830's to deal with individual epidemics, and ending with centralized governmental control and responsibility. The process should perhaps be regarded less as a manifestation of social conscience or humanitarian impulse than as the slowly growing realization that adequate measures of sanitation and public health eventually affected the whole economy and thus should be the concern of the whole community. Happily this consideration ultimately prevailed even with those who propounded the strong contemporary political and economic philosophies that found the concept of government control extremely distasteful. The evolution of adequate public health measures also pointed out the great value of public education and understanding of the problems, a value also realized by workers for pure food and drugs.

In view of our discussions it is refreshing to read how John Roberton, in his *Treatise on Medical Police* (1809), described the average London shopkeeper of the first decade of the nineteenth century:

The generality of shopkeepers in the city, however, enjoy an affluence of circumstances independent of particular patronage or favour, from the fullness of customers in the *market* (as all that part of the metropolis may be justly called) that gives them an independence of manners as curious as it is fortunate. A city shop-keeper acts out of his shop, as if he had not a master in the world.[9]

Roberton went on to paint a picture of the so-called "higher order of traders" that bears little resemblance to the situation described by Accum and others:

In short, in respect to almost every description of traders in this city, it may generally be asserted, that their independence, and the ancient habits of their country, render their moral character equal, if not superior, to almost any other nation. It has been asserted, that the bustle of commerce, and the love of gain, have tended to degrade and vitiate their minds. In some instances this is probably too true; but in general, with the power, they have acquired the resolution to be just. Many, nay a great proportion of them, would sooner suffer death than commit a fraud; being well aware, that such an act would at once be dishonest and destructive to themselves.[10]

Roberton's national pride apparently interfered with clear observation of existing conditions.

The social repercussions and misery caused by the Industrial Revolution were complicated by the Napoleonic Wars and the hysteria of the anti-Jacobin reaction; social reforms were needed in many areas. Parliament reflected the pronounced laissez faire attitude toward business of the English people. These circumstances provided tempting opportunities for adulteration practices.

Seen against this background of the period surrounding his crusade of 1820, Accum's unsuccessful and personally disastrous efforts can be better understood. In a "nation of shop-keepers" it was difficult to throw stones through shop windows without getting cut.

Social reform came only slowly in nineteenth-century England. The Reform Acts of 1832 and 1867 gradually extended the franchise. Free, universal, and compulsory education came only with the Education Act of 1870.

The established church in England supported laissez faire and stressed private philanthropy rather than public social services. This was the prevailing philosophy of rising British middle-class Liberalism of the second half of the nineteenth century, preaching respectability and morality, but strongly supporting the idea of "self-help," expressed in the work of such authors as Samuel Smiles (1859), in the social paternalism of Thomas Hughes, and the gospel of work of Hughes and Thomas Arnold. These ideas gave the middle classes a morality and an elite theory, but they probably contributed little to alleviating pressing social problems among the lower classes. This may partly explain, however, why the social climate became more favorable for adulteration laws during the second half of the nineteenth century. Probably a more viable force for social reforms touching the lower classes came from the movement later called "Christian Socialism," exemplified by the work of William Booth and the formation of the Salvation Army (in 1870) and the novels of Charles Kingsley.

Combined with the forces of middle-class Liberal morality and Christian Socialism was the general growth of social criticism and reform movements during the last half of the nineteenth century. Robert Owen made a beginning during the first quarter of the century; the Chartists became active during the late thirties and forties; the Fabian Society came into being in the eighties.

While the professions were eager to maintain control over their own affairs and resented any hint at government surveillance, they were equally anxious to gain full recognition under the laws. Consequently the period that saw general social reforms also saw reforms of the professions. The Medical Act of 1858 and the Pharmacy Act of 1868 attest to this, as does the general educational program of the Pharmaceutical Society of Great Britain.

All these movements undoubtedly contributed to the increasing support that food and drug reformers found during the last half of the nineteenth century. The revelations of Hassall were greeted by cries of "exaggeration," and business resisted government interference of any kind, but the thirty years separating Accum's *Treatise* (1820) from the *Lancet's* Commission (1851) saw significant change in public and government attitudes. The spirit of laissez faire continued strong and social reforms came slowly, but the change from *caveat emptor* to *caveat venditor* was unmistakable.

9.

THE EXTENT AND NATURE
OF THE PROBLEM

Ample evidence, foregoing and hereafter, testifies to the wide extent and infinite variety of drug adulterations.[1] This chapter will document this more explicitly by drawing together selected information from a few representative sources. Questions may be raised about the relevance and comparability of data concerning the extent of drug adulteration. And it must be conceded that many reports in the literature were not adequately documented, and that even government reports left much to be desired; furthermore, the regular reporting of government statistics came only in the last quarter of the nineteenth century.

In his sensational *Treatise on Adulterations* of 1820, Fredrick Accum stated flatly that "nine tenths of the most potent drugs and chemical preparations used in pharmacy, are vended in a sophisticated state." [2] This statement was undocumented, as were others that referred to drug adulteration of "so alarming an extent" that it "exceeds belief," "calcined magnesia . . . seldom met with in a pure state," and "a great many of the essential oils . . . so much adulterated, that it is not easy to meet with such as are at all fit for use." [3]

In his earlier papers on adulterated chemicals, Accum tended to use such qualitative terms as "often," "frequently," "in general," and "generally," to describe the extent of adulteration.[4] Even if we assume exaggeration as an element of Accum's zeal as a reformer, we may still infer extensive adulteration. And we can probably attribute the absence of specific statistics to the inadequacy of analytical tools and lack of systematic reporting.

Such statements of the extent of adulteration in general terms, rather than in specific statistics, are found throughout the century in works of reputable authors.[5] Popular, pseudo-scientific works, such as the anonymous *Tricks of Trade*, repeat these qualitative descriptions of extent: "very often," "frequently," "constantly."[6] Only when the author of this book refers to the opinions of others, like Hassall, does he indicate the extent of adulteration in quantitative terms;[7] these reports will be discussed later, when we turn to the original authors.

Among the earlier published statements that attempted to quantify the extent of adulteration were those of the pharmacist Richard Phillips, in his important "Illustrations of the Present State of Pharmacy in England." Phillips' own colleagues questioned whether most of what he reported might better be termed impurities, attributable in part to the inadequacies of the *Pharmacopoeia*, rather than adulterations (see pages 149–150); yet even such a view pointed to the urgent need for reform. Phillips himself considered that the conditions arose from a combination of "carelessness, ignorance, or fraud,"[8] and we look at the results of his survey in this light. Out of a total of 19 substances examined, no pure samples were found for 9, representing a total of 45 samples examined.[9] For the remaining 10 substances tested, the ratio of pure to samples tested ranged from 1:21 to 2:3, and only in the case of 1 substance, silver nitrate, were all the samples tested (2 in all) found to be pure.[10] In terms of total pure samples to samples tested, the ratio was a low 14:101 or less than 14 per cent pure. Even taking the relatively small number of samples examined into consideration (in no case more than 7 for 1 substance and in several as few as 2) the results indicated a need for considerable improvement. This is especially so when we realize Phillips took most of his samples from "among the most respectable members" of the profession.[11]

Most other reports published in the *Pharmaceutical Journal* during the rest of the century, as well as those that appeared in the *British Medical Journal*, dealt with the extent of adulteration in general, rather than quantitative terms (see pages 148–153 *passim* and 156–158 *passim*). Two exceptions appear in the first volume of the *Pharmaceutical Journal* where one writer estimated that nine-tenths of all milk of sulfur sold was adulterated, while Jacob Bell reported impurities in scammony amounting to as much as 80 per cent, with 25 per cent to 30 per cent being "considered as a fair average."[12]

An examination of the *Analyst* reveals a similarly non-quantitative approach, with the exception of a period from 1877 to 1883, when the editor G. W. Wigner reported annually on the "Working of the

Sale of Food and Drugs Act" during the preceding year. His reports took as their bases the same information utilized for the annual reports of the Local Government Board (for 1876 and after) and it will be more meaningful to discuss them both at the same time. Aside from the reports of Wigner there are few statistics concerning adulteration published in the *Analyst,* and of these very few concern drugs, for the journal, like its sponsor the Society of Public Analysts, was always more concerned with food than with drug analysis. One correspondent claimed that his examination of 165 drug samples in London over a 5-year period showed 71 (or about 43 per cent) adulterated, some considerably. He reported liquor arsenicalis with up to 60 per cent adulteration in one sample; samples of scammony containing up to 10 per cent chalk, some starch besides, and 5 out of 6 deficient in resin; and iron and quinine citrate, for which 11 of 17 samples contained from 4.1 to 10.3 per cent of alkaloid (16 per cent standard) and from 10.3 to 33 per cent ferric oxide (20 per cent standard).[13] Still another correspondent, Dr. C. A. Cameron, analyst for the County of Limerick, Ireland, complained that 5 out of 7 drug samples sent to him from one source were adulterated, and all the samples of 9 drugs from another source.[14]

Most accounts of drug adulteration published in the *Lancet* before the time of the Analytical Sanitary Commission were equally general, although in the 1830's one writer, somewhat reminiscent of Accum, wrote that "many hundred persons are supported in London by the art of adulterating drugs"; still another estimated that in Great Britain there was "not more than one establishment in twenty free from this deadly and abominable traffic." [15]

With Hassall's reports and their subsequent publication in book form we begin to get more regular statistics on the extent of adulteration. Thus he reported that of 23 samples of gum opium analyzed, 19 were adulterated, many extensively; of 40 samples of powdered opium, only 1 was genuine; of 13 samples of resin of scammony as imported, only 1 was genuine, whereas only 1 of 17 was genuine as purchased from various chemists and druggists; 14 of 33, or nearly half, of the samples of powdered jalap were adulterated; 18 of 33, or more than half, of the samples of powdered ipecacuanha were adulterated; and 11 out of 28 samples of liquorice powder were adulterated.[16] Taken all together, Hassall's figures point to an over-all rate of about 55 per cent adulteration. In addition to this handful of drugs on which he reported in detail, Hassall also published a list of some nearly 50 other drugs, along with adulterations according to his own experience and those of numerous authorities of the time—a list he indicated "might have been greatly extended." [17] The actual extent of adulteration of a particular drug may be seen from Hassall's statement that the adulteration varied from 8 per cent to 75 per cent in the case of resin of scammony and from 18 per cent to 65 per cent in the case of powdered scammony, with one sample of resin being reported as completely factitious.[18] In his earlier book, *Food and Its Adulterations* (1855), Hassall referred to drugs only in the introduction, where he estimated that "nearly all the most useful and important articles of the materia medica are grossly and systematically adulterated, often to an enormous extent." [19] In later years, Hassall estimated that the over-all adulteration of all kinds, including foods and drugs, as represented by his reports for the period 1851–1854, amounted to about 61.59 per cent; [20] this figure was sometimes rounded off to 65 per cent.[21]

When we come to examine the testimony of witnesses before various Parliamentary Select Committees (1855, 1856, 1874, 1878–79, 1894, 1895, 1896), we find a wide range of views expressed, although mainly in general terms. Thus rather extensive adulteration was indicated by Hassall, Maurice Scanlan (an analytical chemist), J. Gordon (Mayor of Cork), Alphonse Normandy (physician and chemist), John Simon (officer of health), R. D. Thomson (physician and surgeon), and Thomas Herring (wholesale druggist) at the parliamentary hearings of 1855.[22] Charges of exaggeration were laid against the foregoing by Theophilus Redwood (professor of the Pharmaceutical Society), George Phillips (Chief Officer, Chemical Department, Board of Inland Revenue), and Richard A. Wallington (solicitor and chairman of a local board of health).[23]

Many of these same witnesses admitted that the picture was not entirely black and white. Scanlan and Herring indicated that pure drugs were available and that the situation was in general improving through the efforts of the Pharmaceutical Society of Great Britain; Redwood admitted some adulteration, but also referred to the salubrious effect of the Society.[24]

The deliberations of the Select Committee of 1856 again found witnesses lining up on opposing sides. Attesting to extensive adulteration of drugs were persons such as John Challice (a physician), Thomas Wakley (editor of the *Lancet*), Hassall, William Bastick (analytical chemist and sometime writer of "scare" tracts); [25] while opposite views were expressed by such people as James Baiss (wholesale druggist and drug grinder), James Drew (wholesale druggist), William Atkinson (manufacturing chemist of medicinals), Stafford Allen (manufacturing chemist), and Jacob Bell (*Pharmaceutical*

Journal editor).[26] On the subject of adulteration in general, that is, including foods, one witness (Richard Gay, formerly a spice and drug grinder) believed that "seven out of ten of all articles are adulterated"; and the Birmingham surgeon William Postgate found in his experience "about two-thirds of the articles . . . to be adulterated." [27] Such statements scarcely can be reconciled with that of Hassall that "there is not one-twentieth part of the adulteration now prevailing that did prevail some four or five years ago!" [28]

In the final analysis, it was how the Select Committee interpreted this testimony that was important. With regard to adulteration practices in general, it expressed the opinion that: "Though the witnesses differed both as to the extent to which adulteration is carried on and as to its nature and effects, your Committee cannot avoid the conclusion that adulteration widely prevails, although under circumstances of very various character." [29] The Committee's opinion with respect to drugs was similar; namely, that drugs were extensively adulterated and that it was "difficult to exaggerate the evils arising from the prevalence of the practice." [30] At the same time, the Committee recognized the beneficial results that have been achieved by the Pharmaceutical Society.[31] It is interesting that a considerably more detailed report touching pharmacy and drugs did not get beyond the draft stage.[32]

When the Select Committee of 1874 brought in its report there had already been time for the accumulation of some beneficial effects from legislation passed during the preceding decade and a half. The bulk of the testimony touching drugs—excepting that of William Henry Allen, a public analyst, lecturer on chemistry, and author, and of Henry C. Bartlett, a chemist—pointed to a considerable decrease in the practice of adulteration.[33] And Arthur Hill Hassall testified to the "vast diminution" of adulteration since he last appeared before such a committee eighteen years earlier.[34] The Committee's final report remained completely silent on the question of drugs.[35] That drugs occupied but little of the attention of those few analysts appointed (60 out of a possible 223 appointees) is obvious from an appendix to the *Report* that showed only 2 convictions for drug adulteration out of a total of 260 convictions during the year 1873.[36] One witness, when pushed to give some details of cases in which pharmacists had suffered hardships under the Act, was finally forced to admit that they had been "a good deal frighted [at the possible consequence], and not very much hurt." [37] Still another witness, while arguing that drugs should not come under the Adulteration Act since they were already covered in the Pharmacy Act (1868), admitted that he knew of no convictions for adulteration under the Act.[38]

Subsequent Select Committees during the remainder of the nineteenth century paid little or no attention to drugs. Thus nothing in the proceedings of the Committee of 1878–79 concerned itself with the extent of drug adulteration; there was considerable discussion however about making the *British Pharmacopoeia* the official standard for drugs under the Adulteration Act. During the hearings of the 1894 Committee, one of the general inspectors of the Local Government Board concluded that the evidence suggested that the adulteration of drugs was "probably not nearly so common as it may have been in times past." [39] The evidence in question was the reports of public analysts for 1893 that showed about 13 per cent of those drugs examined to be adulterated (as compared to 17 per cent for all articles). Yet the number of samples taken (751, of which 85 were adulterated) was still small compared to the total number of samples taken (37,233); and of the 85 samples reported as adulterated, only about one-third (35) were proceeded against and fewer still (28) had penalties imposed.[40]

And finally three witnesses before the Select Committee of 1895 agreed there was little material or systematic adulteration of drugs; and presumably on this basis the Committee concluded in 1896 that "the Act of 1875 has had excellent results in securing the purity of drugs on sale in the United Kingdom, and that at the present time they are not surpassed in this respect." [41]

One of the functions of the Local Government Board, created in 1871, was to provide a central body to look after the health needs of the country, including the administration of the Adulteration Acts. Beginning with the 6th Annual Report (for 1876) of the Board there were published percentages of adulteration and from the 7th Report onward, efforts were made to tabulate statistics reported by public analysts functioning under the Acts. While these reports did bring together a great deal of useful information, they retained throughout the century certain flaws. A leading analyst complained in 1894 that nowhere were full statistics available on the nature and average extent of adulteration, and that the Local Government Board reported only the percentage of samples found adulterated.[42] It was for similar reasons that Wigner had published his own analyses in the *Analyst* a quarter of a century earlier.[43]

In spite of flaws, these reports provide a better picture, based on a much broader sampling, than we could get in any other way. The results can best be summarized in tabular form (see Table 2).

TABLE 2

The Extent of Drug Adulteration, 1851–1931, as Reported in the Annual Reports of the Local Government Board

Year	All Articles					Drugs				
	Total samples taken	Total samples adulterated	% Adulteration	% Prosec.	% Fined	Total samples taken	Total samples adulterated	% Adulteration	% Total samples taken	% Total adulteration
1876	9,977	1,753	17.6	—a	—a	250	47	18.8	2.5	2.5
1877	14,706	2,826	19.2	—	—	503	110	21.8	3.4	3.8
1878	16,191	2,782	17.2	—	—	491	125	25.4	3.0	4.5
1879	17,049	2,535	14.8	—	—	613	171	27.8	3.6	6.7
1880	17,673	2,772	15.7	—	—	405	63	15.5	2.3	2.3
1881	17,823	2,613	14.7	—	—	398	60	15.5	2.2	2.3
1886	23,596	2,813	11.9	—	—	435	47	10.8	1.8	1.7
1891	29,028	3,540	12.2	60.4	52.0	740	121	16.4	2.6	3.4 b
1896	45,555	4,202	9.2	66.7	55.9	1,380	156	11.3	3.0	3.7
1901	67,841	5,989	8.8	60.1	49.0	2,301	268	11.6	3.4	4.5
1906	90,504	8,446	9.3	45.9	34.6	2,726	191	7.0	3.0	2.3
1931	136,169	6,324	4.6	—c	—c	5,257	236	4.5	3.9	3.7

Source: Statistical data were drawn from: "Sale of Food and Drugs Act," Annual Report of the Local Government Board, 1876–77, bound in House of Commons, 1877, Vol. 37.1, lxxvii–viii; LGBR, 1877–78, in H. of C., 1878, 37, Pt. I.1, xciv; LGBR, 1878–79, in H. of C., 1879, 28.1, cxxx; LGBR, 1879–80, in H. of C., 1880, 26.1, cx; LGBR, 1880–81, in H. of C., 1881, 46.1, lxxxvii; LGBR, 1881–82, in H. of C., 1882, 30, Pt. I.1, c; LGBR, 1886–87, in H. of C., 1887, 36.1, cxxxvii; LGBR, 1891–92, in H. of C., 1892, 38.1, cxli; LGBR, 1896–97, in H. of C., 1897, 36.1, cxl; LGBR, 1901–02, in H. of C., 1902, 35.1, clii; LGBR, 1906–07, in H. of C., 1907, 26.1, 238; and Annual Report of the Ministry of Health, 1931–1932, in H. of C., 1931–32, 10.1, 279.

a The reports for the years 1876–1886 did not include data on prosecutions and fines.

b 29.9% were prosecuted and 19.0% were fined.

c In 1931, the form of the report was again changed and data on prosecutions and fines were not given.

Drugs apparently were somewhat more often adulterated than the average, although staples such as milk, butter, coffee, and condiments were also heavily adulterated, and potable spirits usually exceeded all other substances in degree of adulteration.[44]

The figures do not tell the whole story. In 1877 the *Report* warned against "making broad distinctions" on the basis of the statistics, especially as to what constituted adulterated versus unadulterated. Some analysts apparently classified as "adulterated" all samples that were not chemically pure; others gave their results, but not the conclusions to be drawn therefrom; still others designated as adulterated only those samples in which the admixture was unusually high. The *Report* further admitted that a large proportion of the samples were so loosely categorized as adulterated that legal proceedings could never have been successfully sustained.[45]

The total number of drug samples taken gave cause for comment in a regular pattern throughout the century, beginning with the first *Report* (1877): "We regret that a larger number of samples of drugs have not been submitted to analysis." [46] Wigner also repeated the theme that "drugs need much more attention." [47] In general, compliance with the Acts remained disappointing to those concerned with their administration, but some of the most serious omissions concerned drugs. For example, in 1877, 18 out of 32 English and 2 out of 3 Welsh counties reporting took *no* drug samples; 2 counties took only 1 sample each; 5 more took fewer than 10 each; and of the remaining 7, 1 county took between 10 and 20 samples, 2 took between 20 and 30, 2 more took between 30 and 40, 1 took between 50 and 60, and only a single county took more than 100 samples.[48] That same year several English counties took no samples of any kind and 5 more together took a total of only 30 samples.[49] The same story was repeated with each report, so that nearly two decades later, in 1906, we find 3 out of 42 English and 6 out of 13 Welsh counties still took *no* samples of drugs. Of the remaining 39 English counties, 8 took fewer than 10 samples each, 20 took fewer than 100, 5 took between 100 and 200 samples each, 2 more took between 300 and 400, and London (with a population in excess of 4.5 million) took 437. Among those counties that took fewer than 100 samples each were 3 that had populations over 1 million (2 of these took fewer than 40).[50] The total number of samples of all kinds in relation to population also offers some gauge of compliance (see Table 3).

Equally significant is the number of cases in which prosecutions were made and penalties assessed, in relation to the total number of samples considered adulterated. Figures on drugs are available only

TABLE 3

Total Number of Food and Drug Samples Analyzed, 1877–1906,
in Relation to Population

Year	Number of samples analyzed	Ratio of samples to population
1877–81	16,888 [a]	1:1520
1882–86	21,772 [a]	1:1237
1887–90	26,846 [a]	1:1060
1891	29,028	1:999
1896	45,555	1:636
1901	67,841	1:479
1906	90,504	1:359

Source: Statistical data were drawn from "Sale of Food and Drugs Act,"
Annual Report of the Local Government Board, 1891–92, bound in *House of
Commons, 1892,* Vol. 38.1, cxxxix–cxl; *LGBR, 1896–97,* in *H. of C., 1897,* 36.1,
cxxxviii; *LGBR, 1901–02,* in *H. of C., 1902,* 35.1, cli; and *LGBR, 1906–07;* in
H. of C., 1906, 26.1, xcviii.

[a] Figures shown are averages for five-year periods.

for 1891. As Table 2 shows, fewer than one-third of the drug cases in
which adulteration was found analytically were brought to trial, and
fewer than one-fifth had penalties assessed. Of all drug samples
examined, fewer than 5 per cent were taken to court, and only about
3 per cent had penalties imposed.

The low incidence of prosecutions and penalties may be attributed
to factors revolving around the definition of adulteration and attitudes about punishment, among other problems involved in administering the Acts, which we shall discuss in more detail later. A
further complication was a question of what constituted "adulteration" as opposed to acceptable "trade practices." [51] On the other hand
the statistics may be somewhat unbalanced in the sense that analysts
tended to collect samples according to what the current trends suggested might prove to be adulterated. This of course would not be an
accurate picture of the purity of drugs in general. For example, sweet
spirits of nitre was almost always reported in violation, amounting to
more than half the total adulterated drug samples in 1886, about 25
per cent of the total in 1896, and about 30 per cent of the total in
1906; nitre along with rhubarb constituted almost half of the total in
1895.[52] In the case of this particular drug the problem was often loss
of strength through high volatility rather than intentional dilution.

Adulteration often had more serious implications than in the case
of sweet spirits of nitre, even though the number of cases involved
might be small. Thus jalap was reported containing two-thirds

strychnine; "quinine wine" was totally lacking in quinine; tincture of rhubarb was barely half strength in one shop; paregoric lacked opium; tartaric acid contained lead in sufficient quantity to cause injury; borax contained arsenic.[53] (The bulk of the cases involving paregoric without opium apparently involved "small shopkeepers" who were not pharmacists and therefore not permitted to sell poisons under the Pharmacy Act.[54]) Of all the reports examined only that of 1906 listed by name all the drugs examined and the number of samples of each found to be adulterated.[55] In most instances only a few examples were mentioned of the more noteworthy adulterations. We can get some further idea of the nature of drug adulterations from the legal reports published in the *Analyst*, but the same impression is gained of general inadequacies of sampling and concentration on so-called "trade" questions, which usually involved products whose names were little or not at all related to their composition, or whose names carried over from earlier editions of the *Pharmacopoeia*, but whose composition changed in later editions.[56]

Although the number of samples submitted for analysis by the public always remained small, the extent of adulteration in such samples was always several times greater than the average adulteration. Thus, in 1886, samples of all substances submitted by the public were found to be nearly 21 per cent adulterated, as opposed to 10.8 per cent on the average (see Table 2); in 1891, 34.5 per cent, as opposed to 12.2 per cent; in 1896, 20 per cent, as opposed to 9.2 per cent; in 1901, 29.4 per cent, as opposed to 8.8 per cent; and in 1906, 20 per cent, as opposed to 9.3 per cent.[57] It was recognized at the time that this was primarily because private persons had to be quite convinced that adulteration existed before they went to the effort and expense of having samples analyzed.

At this point we recognize more clearly the difficulty of giving an unqualified answer to the question of the extent of drug adulteration. We can safely conclude, however, that there was a drastic diminution of the problem during the period under consideration.

The persons indicted for these practices will be met again briefly when we examine the over-all role played by the Pharmaceutical Society of Great Britain, so here we shall only summarize the general views or evidence on the subject. Renegades representative of all occupational classes involved in marketing drugs—from the time of their collection to the time of their delivery to the patient—were implicated at various times, but with significantly different frequency. These included drug collectors (usually natives of foreign countries), importers, roasters and grinders, wholesalers, manufacturers, and retailers (primarily spicers or herbalists), grocers, and pharmacists (dispensing "chemists and druggists").

Accum accused all classes, yet perhaps pointed the finger most at the drug grinders in his statement that "every chemist knows . . . there are mills constantly at work in this metropolis, which furnish bark powder [cinchona containing quinine] at a much cheaper rate than the substance can be procured for in its natural state." He referred also to the "amazingly large scale" on which certain "manufacturers" (meaning grinders?) turned out other powdered drugs.[58] And Phillips of course directed his attention in the 1840's toward his fellow pharmacists.

Hassall likewise laid much of the blame upon the drug grinders and, to a lesser extent, upon the wholesalers, without completely exonerating the others. Thus in the case of jalap he accused the wholesalers and grinders, while excusing the pharmacists; in the case of scammony resin he recognized its adulteration before import; and in the case of laudanum, he claimed only one pharmacist in six prepared it with sufficient opium.[59] In his testimony to the Select Committee of 1855 he again referred to adulteration abroad before importation and to some extent by the retailers, but expressed no hesitation in saying that "a very large proportion of the adulteration practised with drugs . . . is due to the drug-grinder." [60]

And the testimony of other witnesses at that and subsequent Select Committee hearings seemed to bear out Hassall's convictions. Warrington, Gordon, Redwood, Letheby, all spoke in 1855 of the guilt of drug grinders.[61] Thomson spoke of circumstances under which certain wholesale druggists would supply any powdered drug at a minimum price, while Herring and Letheby defended the general honesty of the wholesale dealers.[62] Herring conceded that some pharmacists were willing to sell impure drugs, while Postgate felt they were often imposed upon by the manufacturers who supplied them.[63]

During re-examination the following year, before the Select Committee of 1856, Hassall repeated his opinions, and again thought "more generally the drug-grinder is at fault." [64] While a great deal of new testimony focused upon the drug grinder, only one witness accused the generality of drug grinders of making up the usual losses in weight through grinding or evaporation by adding inert matter. All the others conceded that this might have been customary in former times but was so no longer.[65] Considerable discussion during the 1856 hearings dealt with preventing the importation of adulterated drugs.[66]

By the time of the Select Committee of 1874, according to testimony, adulteration before importation seemed the primary problem.[67] By the end of the nineteenth century in Britain the extent of drug adulteration thus had diminished considerably, as had the extent of involvement of the various groups through whose hands these drugs passed on their way from the source to the consumer.

10.

CHANGING CONCEPTS
OF DRUG ADULTERATION

It is impossible to frame an enactment on this subject which shall rely on strict definitions.[1]

One of the most bothersome difficulties that arose in administering English food and drug laws hinged upon a fundamental element, "the want of a clear understanding as to what *does* and what *does not* constitute adulteration."[2] This deficiency was recognized by Parliament's Select Committee of 1874, by many individuals, and by the Society of Public Analysts. Yet, the major British Sale of Food and Drugs Act of 1875 that was to be amended repeatedly and remain in effect until 1928 avoided even the word "adulteration"; and no satisfactory definition was incorporated into the legislation during the entire period under consideration (to 1906).[3]

Two major species of adulteration received consideration during the nineteenth century: fraudulent adulteration intended to increase weight or bulk, or improve the appearance of a substandard product; and the addition of deleterious substances that could be injurious to health. Primary concern centered upon the latter type, as reflected in the conclusion of the 1874 Select Committee that the public was exposed to fraudulent rather than to deleterious adulteration.[4] In other words, their pocketbooks suffered rather than their health.

In spite of the tendency to stress deleterious rather than innocuous fraudulent adulteration, most reformers, such as Arthur Hill Hassall in England, felt strongly that legislative control of both types was necessary. Accordingly, he defined adulteration as consisting of the

126

"intentional addition to an article, for purposes of gain or deception, of any substance or substances, the presence of which is not acknowledged in the name under which the article is sold." [5]

Many others felt a need to recognize and differentiate the two main species of adulteration (deleterious and pecuniary). Accum nowhere specifically defined adulteration; but he clearly distinguished between innocuous adulteration ("the sophistication [which], though it may affect our purse, does not injure our health") and adulteration deleterious to health ("of all possible nefarious traffic and deception, practised by mercenary dealers . . . [it is] the most criminal, and in the mind of every honest man, must excite feelings of regret and disgust").[6] The distinction also was made by Accum's successors in the field of popular treatises on adulteration: *The Domestic Chemist* (1831) and *The Tricks of Trade* (1859).[7] The anonymous author of *Tricks of Trade* considered that "adulteration always implies cheating . . . taking advantage either of the confidence or ignorance of the purchases"; but he clearly distinguished between innocuous and injurious adulteration as "misdemeanor" and "criminal." "If for the sake of extra profit, the dealer adulterates his goods with what he knows to be injurious substances," continued the writer, "he places himself in the same category with the man who deliberately poisons another to obtain his property. The former is simply committing in detail the crime which the other perpetrates in gross." [8] Hassall and Postgate, recognizing the need for controlling both types of adulteration, still saw a reason to differentiate between fraudulent and injurious adulteration; and this recognition also appeared in the 1856 *Report of the Select Committee*.[9] These remarks show that the duality of definitions covering adulteration extended to the nature of the punishment that should ensue. The importance of this will become clearer in our discussion of changing official sanctions against adulteration.

By stressing the intentional character of the act of adulteration, Hassall ruled out substitutions, impurities, and accidental contaminations.[10] Intent was one of the main grounds upon which most legal definitions of adulteration were based, but it also created one of the many legal problems associated with enforcement of adulteration legislation. The problem was to *prove* willful admixture.

This problem was already acute in enforcement of the first broad British Adulteration Act (1860), which applied only to food and drink. One committed an offense by selling an article "with which to the knowledge of [the seller], any Ingredient or Material injurious to the Health of Persons eating or drinking such Article has been mixed," and also by selling as pure and unadulterated what was in fact adulterated or impure.[11] As a result of this clause, and for other reasons, the Act proved practically inoperative. The problem had perhaps been foreshadowed already by the opinion of the 1856 Select Committee on Adulteration which considered that "the object of the law [is] . . . to strike at fraud, and wherever a fraudulent intention can be proved, there to inflict a penalty." Unfortunately for advocates of control, the Committee's *Report* also expressed the opinion that "what constitutes fraud must be left to the interpretation of the administrators of the law." A defendant was expected to prove satisfactorily that he was unaware of the adulteration, unless he had "evinced a culpable ignorance of the trade which he professed to follow." [12] Considering that administrators of the law had little experience, and often as little qualification, it is not surprising that proving guilty knowledge should become an insurmountable obstacle, even in those few areas where an attempt was made to carry out the law.

The same interpretation—that is the necessity of proving guilty knowledge—was subsequently read into the Sale of Food and Drugs Act of 1875, but the burden of proving absence of such guilty knowledge now rested with the defendant and not with the government prosecutor as it had in the previous Acts of 1860 and 1872 (extending the 1860 Act to drugs).

Following an opinion of some of its leading witnesses (such as Hassall and John Postgate, the Birmingham surgeon whose interest in pure foods and drugs stimulated action in Parliament), the 1856 Select Committee recognized both fraudulent (or pecuniary) and deleterious (or pernicious, injurious, poisonous) adulteration as requiring government action. But it carefully stipulated that innocuous admixture should not be legally restricted if known to the buyer and to his financial advantage, or if done for reason of preservation. It saw such a restriction as impeding freedom of commerce and clearly indicated that the consumer could be guarded against any danger from such admixture by requiring that such mixtures not be passed off as pure substances.[13] The 1856 *Report* concluded: "Subject to these qualifications [i.e., innocuous mixtures, proof of innocence, or culpable ignorance], the law should be clear and positive in forbidding adulteration, and in punishing those who practice it." [14] Rather ironically, the law of 1860 was neither clear nor positive; and its 1872 amendment, which included drugs for the first time, clarified little.

The 1872 Act considered the adulteration of drugs to consist of willful admixture or the direction to another person to carry out such admixture. Like the 1860 Act it made it an offence to sell impure or adulterated goods as pure and unadulterated, and it added a new section (3.) regarding fraudulent admixture. It became unlawful to sell a drug known to be fraudulently mixed with other substances, for purposes of increasing its weight or bulk, without declaring such admixture.[15] This last seems obviously modeled upon Hassall's all-embracing definition.[16]

From the beginning, the adulteration of drugs was considered more reprehensible than the adulteration of food. It was clear to Hassall, to the English chemist and author Alphonse Normandy (an important witness before the 1855–1856 Select Committee hearings), and to many others that the adulteration of drugs constituted a practice dangerous to health, whether innocuous or deleterious admixture took place.[17]

That foods might be unhealthy as the result of innocuous adulteration because of reduced nutritional value was also recognized. As a result, it seemed desirable not only to control the fraudulent admixture of innocuous ingredients but also to control the fraudulent extraction of important constituents. This found expression in the *Report of the Select Committee* investigating the Act of 1872, just barely two years (1874) after it went into effect. But the Committee carefully pointed out "that a distinction should be drawn between this and the fraudulent or noxious addition of ingredients which more strictly speaking constitutes adulteration."[18] The Act of 1872 already included provisions against fraudulent admixture, and the Act of 1875, following upon the recommendations of the 1874 Committee, forbade unacknowledged extraction of constituents affecting "injuriously [the] quality, substance, or nature," of a substance. But the offense applied only to food.[19]

How did the Act of 1875 define drug adulteration? Perhaps as a result of the findings of the 1872 Committee that the 1872 Act had "inflicted considerable injury, and imposed heavy and undeserved penalties upon some respectable tradesmen," the new Act of 1875 avoided completely the term "adulteration."[20] It defined "drug" as including "medicine for internal or external use," thereby creating problems over certain commercial products and quasi-medicinal products.[21] The statute considered the following acts as offenses with respect to drugs: (1) the mixing, coloring, staining, or powdering of drugs or the ordering or permission to any other person so to treat— "with any ingredient or material so as to affect injuriously the quality or potency of such drug, with intent that the same may be sold in that state," or the sale of a drug so treated; [22] (2) the sale to the "prejudice" of the purchaser of a drug, "not of the nature, substance, and quality of the article demanded," except for (a) a non-injurious, non-fraudulent, non-concealing addition, required for purposes of preservation or production, (b) a proprietary medicine, (c) a compound (prescriptions), (d) unavoidable admixture of extraneous matter, in the process of collection or preparation; [23] (3) the sale of a compounded drug—that is, a prescription or recipe, medical or otherwise—"not composed of ingredients in accordance with the demand of the purchaser"; and (4) false labelling.[24] The major exceptions, or protections for the seller, aside from those already mentioned included the possession of a written warranty from the manufacturer indicating the article to be of the nature demanded and written (label) or verbal notice to the purchaser of admixture (non-injurious and non-fraudulent).[25] This legislation remained fully in effect, with amendments, until 1928, when only portions were still retained. Unsatisfactory as the measure was in many respects, it influenced the development of comparable comprehensive legislation in other countries, notably Canada and the United States.[26]

Before 1906, the Act underwent two amendments. The first, in 1879, clarified the meaning of "prejudice" under section 6 to include samples purchased for analysis; and, under the same section, forbade the claim that an article, "though defective in nature or in substance or in quality, was not defective in all three respects." [27] The second amendment, in 1899, required distinctive labelling of permissible admixture (sec. 8, 1875), without causing interference with labels or trademarks in use for at least seven years and allowed the sale (to inspectors) of unopened tins or packets, duly labelled.[28]

In the light of modern legal definitions of drug adulteration, it is striking that none of this British nineteenth-century legislation indicated how the courts or the analysts were to determine the existence or degree of adulteration. The 1875 Act described a variety of offenses, but set no guides. Hassall expressed the desirability of "some specification drawn as a guide," for those administering the law, and of some central power to oversee such administration. Postgate likewise referred to the need of some central body or authority—such as the Board of Health—to decide what constituted injurious, pernicious, and poisonous adulteration.[29]

Where then were the references to standards or limits of purity? How did the *British Pharmacopoeia* come into the picture? Neither it nor any other standard of drugs was recognized officially by the Act of 1875, or by any of its amendments during the nineteenth century.

In practice, however, analysts and the courts considered the *Pharma-copoeia* as their standard for all preparations it contained, in spite of recognized inadequacies of that work.[30] We have seen that section 6 of the Act, considering it an offense to sell to the "prejudice" of the purchaser any drug "not of the nature, substance, and quality of the article demanded," was interpreted in the light of the *Pharmacopoeia* for any preparations contained therein. If many pharmacists doubted the legality of the *British Pharmacopoeia* as a standard under the Sale of Food and Drugs Act, the average practitioner probably felt morally obligated to use it as the standard. As a matter of fact, the Pharmacy Act of 1868 made it an offense to "compound any Medicines of the *British Pharmacopoeia* except according to the Formularies [sic] of the said Pharmacopoeia."[31] Accordingly, any person asking for a preparation contained in the *Pharmacopoeia* and not receiving it could consider himself "prejudiced" in the transaction. Strictly speaking, the *British Pharmacopoeia* had no official legal status in the Act of 1875, although it was "official" after 1868 through the Pharmacy Act. It had such status briefly through the 1872 amendment of the Adulteration of Food Act of 1860 which (in sec. 4) incorporated the Pharmacy Act of 1868.

As a result of the rather peculiar British system of amending and incorporating, without repealing existing statutes, this action gave double recognition to the *British Pharmacopoeia*. Because the 1872 Act included the whole of the Pharmacy Act, it gave legal force to the *Pharmacopoeia* through section 15 of that Act (referred to above); at the same time it incorporated section 24 of the Pharmacy Act, extending the 1860 Adulteration Act to medicines. This section clearly stated that "all Articles usually taken or sold as Medicines, and every Adulteration of any such Article shall be deemed an Admixture injurious to Health; and any Person registered under this Act who sells any such Article adulterated shall, unless the contrary be proved, be deemed to have Knowledge of such Adulteration."[32]

We see then that drug adulteration came under legislative control in 1868, and that from 1872 to 1875 the *British Pharmacopoeia* received official legal recognition under the Adulteration Acts. Did no one realize the importance of official standards to the meaningful administration of the 1875 Act and its later amendments? The group most intimately associated with the administration of the Food and Drug Acts, the Society of Public Analysts—founded in 1874, partly as a result of the criticism levied by the Select Committee of that year against the conflicting decisions and inexperience of public analysts —stressed the importance of clear definitions of adulteration and standards or limits of purity. In fact, the first task set for the organizing committee of the Society, centered about drawing up definitions of adulteration, and suggestions for limits or standards. The definition submitted a few months later by that committee— consisting of the chairman, Theophilus Redwood, energetic leader of the Pharmaceutical Society of Great Britain and first president of the Society of Public Analysts, and the Society's secretaries Charles Heisch and G. W. Wigner—is almost identical to the one incorporated into virtually all the subsequent legislation on adulteration in America. Wigner incorporated the same definition into the model adulteration act that won the first prize of the National Board of Trade of the United States (1880), and it subsequently found its way into the adulteration laws of New York State (1881), Massachusetts (1882), New Jersey (1881), Canada (1884), and in a somewhat changed form into the rough draft of an adulteration law for New York State proposed in 1879 by the American physician Edward R. Squibb.[33] Ironically, as we have seen, the definition did not enter the Act of 1875 or its 1879 and 1899 amendments, in spite of the efforts of the Society. As originally proposed, the definition stated that a drug be considered adulterated:

(1) if, when retailed for medicinal purposes under a name recognised in the British Pharmacopoeia, it be not equal in strength and purity to the standard laid down in that work, or
(2) if, when sold under a name not recognised in the British Pharmacopoeia it differ materially from the standard laid down in approved works on materia medica, or the professed standard under which it was sold.[34]

The issue of standards and definitions came up again when a special Select Committee deliberated in 1878 and 1879 on the working of the 1875 Act. Perhaps one of the most telling blows against adopting the *British Pharmacopoeia* as the official standard under the Act came from James Bell, chief of the laboratory at Somerset House (of the Department of Inland Revenue), which was the court of reference for all disputed cases of analysis. Bell felt such a provision would be "very difficult to carry out," because "in the preparation of many compounds you cannot in practice get the article of the exact composition laid down in the British Pharmacopoeia." He felt that such action would mean prosecution for the slightest deviation from the *Pharmacopoeia* and although Somerset House referred everything to the *Pharmacopoeia*, he felt a certain allowance needed to be made; and that "As the Act stands it will gradually be applied to drugs, and that it will be found to work." [35] Bell's view was opposed by others, including some government officials, who considered the desirability of incorporating section 15 of the Pharmacy Act (1868), as it had been incorporated in 1872.[36] These officials saw no necessity to label a preparation as deviating from the *British Pharmacopoeia* if it were merely stated that it had not been prepared according to the *British Pharmacopoeia*.[37]

In an appendix to the *Report of the Select Committee* (1879), Charles Graham, an analyst and Professor of Chemical Technology at University College, London, made, under the heading "Provisions for Definitions of Genuineness and Adulteration," the following telling point concerning the "abundance of disagreement" in the administration of the 1875 Act:

If it be deemed advisable that the alcoholic strength of genuine spirits be defined by Parliament, much more needful is it that some competent authority, such as the Local Government Board, should define what constitutes adulteration or admixture in important articles of food and medicine.[38]

Graham freely acknowledged the significant contributions to the standards by the Society of Public Analysts, but noted that they were only suggestive and could not be forced upon their own members, much less upon non-members such as himself.[39]

The question of definitions, standards, systematization of analytical methods, and detailed analytical investigations of foods and drugs came up again at the end of the century. As a result of renewed interest in improving existing legislation, the Society of Public Analysts called a semi-public meeting, in 1893, to consider the advisability of establishing a board of reference—with broad representation from appropriate bodies—to consider these questions. The Society also drew up a draft Sale of Food and Drugs Bill;[40] and participated actively in the proceedings of the Select Committee that met during 1894, 1895, and 1896. In spite of the good that came of Society participation, the Society and others were extremely disappointed that the 1899 amendment ignored their suggestions for a court or board of reference to deal with questions of definitions and standards. The chief benefits derived in the amended legislation were an enlarged definition of the term "food" and a provision for the Board of Agriculture to define limits in connection with certain dairy products.

The problem of adequate and clear definitions of drug adulteration plagued the administration of food and drug legislation from the time of the first Act of 1860 and still remained with the 1899 amendment to the great Act of 1875. Many individuals sought to correct this defect, but English government leaned too strongly in the direction of laissez faire throughout the period to introduce such a restriction.

The earliest definitions stressed deleterious rather than fraudulent adulteration, but both had evoked concern from the beginning. Innocuous admixtures, appropriately declared, were accepted by 1872, in an effort to recognize public demand for different grades of substances and to avoid undue harassment of trade and commerce.

The stress upon non-interference became even clearer with the 1874 investigations and the 1875 Act, which avoided the term "adulteration" completely, and defined in detail offenses under the Act, with numerous exceptions. The Act did define the term "drug," but not clearly enough to avoid difficulties.

In spite of repeated efforts to establish official standards for drugs, by means of the *British Pharmacopoeia* or otherwise, the *Pharmacopoeia* received only brief official recognition (1872–1875) under the Adulteration Acts. It received official sanction under the Pharmacy Act of 1868, and was regarded as the standard for drugs by analysts and the courts administering the 1875 Act and its amendments.[41] Under the provisions of the 1875 Act, it was considered to the "prejudice" of the purchaser (a punishable offense) to sell an article differing from one recognized in the *Pharmacopoeia,* because it was not of the "nature, substance, and quality" of the article demanded. For non-*Pharmacopoeial* preparations, no standard existed.

The proof of intent remained part of the legal definitions, but in 1875 the burden of proof shifted from the government to the defendant. Removal of vital constituents received official attention only in connection with foods (1875); though no limits were set. Additions for the purpose of preservation or preparation received official sanction (in 1875), and proprietary articles were exempt (in 1875).

The principal elements of nineteenth-century legal definitions of adulteration centered about the intent and knowledge of the manufacturer and vendor, and recognition of the demands of the purchaser, partly in the light of his inability to distinguish adulteration. In discussing the problem of definitions, it was suggested that "Some time ago when the Committee [1874] who had charge of the Adulteration of Food and Drug Bill, had some difficulty in defining breaches of the law, they should have referred to the [definition made in 1617 by the Apothecaries' Company] . . . as likely to meet every possible delinquent." [42] This definition had given power to punish the possession of any "unlawful, deceitful, inveterate, out of use, unwholesome, corrupt, unmedicinable, pernicious, or hurtful" drug.[43] In spite of difficulties created by the absence of clear-cut legal definition in the nineteenth century, legal sanctions under the Adulteration Acts reflected clearly the official light in which adulteration was viewed.

11.

CHANGING ATTITUDES
AND SANCTIONS

Adulteration is either a fraud or it is not, and it should be punished like any other cheating.[1]

English legislators apparently only agreed with Gilbert and Sullivan's droll directive to "let the punishment fit the crime" when deciding the relative severity of punishment between one form of adulteration and another, but not between adulteration and other forms of crime. Fredrick Accum commented, with a zealous flair, in 1820:

It is really astonishing that the penal law is not more effectually enforced against practices so inimical to the public welfare. The man who robs a fellow subject of a few shillings on the high-way, is sentenced to death, while he who distributes a slow poison to a whole community, escapes unpunished.[2]

Capital punishment for thefts of less than five shillings actually had become illegal in England only a decade earlier (1810), but more than a hundred other petty crimes were not removed from the list for which the law authorized capital punishment until 1834.

The official sanctions against fraud and adulteration (drugs included) had not always been so lenient as Accum depicted them. In the anonymous and sensational *Deadly Adulteration*, the author spoke of "this wholesome severity," referring to the punishment meted out by James I and William III against medical quacks. He spoke of the convicted being exposed to the pillory, whipped, branded, and banished. And, in addition, he described the convicted quack

being led by the hangman through the streets on horseback, seated
toward the horse's rear, with the tail in his hands and with a collar of
urinals dangling around his neck.[3] There is more exaggeration in the
author's style than in the severity of punishments portrayed.

In England any adulterated drugs found in the shops of apothecaries were usually burned in the street before the shop—in accordance with the 1617 Charter of the Apothecaries' Company—and the
practitioner himself punished in various ways, including expulsion
from the Company or banishment from London.[4] In time the inspection of apothecaries and system of punishment became more refined;
the confiscated drugs were burnt more privately and a fine was
inflicted. In medieval Nürnberg, several adulterators of saffron had
been burnt along with their adulterated goods.[5] The English apothecaries' guild had powers of inspection over apothecary shops. While
the College of Physicians also had power to inspect London apothecaries, as well as the "chemists and druggists," these visitations (see
Plate IV) seem to have been carried out infrequently and perhaps
inadequately.[6]

The Apothecaries' Act of 1815 gave to the Society of Apothecaries
the right to enter any shop in England or Wales in which pharmacy
was practiced and to destroy any inferior drugs it found there. This
power seems not to have been used, though the act remained in effect
through the nineteenth century.[7] The changing role of apothecaries
from practitioners of pharmacy to that of medicine was fairly complete by this time, and this may account for the law's remaining
largely a dead letter. Besides, legal clauses that would have controlled
the new class of dispensing "chemists and druggists" were sufficiently amended to hamper serious enforcement among this class.[8]

What forms of punishment found greatest favor during the nineteenth century, and how was this attitude toward punishment reflected in the legal measures enacted? We shall consider here mainly
the official legal sanctions against adulteration, but it is interesting to
see them in the light of the opinions of those associated with the
reform movement.

A few individuals, such as the Edinburgh physician Christison—
heartily opposed by Jacob Bell and other leading figures of the Pharmaceutical Society of Great Britain—still favored some system of
regular inspection of pharmacies. A carry-over from the medieval
system of inspections by professional and craft guilds, these inspections, as we saw, had proved ineffectual in the hands of the Apothecaries' Company and College of Physicians.

Organized pharmacy's opposition to such methods stemmed

clearly from the association of this procedure with medical domi-
nance and with the state of affairs before pharmacy's professional
emergence. Bell carefully pointed out that Christison made this suggestion (in 1838) before the chemists and druggists united for purposes of their own regulation (in 1841), and declared, "If we perse-
vere in the course which has now been adopted, any extraneous and
inquisitorial interference will be altogether superseded." [9] Although
he gave credit for the concern and efforts of the medical profession to
prevent drug adulteration, Bell concluded (in an earlier discussion of
the same subject):

Cases of adulteration have been published in the newspapers, and worthless drugs have been publicly cast into the streets. But it is not by a
septennial visitation of a few Druggists' shops, or an occasional exposure
of pharmaceutical dishonesty, that a complete reform can be effected.[10]

It becomes apparent from other comments made by Bell and
members of the Society that they felt the best results could be
obtained from summary punishment and publication of the names of
offenders. In keeping with the Society's stress upon education to
solve drug adulteration problems among its own ranks, it declared
that publicity of this sort would serve to put the public on its guard,
as would the dissemination of greater knowledge on the subject of
adulteration.[11] The strong reaction against the use of this technique
therefore sounds curious a decade later when the publication of
names by the *Lancet* was deemed sometimes "calculated to convey
an unfair and erroneous impression." [12] The explanation may be that
the members of the Society resented interference into what they
considered their internal affairs.

The lenient attitude of the Society, or some of its members, on
matters touching adulteration did not go unnoticed at that time.
E. M. Holmes, a leading member of the Pharmaceutical Society and of
the Pharmaceutical Conference, upheld (1882) his opinion concerning the limited value of publishing cases as a deterrent and favored
more detailed descriptions of analyses for the detection of adulteration. In 1891 the *Pharmaceutical Journal's* editor answered a criticism from one of England's leading analysts, A. H. Allen, by stating
that the journal raised no objections to the publication of names,
provided the source of the drugs was fully acknowledged (i.e.,
whether from registered pharmacists or unlicensed dealers).[13]

Hassall, Wakley, and others strongly favored publicity over punishment in their evidence before the 1855 and 1856 Select Committees, and in their publications, but the *Pharmaceutical Journal* seems
to have shifted toward summary punishment.[14] Accum, of course,

strongly emphasized the value of publicity to deter adulteration practices, and his daring to do so prematurely perhaps led to his ultimate
self-exile from England.[15] The anonymous *Tricks of Trade* (1859),
which appeared in the midst of the first flurry of excitement over
adulteration, also stressed publicity and pointed out the strong feeling of some legislators on the subject.[16] Hassall and others, as we will
see, did not pin all their hopes upon publicity. They realized that
fines and imprisonment were essential to discourage adulteration,
and felt the Select Committees of 1855 and 1856 did not see clearly
enough the need for severe punishment for the worst offenders.
Hassall wrote in 1857:

What is required is, that adulteration should be branded as a crime, and
this can only be done by affixing to it some punishment which shall entail
discredit and disgrace, such as that of imprisonment. We are therefore
decidedly of the opinion that imprisonment ought to form one of the
punishments for adulteration, it being reserved for the worst cases, and
for second offences. The punishment by fines only will effect little or
nothing for the suppression of adulteration.[17]

Accum had stressed severe punishment, in keeping with the nature
of the crime; the anonymous *Deadly Adulteration* suggested that
"transportation ought to be the mildest punishment of the iniquitous
offender"; the anonymous *Tricks of Trade* considered the misdemeanor criminal and felt punishment should be dealt accordingly.[18]

Several forms of punishment that had not appeared in the British
Acts, yet were commonly applied in earlier times along with public
humiliation and physical chastisement, were the seizure and destruction of the adulterated drugs, or other goods, and in serious
cases the expulsion of the offender from his trade and sometimes
from his town. Hassall pointed to the absence of these means of
deterring adulterators in the *Select Committee Report* of 1856, while
they were included in foreign laws.[19] Expulsion from practice did of
course remain a prerogative of the Pharmaceutical Society, although
we are unaware of its ever being used to punish a convicted adulterator.

Undoubtedly the greatest factor preventing the development of
severe official sanctions against food and drug adulteration lay in the
pronounced laissez faire attitude of British government. This is obvious from the tenor of *Select Committee Reports*, as it is from the
comments of most of the popular treatises on adulteration to appear
in English, from the time of Accum onward. Accum observed:

It has been urged by some that, under so vast a system of finance as that
of Great Britain, it is expedient that the revenue should be collected in

large amounts; and therefore that the severity of the law should be relaxed in favour of all mercantile concerns in proportion to their extent: encouragement must be given to large capitalists.[20]

The predominant note of the *Select Committee Report* of 1874, preceding the Act of 1875, was the strong desire of the government not "to hamper the buyer or fetter trade, still less to interfere between the buyer and seller with the view of regulating prices, or attempting to assist the consumer in ascertaining the real money value of any marketable commodity." [21] The Committee of 1856 had rejected the recommendations of certain witnesses to adopt the inspection systems carried out by some foreign countries as involving "so many hindrances to the free course of supply and demand, as to unfit them for the commercial usages of this country." [22]

That the legislature could deal severe penalties in cases in which they felt it merited, usually in connection with the excise, is obvious from an 1816 Act providing a five-hundred-pound fine, plus forfeiture of the goods in question, against any "druggist, vendor of, or dealer in drugs, or chemist or other person" selling substances to brewers to be used in falsifying or adulterating beer.[23] We already noted that the legislature was criticized for defining standards for alcohol while at the same time ignoring standards for foods and drugs.[24]

Many drugs imported into England came under the laws of customs and excise and were subject to import duties. Such duties seem to have discouraged importation of cheaper substitutes for genuine drugs (the duties being the same), but might have encouraged domestic adulteration of drugs carrying high import duties. Certain members of the Pharmaceutical Society thought this system was "of necessity inquisitorial and oppressive," while at the same time they regretted that "less oppressive and objectionable" methods could not be found for raising revenue.[25] Import duties acted indirectly as a levy or fine against adulteration and for this reason are mentioned briefly here. How effective were these duties? In spite of their so-called "inquisitorial" character, it seems doubtful that they prevented the importation of adulterated drugs as much as some individuals believed. An earlier practice of remitting half the duty on damaged or inferior drugs apparently had been stopped upon the protest of certain wholesale houses. But drugs of depreciated quality unclaimed and "considered not to be worth the charges due thereon" continued to be sold at public auction.[26]

Although the expert witnesses testifying before the Select Committees on Adulteration of 1855 and 1856 did not all agree as to the form that punishments for adulteration should take, few of them probably agreed with the minimal fine included in the 1860 Act that resulted from these hearings, a fine not exceeding £5,[27] together with costs, for each offense. No distinction was made between the act of adulteration and the sale of an adulterated preparation; and apparently any number of offenses might be committed without any increase in the amount of the fine, which amounted to little more than a license fee to the miscreant. Even the relatively minor good that might result from this legislation was partly negated by the fact that compliance with it in specific areas remained entirely voluntary, according to the inclination of district boards or town councils. Besides, it proved virtually impossible to prove willfulness on the part of accused persons, as the law provided; those analysts who were appointed had no guides or standards to follow in judging purity; there were no courts of reference to settle disputes between analysts if these arose.

The Pharmacy Act of 1868 gave extra stringency to the measure by considering all adulterations of medicines to be injurious, and by assuming "guilty knowledge" (willfulness) unless proved otherwise. The extent of the punishment which the Pharmaceutical Society of Great Britain could inflict under the Pharmacy Act was to strike the name of the convicted offender from its register.[28] The Pharmacy Act of 1868 did give powers of registration and examination of pharmaceutical chemists, and of dispensing chemists and druggists, to the Pharmaceutical Society, but it offered no control over a myriad of merchants dealing in drugs commercially or in quasi-medicinal substances.

The 1872 amendment of the 1860 Adulteration Act extended this legislation to drugs and increased the scope of punishable offenses somewhat. Yet while the 1872 Act increased penalties for adulteration and adjusted penalties in terms of the nature of the offense, this law suffered from the same administrative difficulties as its earlier version. Willful admixture of ingredients injurious to health was now punishable by a maximum fine of £50, plus costs, for the first offense; and a maximum imprisonment of six months with hard labor for the second. The sale of an adulterated article as pure or unadulterated brought a fine of £20, plus costs, for the first offense; and the publication—at the offender's expense—of the name, address, and offense "in such newspaper or in such other manner as . . . shall seem desirable" for a second offense of the same nature. (Fraudulent admixture was considered to be adulteration under this Act.[29])

The significance of these stricter penalties dims considerably in the light of the findings of the Select Committee (1874), appointed to look into the operation of the Act. Among their conclusions was a revealing comment upon the effectiveness of application of the Act and so of its penalties: "The adoption of the Act has been by no means general" (26 boroughs and 34 counties, out of 171 and 54 respectively, had made appointments of analysts). "The deterrent effects are undoubtedly great, and the opinion of the promoters has been substantiated, that the most beneficial effects of the Act would be to prevent adulteration, rather than to punish it" (the number of convictions made in 1873 was small); ". . . in some instances, the magistrates, considering the prosecution to be a criminal one, would not allow the defendant to be examined." [30]

The Act of 1875 made no change in the severity of punishment for drug adulterations of an injurious nature (to potency or quality)—i.e., maximum penalties of £50 for the first offense, and six months imprisonment with hard labor for subsequent offenses—but it did make a significant change in the case of drugs not of the "nature, substance, and quality" demanded by the purchaser. A maximum fine of £20 was stipulated for this offense, but the provision for publication of the offender's name, address, and offense, in the case of repeated misdemeanors of the same nature, was now missing from the Act. This is a revealing omission, in light of the conscious efforts of the legislature to inflict as little inconvenience as possible upon trade and commerce. It seems contrary to an avowed objective of the Select Committee (1874),[31] to the opinion of several expert witnesses, and to the approach of Accum and the *Lancet* Commission. The avoidance of publicity of offenses probably should again be interpreted in terms of the pronounced laissez faire attitude of the government.

This also might be inferred from the nature of other fines provided under the legislation of 1875. Maximum fines of £20 were provided for the other offenses under the Act, and a £10 maximum penalty for refusing a sale to an inspector under the Act. In no case did the Act provide for increased penalties in the event of repeated convictions for the same offense.[32]

In the sense that proof of innocence of guilty knowledge (with reasonable diligence) now rested with the accused, rather than proof of guilt with the prosecution, the measure might be considered more severe. This point of view found expression in a sense in the pages of the *Pharmaceutical Journal*. For, the Law and Parliamentary Committee of the Pharmaceutical Society, commenting upon the proposed legislation during its passage through Parliament, considered the £50 fine for a first offense (under secs. 3 and 4) too severe, unless the word "knowingly" was retained. If the term "knowingly" were retained, the Committee felt that this would serve to soften correspondingly the severity of punishment.[33] The accused person of course had additional possibilities of protection by asking for guarantees of purity from the manufacturer and by labelling admixtures as such. He also benefited somewhat from the limiting and vague definitions set down in the Act, by the lack of adequate specifications for standards of purity, and by the unsatisfactory court of reference in Somerset House.

The appointment of analysts now for the first time (1875) became compulsory throughout England. But this directive was slowly carried out and often was meaningless in cases where token appointments were made without any real action being taken.

A quarter of a century passed before major changes took place in the severity of punishment under the Act. The 1899 amendment provided maximum fines for first, second, and subsequent offenses of any kind, of £20, £50, and £100, respectively. The 1899 Act also made the following significant stipulation:

Where, under any provision of the Sale of Food and Drug Acts, a person guilty of an offence is liable to a fine exceeding fifty pounds, and the offence, in the opinion of the court, was committed by the personal act, default or culpable negligence of the person accused, that person shall be liable (if the court is of the opinion that a fine will not meet the circumstances of the case) to imprisonment, with or without hard labour, for a period not exceeding three months.[34]

Official sanctions against drug adulteration in nineteenth-century statutes remained lenient by today's standards. Short terms of imprisonment were imposed in extreme cases, but a system of fines predominated. No provision appears to have been made for either the forfeiture or destruction of adulterated drugs, and public humiliation in the form of publicity of the offense was recommended only in the case of habitual offenders. Laissez faire attitudes minimized the severity of official sanctions and consequently restricted the effectiveness of official controls against drug adulteration.

12.

THE PROFESSIONS
AND THE PROBLEM

*The great majority of men are unaware of injustice until
it is pointed out to them. The denunciation of abuses is an
essential preliminary to a demand for reform; a clearly for-
mulated idea, the prerequisite of a loyal following.*[1]

This comment, from another context, sums up the processes bringing
about social controls of adulteration in nineteenth-century England.
Action came first, largely through voluntary efforts, catalyzed by a
few dedicated individuals. Professional groups played a comparatively minor role—although organized British pharmacy provided its
members with the tools necessary to effect such controls—and it was
individuals within these groups who took the initiative. In England,
physicians rather than pharmacists played the greatest role, perhaps
because pharmacy as a distinct profession emerged relatively late.
And in spite of the importance drug adulteration and its detection
assumed from the very first in the activities of the Pharmaceutical
Society of Great Britain, the Society was long occupied with organiza-
tional problems and with struggles for public recognition.

Voluntary efforts of the comparatively small group of individuals
eventually stirred the government to action. Demands for government action were met first, though weakly and ineffectually, by
measures dealing with foods. Only when it became apparent that the
Pharmaceutical Society lacked power to guarantee a pure drug supply did legal measures extend to drugs.

In democracies, such as those of England and the United States, we expect that significant social controls should develop as the result of voluntary efforts. Unlike the socio-politic tradition of Continental Europe, in which more or less arbitrary government intervention and control was looked for and accepted, the vigorous spirit of freedom of the Anglo-American countries fostered a view of government intervention as oppressive, as an evil to be tolerated only after other avenues of approach to the problem had been found seriously wanting.

It is in this light that we examine here the view of an English faction which saw adulteration as a form of competition and as perhaps merely a natural phenomenon for a "nation of shop-keepers." An illustration of this point comes in the concluding lines of the official report of an early English Parliamentary Select Committee, appointed to look into the question of adulterated food, drugs, and beverages: "[It is] some consolation to the public to know that in the matter of adulteration they are *cheated* rather than *poisoned.*" [2]

This general attitude on both sides of the Atlantic helps account for the defensive, at times almost compromising, stand taken by some professional organizations. Although they were well aware of the problems, they sought a solution in self-regulation rather than in government-inspired and -administered control. Such prevailing outlooks made the task more difficult for the few individuals in both countries who viewed adulteration in quite a different light and applied almost missionary zeal to accomplish reforms. But the determining factor was the attitude of the general public. For as long as the public remained indifferent to its own welfare, the agent of its wishes, the government, remained reluctant to interfere with prevailing conditions.

PHARMACY

Organized pharmacy emerged in Great Britain as a modern profession, distinct from medicine, with the formation of the Pharmaceutical Society of Great Britain. A distinct class of "chemists and druggists," as they were called, did not become prominent until the end of the eighteenth century and the beginning of the nineteenth, although English pharmacy had one of its main roots in the calling of the medieval guilds of "pepperers" and grocers.[3] At least part of this late emergence may be associated with the confused development of British medicine during the eighteenth century, which saw "apothecaries"—that is, members of the Society of Apothecaries—becoming more and more medical practitioners. As this happened, their pharmaceutical functions passed gradually into the hands of the chemists and druggists. This transfer of pharmaceutical duties to the chemists and druggists was largely complete by the end of the eighteenth century, and numerous attempts by the apothecaries to regain control failed. Recognition of the special function of pharmacists came with the Apothecaries' Act of 1815, which specified noninterference with the customary rights of chemists and druggists, defined as including the buying, preparing, compounding, dispensing, and vending of drugs and medicinal compounds, wholesale and retail.

Now problems of adulterated drugs faced the early forebears of modern British pharmacy, just as they did the newly formed Pharmaceutical Society. Virulent tracts inspired by physician-apothecary-chemist-druggist disputes of the seventeenth and eighteenth centuries often centered about accusations of drug adulteration. These accusations were often exaggerated, yet contemporary literature leaves little doubt that drug adulteration was a serious problem. While bias and emotion in the tracts usually obscured the actual circumstance, it can be said that the records of the Grocers' Company, the Society of Apothecaries, and the College of Physicians indicate no abatement of adulteration practices throughout this period. Powers of inspection, which had sought to control the practice from medieval times, shifted among different organizations. In 1820 this power remained divided between the Apothecaries' Society and the College of Physicians. Only the latter possessed prerogatives of inspection involving the new class of pharmacy practitioners, and these prerogatives seem to have atrophied before the Pharmaceutical Society came into being in 1841.

When in succeeding decades the problems of adulteration came before the public with sufficient force to induce legislation, the Pharmaceutical Society could claim in truth that the adulteration of drugs had always been a primary concern to the Society and one which it had endeavored to correct from the beginning. No direct mention was made of adulteration as one of the objects for the founding of the Society; but at its first annual meeting, the Society's president, William Allen, pointed out that "another end to be answered by the Society was the detection and prevention of adulteration." [4]

A few months after the founding of the Society (April 1841), Jacob Bell, one of the founders and key figures of the Society, issued a brochure of general information explaining the purposes of the Society to the pharmacists of the country; in it he referred to adulteration. A lengthy extract from this pamphlet will be instructive, both as to the nature of the problem, as Bell saw it, and the form of the solution suggested:

The want of a uniform education among Druggists, and the variable quality of the drugs which are found in the market . . . are continually brought before the public in a manner which is particularly galling to those who are solicitous of maintaining an unblemished reputation.

As long as Chemists and Druggists *collectively* neglect to take those means which are within their reach for rectifying these evils, the stigma, which ought to be confined to some individuals among them, is extended to all—as long as they continue to be subject to no educational regulations, they are exposed to the imputation of ignorance—and as long as they are disjoined, unrecognized, and indifferent, the influence which they would possess as an organized body, is lost in the confusion of inoperative individual efforts.

.   .   .   .

The difficulty which exists in a majority of cases in estimating, with any degree of precision, the qualities of drugs, increases very much the responsibility of the Druggist by placing the Public in a great measure at his mercy. The chief ground therefore on which he can hope for success in his business is, the *confidence of the Public in his integrity and experience;* and any circumstance which could tend to increase that confidence must necessarily be of great importance.

The practice of selling inferior drugs on the score of economy is as much at variance with sound policy as it is with moral principle; for, although these misdemeanors may be difficult of detection, a person who is guilty of them is never safe, and his reputation must suffer sooner or later.

.   .   .   .

Apart from all selfish considerations another circumstance ought to be kept in view, namely that the public good requires a systematic regulation with regard to Chemists and Druggists. The complaints which are frequently made on this subject, and some of them not without reason—the misunderstandings and skirmishes with the medical profession, and the acknowledged inferior quality of the drugs which are often found in the market, ought to be considered unanswerable arguments in proof of the necessity of some effectual remedy.[5]

In these few paragraphs, we see essentially the attitude of the Pharmaceutical Society, as it continued to be expressed for decades following. To justify its existence to the public and to the medical profession, the Society hoped to raise members' qualifications in general, and particularly their capacities for detecting adulteration, by means of a uniform system of education under the auspices of a tightly knit professional organization. The strengths to be gained from education and unity continued to be stressed by the Society long after it was beyond its initial growing pains. And a lack of such strengths was offered in explanation of the low status of British pharmacists as compared with those of Europe and even the United States.[6] American pharmaceutical development was held up periodically as an example of what could be accomplished through concerted effort and education. Bell's reference to a paucity of scientific means of detecting adulteration in many drugs and preparations reminds us that this problem remained unsolved until the second half of the nineteenth century. Clearly, moral questions by no means dominated the basic reasons for the control of adulteration suggested by individuals of all classes during the nineteenth century.

The problem of adulteration and its control was frequently discussed at meetings of the Pharmaceutical Society. Jacob Bell, one of the Society's most energetic promoters, was to estimate that during the first fifteen years of the Society's existence "the subject of adulteration formed a portion of the business of at least one meeting in three." [7] Adulteration also formed the topic of many papers published in the *Pharmaceutical Journal*, from the first volume onward, with the acknowledged purpose of encouraging higher moral practices among Society members and of providing them with suitable information for the checking or detection of such frauds.[8]

One of the earliest papers comes again from the hand of the prolific Jacob Bell, astute editor of the *Journal*.[9] This lengthy paper was an important one, for it pointed out the extent of drug adulteration and the urgent need for controls. It also clearly set forth the duties of pharmacists and the Society in the matter and their responsibilities to the public. The reasons for and solutions to adulteration he suggested are of special interest, and follow the general pattern suggested in his *Observations*.

Added to his statement that "no one would pretend to deny the prevalence of systematic sophistications" was the one that "the extent to which such abuses prevail, exceeds the limits of remedies which ought to exist." [10] Bell pointed to the serious variations in therapeutic results that might result especially in using potent drugs such as the alkaloids.

To the usual factors accounting for adulteration, Bell added one that would be repeated until the end of the century—"the rage for *cheap medicines*." [11] He clearly saw the demoralizing effect this desire had upon the whole drug trade—drug gatherer, wholesaler, and retail pharmacist—but laid the blame to the "mistaken idea that the [pharmacist] must humour this prejudice in his customers." [12] The solution lay, he believed, in the education by vocal pharmacists of the public to the danger inherent in inferior drugs. He saw this as contributing to the credit of the profession as well as to the welfare of the public. Moreover, he felt the pharmacist would be fully compensated for using only the best drugs by making a fair charge for his services. Bell also insisted that through rigorous, periodic inspection of their stock, pharmacists must guard against retaining drugs that had undergone natural deterioration, no matter what the immediate pecuniary loss would seem to be.[13]

Just as he saw the whole question in his *Observations* as more a reflection on the profession than on any individual pharmacist, so did he in this article. He foresaw great benefit in special attention by individual pharmacists and the Society to investigating the extent and nature of the practice of adulteration and developing effective means of detection. Apparently conscious of objections by some pharmacists to "an officious interference with [their] prerogative[s]," Bell stressed the general benefit to be derived from careful surveillance.[14]

Bell suggested various means for controlling adulteration. In support of his rejection of the older forms of control—periodic inspections, destruction of inferior drugs, and the public announcement of offenses—as inquisitorial, Bell pointed to the ineffectiveness of such methods in the past in the hands of the medical profession. The plan he proposed instead, in keeping with his earlier suggestions, was the one the Society supported over all others. "The most effectual means of checking the evils under consideration," he wrote, "is the education and improvement of dispensing Chemists, and the extension of pharmaceutical knowledge." [15] Self-regulation of pharmacy for the correction of its own deficiencies has remained a prominent theme throughout the history of Anglo-American pharmacy, on the ground that to admit more government regulation than was absolutely necessary risked oppression and shirked professional responsibilities. This view of a solution to adulteration problems in terms of the greater benefit of the profession and public welfare, that is, as a professional rather than a "trade" problem, perhaps explains why the Society came to be criticized by certain members of the profession for failing to concern itself with the more practical trade questions involved.[16]

Among the convincing proofs that such criticism was not unfounded is a series of articles (1842–1844) by the distinguished pharmacist-chemist Richard Phillips. We have repeatedly referred to Phillips' part in adding tests of purity and identification to the last editions of the *London Pharmacopoeia*, and this especially fitted him to investigate various preparations of the *Pharmacopoeia* as then made up by London pharmacists.[17]

Examining mainly chemical preparations obtained from some of the city's respectable pharmacies, and relying upon the simplest physical and chemical tests, Phillips made some startling reports.

Most of the samples he examined varied considerably from the standards of the *Pharmacopoeia*, causing him to state that "agreement with the directions of the Pharmacopoeia forms the exception, and that a scanty one; while a violation of them seems to constitute the rule." [18] Phillips closed the series with a charge to the Pharmaceutical Society to effect a control among its members, and a promise to reopen his investigations after a reasonable period of time had elapsed to allow the application of remedies.

The editorial reactions in British pharmacy to Phillips' series foreshadowed a different Society viewpoint, which at times bordered on compromise. In defending the Society's members against the implications of Phillips' report, Bell seemed to abandon his earlier position for reform by means of greater competence of the average practitioner and more reliable quality of drugs.[19]

Is it possible to reconcile this attitude with the serious aims of the Society and its members? The following discussion attempts to answer this important question. As we look at the first few decades following the founding of the Pharmaceutical Society, its leaders stretched logic and effort to maintain, on the one side, the ideals to which they aspired for the rising class of "chemists and druggists." On the other side, they tried to rationalize, if not justify, the shortcomings of a lower stratum of that class, whose abilities and practices by no means conformed to the Society's aspirations. Adulterated drugs—even if substandard through incompetence rather than intent —repeatedly would embarrass the Society's leadership group. Again and again thoughtful pharmacists and pharmaceutical scientists raised a charge of "exaggeration" [20] to shield the Society and the would-be profession's reputation against accusations of drug adulteration. While the unbridled prose of the early nineteenth century properly may be discounted, few denied the reality of the problem.[21]

That even the most conscientious could not bring legal controls within range of their program for improvement finds partial explanation in two circumstances of the mid-nineteenth century. First, the English middle classes remained firmly committed to the concept of laissez faire in societal relations. Secondly, a far-reaching confidence in the purifying and controlling influence of better education of pharmacists was perhaps buoyed up by general approval toward self-improvement through education, the slow maturing of the public system of education, and the extension of scientific instruction and facilities, including the Society's school (founded in 1842) and laboratory (founded in 1844).[22]

Like professions of most places and times, the Society's members were chagrined when their self-improvements were smeared or ignored by their critics in favor of more attention-catching derelictions, such as drug adulterations. The reaction to the Phillips reports by one reader of the *Pharmaceutical Journal* may have reflected the feelings of a good many others who found themselves judged according to actual deficiencies within their ranks rather than by their good intentions. "Although it is true that such discrepancies [in *Pharmacopoeial* drugs] exist in the year 1843 among Chemists and Druggists," he wrote to the editor, "it could not be forgotten that we are but just beginning to produce that improvement which our union is likely so greatly to increase, and that many of our members have not had the opportunity of acquiring that information which the rising generation possess in the talented Lectures of the Society." [23]

During the decade that followed the founding of the Society, some of its most knowledgeable members repeatedly called attention to adulterations and substandard drugs, without necessarily implying that qualified pharmacists were responsible for market conditions. Jacob Bell claimed that a widely used drug, senna, was "systematically" adulterated. He further maintained that the competitive prices advertised for many other drugs made it obvious that the drugs hardly could be "genuine and sound." [24] A Scot complained, through the Society's journal, that he could not get extract of Roman chamomile and had been informed that no "real" extract of this popular botanical drug was available on the market. [25]

In the late 1840's two of the men most instrumental in the founding and early development of the Society were recognizing the problem of drug adulteration frankly and publicly. The one, Theophilus Redwood, usually claimed that others exaggerated the extent of the problem, [26] and the other, Jacob Bell, maintained that adulterated drugs coming into the market were "extensively bought by those . . . not knowing the difference between good and bad rather than by the regular chemist." [27]

Concrete evidence of adulteration—not to mention of the statistical extent of the practice—remained in the background, however, until the *Lancet* established its "Analytical Sanitary Commission" in 1851 under the direction of Arthur Hill Hassall. When Hassall's studies first began to appear in the *Lancet*, the *Pharmaceutical Journal* welcomed the reports and commended their purpose. [28] But as the investigation began to touch the drug market, the editor noticed Hassall's doubtful competence for chemical testing, made clear why the report might give a wrong impression, and argued that the dispensing chemist often was the victim rather than the perpetrator of adulteration, and in any event was constantly being improved by the beneficial effects of the still new program of education (though it remained an optional study until 1908).[29]

The sensitivity of the Society to criticism was further suggested by the report of its Council for 1855–56, referring to the investigation by the Parliamentary Committee. "The sweeping and indiscriminate charges which have been brought against the entire body of chemists, and extensively circulated by the press," sadly observed the Council report, "have caused no less surprise than annoyance to those who have been for many years successfully using all their endeavours to bring about an improvement. The Statements, which have been industriously circulated with a view of exciting alarm, are in most instances greatly exaggerated, and calculated to mislead the public." [30] Actually it was only certain zealous witnesses whose views expressed to the Parliamentary Committee may have spurred the Council to this defense. Other witnesses had recognized the role of the Pharmaceutical Society in helping to control and eliminate the adulteration of drugs. The official report of the Parliamentary Committee itself recognized the beneficial influence of the Pharmaceutical Society upon the problem at hand and recommended—in line with the Society's own philosophy—that a further improvement would result only after measures had been taken to require proper qualification of pharmaceutical practitioners.

As usual, the opinion of expert witnesses diverged widely on the extent of the practice of adulteration. Hassall, Wakley and Postgate, for example, considered it almost universal. Others, including Bell, Redwood, and Letheby, admitted a certain amount, but denied that the practice was nearly as extensive as formerly practiced or as indicated by extremist witnesses.[31]

Whatever the actual prevalence, the Committee reached a conclusion that was in accord with the prevailing social philosophy of a majority of "solid citizens" of England, including its pharmacists. It recognized the types of control imposed by France, Germany, and to some extent America, "as being worthy of imitation," but felt them to be entirely too inimical to English commerce. Perhaps in keeping with the general opinions of the Select Committee Report concerning the capable activities of the Pharmaceutical Society, Parliament decided to exclude drugs from the Adulteration Act of 1860.[32] We have seen that the 1872 amendment first extended the law to drugs, although some provisions had already been made in the Pharmacy Act of 1868.

The Pharmaceutical Society was vitally concerned with all these legislative procedures, but in general the subject of drug adulteration —aside from its legal consideration—seems to have found much less prominence in the pages of the *Pharmaceutical Journal* than it had in the years immediately after its founding. The shift of interest appears to have been from one of discovering and pointing out adulteration to one of ensuring the Society a proper voice in the promulgation of legislation, and further ensuring that regulatory measures were carried out fairly as far as members of the profession were concerned. Printed discussions concerning the extent of adulteration practices were spare and isolated, and the over-all impression is that of marked improvement from the time of the Society's founding in 1841 and subsequently (especially after the Acts of 1872, 1875, and those following). Adulteration, nevertheless, remained a problem and continued to elicit concern from some pharmacists and their well-intentioned friends.[33] This general view found support in the evidence given before the various Parliamentary Select Committees.

Having seen how the Pharmaceutical Society viewed and interpreted the extent of adulteration practices, we now look briefly at what the members regarded as the causes of adulteration, and consequently at what they considered the most promising solution.

The attributed causes tended to be similar to those offered for centuries preceding: scarcity of supply, the nature of the demand, high price, careless collection, and deterioration. Charges and counter-charges implicated, alternately, natives in foreign countries, the drug broker or wholesaler, the drug grinder, the retail pharmacist, the public, and the unqualified vendors of drugs, including grocers, oilmen, and chandlers—in other words the dishonest or careless human being, wherever found.[34] Underlying all of these stated causes of adulteration was "indifference," on the part of both the public and the profession.[35] Another factor pointed to throughout the century was, as we have seen, economic—the "rage for cheap medicines." This aggravated already intense competition within the profession by encouraging a host of unqualified practitioners.

In the first major paper on the subject of drug adulteration to appear in the *Pharmaceutical Journal,* the eminent Jacob Bell set forth as one of his primary objects, "to show that one of the chief sources of the evil consists in the demand for *cheap medicines,* and the imperfect acquaintance which the public possess of the tendency of this prejudice." [36] More than five decades later the *Journal's* editor still felt, "There is much force in the contention that competition and the mania for cheapness, regardless of real value, are at the bottom of the evil"; while a contemporary echoed: "The demand for cheap stuff is very largely at the bottom of the whole difficulty." [37] In the intervening period the literature had quoted pharmacists repeatedly on this subject.[38] Members of the Society laid the blame for maintaining this "mania," in turn, on the wholesaler for supplying inferior goods, on the retail pharmacist for acceding to the public demand and for failing to educate the public on the inherent dangers of the practice, on the public for demanding cheap medicines, and on unqualified drug vendors for encouraging the system and for being unable to discern between good and bad drugs.[39]

Some members of the Society felt that severe competition within the profession itself tended to impose the sale of inferior drugs upon pharmacists.[40] Before the Pharmacy Act of 1868, most members of the Society considered this competition attributable to the "inroads" —particularly in smaller communities and poorer districts—made by "persons entirely destitute of proper education, with whom it is ruinous to compete, and who are, nevertheless, in some cases, formidable rivals." [41] Consequently, at least part of the solution to adulteration problems, as the Society and its members saw it, lay in the legal recognition of properly qualified and examined pharmacists.[42]

As might be expected, members of the Pharmaceutical Society proposed solutions to adulteration problems in keeping with their ideas of cause. We shall merely summarize proposed solutions here, since we have already referred to most of them. From the very first, and particularly before the Pharmacy Act of 1868, the most effective solution to adulteration in the eyes of pharmacists was through raising the level and qualification of pharmacists by education.[43] A great part of the stress upon education of course centered about the early desire of the Society for the legal recognition of qualified practitioners and the elimination of unqualified competition, but without implying pharmaceutical monopoly.[44] And, at least some pharmacists felt that a solution to adulteration problems, arising out of the demand for cheap drugs, lay in the education of the public (by the pharmacist) to the dangers of this habit.[45]

As part of its function to educate its members, the Society saw a "duty" to inform them fully about adulterations and their detection.[46] It was the fulfillment of this purpose that was most frequently raised in the Society's defense when it came under fire for the state of the drug supply.[47] One manifestation of this clearly felt duty on the part of the Society may be seen in the appointment, in 1882, of a special committee to consider the subject of the sale by drug importers at auction of spurious and worthless drugs. Unfortunately, as a later observer pointed out, the committee became "a dead Committee, and nothing was done." [48]

In general, members of the Society were opposed to severe laws and penalties for controlling adulteration.[49] Organized pharmacy looked to government action mainly to inspect imported drugs. Willingness to accept governmental control in this area stemmed from the opinion that the greatest source of adulteration lay in fraud practiced before or during importation, and from the inauguration of this means of control in the United States (in 1848).[50] However, one voice feared "more Government interference than they liked." The difficulty was "to remedy the grievance without establishing another." [51] Another writer felt the American law was valuable but too strict for British purposes.[52] Yet the willingness of some members of the Pharmaceutical Society to tolerate government control over imported drugs is clear from their support of taxes upon imported drugs, as a means of checking "the importation of spurious or worthless articles." [53]

Reflecting the attitude of the Society and its members against government interference, pharmacists played a noticeable part in parliamentary hearings by Select Committees upon adulteration, and in proceedings involving adulteration laws. The feeling of the profession over government interference may perhaps be summed up in the opinion of one pharmacist that "no class of men would be wise if they willingly permitted themselves to be placed under tyrannical and oppressive laws, even if the main object aimed at was the public welfare." [54]

The Society and its members thus resisted government interference in the matter of adulterated drugs because the dominant feeling was that this fell within their own sphere of activity and that they had already done much to alleviate the problem. However, after the adulteration laws were extended to drugs in 1872, they centered their attention mainly upon how the law impinged upon professional prerogatives. As a result they objected when official reports upon the extent of drug adulteration practices did not distinguish sufficiently between offenses committed by registered pharmacists and non-registered drug vendors.[55] The Society and its members were equally vociferous when the clause in the Adulteration Act of 1872 dealing with the appointment of analysts seemed to imply medical knowledge as a primary requisite for appointees.[56]

The Society refused to defend its members against prosecutions under the adulteration laws when the fault lay with objectionable "trade" questions, such as those in connection with the sale of effervescent citro-tartrate of soda under the name of "citrate of magnesia," or in general the sale of articles under names which bore no relationship to their true constitution.[57]

Perhaps this attitude helps explain why W. S. Glyn-Jones, dynamic leader of the Proprietary Articles Trade Association, should remark early in the twentieth century that in the past the Pharmaceutical Society had been slow to act on the problem created by adulteration legislation; and as a result it was no wonder that the public and the government should see nothing wrongful in the effect of the legislation if the Society remained silent on the matter.[58] As a direct result of an apparent felt need for an organization to protect pharmacists from unjust prosecution under various laws, Glyn-Jones promoted the organization of the Chemists' Defence Association, founded in 1899. An offshoot of the Proprietary Articles Trade Association, the Defence Association was intended to give its members legal advice, to defend members prosecuted under various trade Acts, to indemnify members against loss for mistakes in dispensing or retailing, to keep members informed on the progress of new legislation and on existing laws, and to watch legislation in the interest of members.[59]

The Defence Association was organized as a limited company, in which members purchased shares. For an annual fee, each member was entitled to the benefits of the Association. A member being legally prosecuted was entitled to defense up to a value of ten pounds.[60] Besides the services of a competent attorney, the Association retained the noted analyst C. G. Moor. Members were entitled to the free analysis of one sample per year, and might have further analyses made at a stated fee.[61] W. S. Glyn-Jones felt this organization differed materially from other organizations of a similar nature set up in the past, because of the direct benefits accruing to each subscribing member.[62]

The Chemists' Defence Association attracted both wide attention and increasing numbers of members from its formation in 1899 to beyond the terminus of our present interest (1906). The apparent success of its legal proceedings even elicited the admiration of non-pharmacy organizations which also felt their members sometimes harassed under the adulteration laws.[63]

In spite of the inadequacy of the professional Pharmaceutical Society to deal with "trade" problems, to which the formation of special organizations testified,[64] the Society did actively look to a solution of the problem of adulterated drugs. This solution lay primarily in the faith the Society placed in the beneficial effects resulting from better-educated pharmacists. It looked at adulteration as a professional problem; it thought it saw a solution in professional terms; and it sought to achieve that solution in the same terms. The effectiveness of the Pharmaceutical Society's approach to the problem was much increased by the encouragement of scientific investigations and interests by the British Pharmaceutical Conference.

MEDICINE

During the first half of the nineteenth century reform loomed as one of the most important issues facing British medicine. The question of regulating medical education and restricting unqualified practitioners remained essentially unsolved until the Medical Act of 1858. Although medicine as a distinct profession had a long history in England, not until 1858, with the creation of the General Council of Medical Education and Registration of the United Kingdom, did unity appear among various groups of medical practitioners, such as the College of Physicians, the College of Surgeons, the Apothecaries' Society, the Provincial Medical and Surgical Association, and so on. This perhaps explains why organized medicine, as such, played almost no part in the development of English social controls over adulteration, even over drug adulteration that affected them directly (because they often dispensed their own drugs) or their patients.

By 1858, the Pharmaceutical Society of Great Britain (founded in 1841) had gained a certain degree of recognition, although it also faced the problems of regulating education and restricting unqualified practice. The modern recognition of English pharmacy as a calling distinct from medicine might be dated as 1815, for in that year "chemists and druggists" were exempted from interference by the Apothecaries' Society, provided they did not encroach upon the legally recognized *medical* functions of the apothecaries.

Organized medicine, occupied with issues within the profession, remained on the edge of the turmoil over adulteration. Besides, they seem to have looked upon drug adulteration as coming more within the domain of organized pharmacy, and felt that the Pharmaceutical Society was making suitable progress toward solving the problem. Unlike the corporate profession, individual physicians played a key role in achieving official controls of adulteration. Arthur Hill Hassall, the able microscopist, provided the scientific ground upon which demands for reform could be made; Thomas Wakley, crusading editor of the *Lancet,* provided the medium through which scientific facts of adulteration could be widely disseminated; and John Postgate, Birmingham surgeon, spurred on government action in the wake of the reaction stirred by Hassall and Wakley through the *Lancet.* These key figures and their roles will be considered individually later.

An examination of the history of the British Medical Association and its official voice, the *British Medical Journal,* including the predecessors of the organization and the journal, attest to the minor interest of organized medicine in England in the problem of drug adulteration.[65] Besides medical reform the Association was concerned with such problems as quackery and counter-prescribing. Comments concerning drug adulteration in the Association's journal consisted mainly of book reviews, and remarks upon the progress of legislation touching adulteration. There were few editorials upon the subject, and virtually no reports concerning the detection of adulteration.

One editorial in the *Association Medical Journal* (predecessor to the *British Medical Journal*) proposed that at least part of the problem lay in the relatively small number of physicians or scientists in the British Parliament, "undoubtedly a source of much evil to the country." [66] The *Journal* editor pointed to the good effects in foreign countries of stringent laws and penalties for drug adulterators, as well as regulations governing the qualifications of pharmacists. However, he considered Parliament "by far too tender of interfering with the freedom of trade; and consequently trade makes free with the lives of the public by falsifying nearly every drug to be found in the chemist's shop." [67] At this time there is a recognition of the Pharmaceutical Society, "justly spoken of as the most efficacious means of dealing with the difficulty," and of the need for government assistance in the Society's efforts to improve pharmacists' education and to restrict practice to those properly licensed and examined.[68]

Opposition was expressed to any efforts to bring food adulteration under government control: "We distrust the efficacy of legislation, believing it would but rear another mischievous brood of the 'red-tapeworm' to strive to uproot the evil by enactment." The writer seemed willing however to give full support to any means required to control the "most patent and disgraceful of all adulterations—the adulteration of drugs. . . . To do this, we believe, is within the power of the profession, if it can rouse the existing authorities: nor do we deem it likely that, *for this purpose,* further power would be refused them by the legislature." [69]

During the final passage of the 1860 Adulteration Act through

Parliament, the *Journal's* editor was especially dubious of any good that could come from the optional appointment of analysts, and doubted the efficacy of allowing the public to have their own analyses made. He felt that the poor, in particular, would be unable to derive any benefit from such a provision because of the expenses involved. "We must have the public analyzer, to lash with a whip of scorpions the unparalleled villains who thus prey upon the helpless classes in the population." [70]

A marked antagonism toward the *Lancet's* Analytical Sanitary Commission is evident from the supplementary remarks made to reviews of Hassall's books appearing at this time. The journal remained remarkably silent during the whole of the *Lancet* series. Aside from the book reviews, we found only one editorial comment upon the activities of the *Lancet*. The editorial opposed the *Lancet's* method of attacking individuals, on the grounds that some innocent persons suffered as a result of mistaken analyses—an almost certain occurrence considering the number of analyses made. It also questioned the practice of obtaining most of the samples in poor neighborhoods, where cheapness was known to be a primary concern to the average purchaser. The editor also questioned any long-range benefits of the *Lancet* investigations for remedying adulteration problems, and considered the primary value of the survey in terms of the original scientific light it threw upon existing practices. [71]

That the editor was not oblivious to the adulteration of drugs is also clear from his criticism in 1861 of a second edition of Hassall's *Adulterations Detected* (1857). He considered it grossly misleading to consider this edition "thoroughly revised," when no apparent change had been made in the text, and remarked that "surely, in the space of time which has elapsed since the book first appeared, he might have given us some more information on the adulteration of various drugs—a subject of the highest importance." [72]

The government's general concern with matters touching the Department of Inland Revenue, in contrast to a certain indifference to public health, stands out. "If her Majesty's Government," remarked the editor, "would dispense the same justice to those adulterating shopkeepers who sin against the stomach of us all it dispenses to those who sin against the revenue, we should soon have a stop put to the iniquitous practices of shopkeepers." [73]

The few examples drawn here from the pages of the *Journal* and proceedings of the British Medical Association suggest that although the Association and its members were aware of the problems of drug adulteration, these problems never seem to have occupied a major place in thought or official action. Also evident is their reserve toward the contemporary journal, the *Lancet,* for the methods of its all-out attack upon existing adulteration practices.

Other British medical organizations of the period showed some interest in specific aspects of the administration of adulteration controls. A special committee of the General Medical Council of Education and Registration made clear its feeling concerning the qualifications of public analysts appointed under the Adulteration Acts, although nothing came of its request to gain the authority to define the subject of examination for public analysts or officers of health. Henry W. Acland, chairman of the committee, "warned the Council against deciding on having nothing to do with the subject. . . . Some might say, that the less the Council had to do with Government the better. This was right, as regarded the internal control of the profession; but, in such a matter as the present, the Council should offer its assistance to Government without being asked." [74] The Association of Medical Officers of Health, under the presidency of Henry Letheby, who made some of the chemical analyses for Hassall's *Lancet* reports, suggested greater co-operation between public analysts for more efficient administration of the laws. [75] The interest of both this Association and the Medical Council undoubtedly was sharpened by the large number of physicians, especially those functioning as medical officers of health, who were appointed public analysts.

The most active force in English medicine came from private and individual sources such as the *Lancet,* and the physicians Hassall, Wakley, and Postgate.

13.

INDIVIDUALS
AND THE CHALLENGE

*Time the destroyer, soon effaces all but a few personalities.
The trumpet gives forth a blast, it is true, but the sound is
heard only over a limited space and is soon scattered and
lost in the distance for ever.*

—*Arthur Hill Hassall* [1]

Individual rather than group action was primarily responsible for
blowing up the storm over adulteration. Groups such as the Pharmaceutical Society of Great Britain, the British Pharmaceutical Conference, and especially the Society of Public Analysts, contributed to the
effectiveness of controls once these were instituted. But individuals,
primarily from the medical profession, deserve the credit for bringing the seriousness of adulteration to the public's attention and for
forcing government action. Individual English pharmacists played
little part in this movement, compared with Continental pharmacists
such as Pomet, Vanden Sande, Favre, Guibourt, Chevallier, Hureaux,
and others. An exception might be the German-born and -trained
Fredrick Accum, who was associated with pharmacy early in life, but
the nature of his pharmaceutical training is uncertain. Other pharmacists such as Richard Phillips and William Bastick raised weak
and isolated voices. The much more active and effective proponents
of pure foods and drugs in England were Hassall, Wakley, and
Postgate, all associated with medicine, as were Beck, Peirce, and
Wiley in the United States. This phenomenon perhaps reflects the
better education of the European pharmacist as compared to his

160

English counterpart, at least until the last quarter of the nineteenth century.

Our discussion of individuals will center about those who were outstanding in their efforts to secure social controls of adulteration: Fredrick Accum and Arthur Hill Hassall, and to a lesser extent Thomas Wakley and John Postgate.

FREDRICK ACCUM (1769–1838)

We may exclaim, with the sons of the Prophet,
"There is death in the pot." [2]

When Fredrick Accum's *Treatise on Adulterations* first appeared in 1820, this striking biblical allusion (II Kings 4:40) appeared at the conclusion of the preface. It was repeated under a death's head on the grisly covers of the book. In succeeding editions, the "death in the pot" reference, again associated with a death's head and menacing serpents, appeared on the book's titlepage.[3] (See Figures 10, 11, and 12.) Consequently, both the book and Accum were nicknamed "Death in the Pot." The biblical allusion was not original with Accum, whose *Treatise* was only one of the so-called "Death" series, culminating in 1830 with John Dingwall Williams' anonymously published *Deadly Adulteration and Slow Poisoning.*[4] Even taking florid nineteenth-century style into consideration, the element of the macabre seems overdrawn in Accum's *Treatise.* On the other hand, the sensational character of the book attracted attention to the seriousness of the problem and stressed the urgency of reform.

Fredrick Accum was most influential in the first quarter of the nineteenth century and was apparently fortunate in whatever field of endeavor he entered.[5] He achieved remarkable popular fame within a relatively short time, even though the place of his success—London, 1793–1821—was not his native land. This London phase of his career ended rather abruptly when he returned to his native Germany, where he lived for another decade and a half. The many books Accum produced during his London period continued to be published and apparently remained popular until past the middle of the century, but they sometimes appeared anonymously.

In spite of Accum's influence, comparatively little is known about his background and his private life.[6] Even his connection with the Brande Pharmacy (apothecaries to George III), both in Hanover and London, remains nebulous.[7] Of Accum's early life we know only that he was born at Bückeburg, Westphalia, in 1769; he studied pharmacy; and he later became associated with the Brande family, who operated drug and chemical firms in both London and Hanover. (At

A TREATISE

ON

ADULTERATIONS OF FOOD,

AND

Culinary Poisons,

EXHIBITING

THE FRAUDULENT SOPHISTICATIONS

OF

BREAD, BEER, WINE, SPIRITUOUS LIQUORS, TEA, COFFEE,

Cream, Confectionery, Vinegar, Mustard, Pepper, Cheese, Olive Oil, Pickles,

AND OTHER ARTICLES EMPLOYED IN DOMESTIC ECONOMY.

AND

Methods of detecting them.

BY FREDRICK ACCUM,

Operative Chemist, Lecturer on Practical Chemistry, Mineralogy, and on Chemistry
applied to the Arts and Manufactures; Member of the Royal Irish Academy;
Fellow of the Linnæan Society; Member of the Royal Academy of
Sciences, and of the Royal Society of Arts of Berlin, &c. &c.

London:

Printed by J. Mallett, 59, Wardour Street, Soho.

SOLD BY LONGMAN, HURST, REES, ORME, AND BROWN,

PATERNOSTER ROW.

1820.

this time the pharmacist's shop was virtually the only place to gain a practical knowledge of chemistry.) The elder Accum's trade of soap-boiler and merchant possibly furnished Fredrick with some interest in chemical technology.[8]

Retaining his connections with the House of Brande, Accum transferred to their London branch in 1793, where he worked as a laboratory assistant, at the same time furthering his studies and attending chemical lectures. About the same time he met William Nicholson and became a frequent contributor to Nicholson's journal (*Journal of Natural Philosophy, Chemistry and the Arts*).[9] During his early association with Nicholson, Accum was instrumental in introducing beet sugar to England from Germany.[10] But more important, through Nicholson's journal Accum manifested his interest in pure drugs, in articles in 1798 and 1800, where he commented upon the prevalence and skillfulness of the adulteration practices of that time, remarked on the inadequacy of existing pharmacopeial standards for testing, and suggested a number of improved purity tests.[11] The embryo of his monumental work of two decades later began to take shape during this period.

In 1800, Accum opened a private laboratory, the full scope of which is indicated by its billhead, which read:

Mr. Accum acquaints the Patrons and Amateurs of Chemistry that he continues to give private Courses of Lectures on Operative and Philosophical Chemistry, Practical Pharmacy and the Art of Analysis, as well as to take Resident Pupils in his House, and that he keeps constantly on sale *in as pure a state as possible,* all the Re-Agents and Articles of Research made use of in Experimental Chemistry, together with a complete Collection of Chemical Apparatus and Instruments calculated to Suit the convenience of different Purchasers. Philosophical Gentlemen residing in the Country or Abroad, desirous of becoming purchasers of large or small Collections of Chemical Preparations, etc., may have explanatory Lists previously made out agreeable to the Expense they are willing to incur, and Chemical Catalogues may be had at the Laboratory.[12]

Figure 10 (*facing page*). Titlepage of Fredrick Accum's *Treatise on Adulterations* (first edition, 1820). The symbolic design pictured on the titlepage here disappeared from later editions, to be replaced by the one shown in Figure 12. We see here an hourglass and a staff of life, both ominously overturned, while in the center of this graphic representation moths hover perilously near the flickering flame of a candle, at whose base one victim already lies. Except for this illustration, the style and wording of the titlepages of the succeeding editions remained largely unchanged. (Reproduced from E. Stieb's personal copy, originally in the library of Charles R. C. Tichborne, Ph.D., F.C.S., M.R.I.A., chemist to Apothecaries' Hall of Ireland, president of the Pharmaceutical Society of Ireland, and member of the General Council of Medical Education and Registration of the United Kingdom.)

The design of the Treatise will be fully answered, if the views here given should induce a
single reader to pursue the object for which it
is published ; or if it should tend to impress on
the mind of the Public the magnitude of an evil,
which, in many cases, prevails to an extent so
alarming, that we may exclaim, with the sons of
the Prophet,

" 𝕿𝖍𝖊𝖗𝖊 𝖎𝖘 𝖉𝖊𝖆𝖙𝖍 𝖎𝖓 𝖙𝖍𝖊 𝖕𝖔𝖙."

For the abolition of such nefarious practices, it
is the interest of all classes of the community to
co-operate.

FREDRICK ACCUM.

LONDON,
1820.

Figure 11. "Death in the Pot" Preface from Accum's *Treatise on Adulterations*
(1820). The "Death in the Pot" biblical allusion that appeared on the last page
of the preface to Fredrick Accum's *Treatise on Adulterations* provided a rousing
battle cry for the British anti-adulteration movement. (Reproduced from personal copy of E. Stieb.)

In 1801, upon the recommendation of the founder of the Royal
Institution, Count Rumford (Benjamin Thompson, American expa-
triate), Accum was appointed "Assistant Chemical Operator" there,
where he collaborated with Humphry Davy, who had also just been
appointed to a lectureship.[13] Accum proved very successful with the
fashionable audiences. His popular writing for Nicholson probably

served him in good stead here, but he also possessed considerable talent in public lecturing, and some charm as well.[14] This must have been an important requisite at a time when public awareness of chemistry seems to have been more a social phenomenon than an expression of scientific awareness. Accum may have had as much theatrical flair as scientific prowess, in view of his somewhat high-strung and artistic nature and a fondness for publicity, sometimes obtained by sensational means.[15] When Accum resigned his position at the Royal Institution in 1803, he remained a subscriber,[16] a fact of later import, as we shall see.

Encouraged by his success at the Royal Institution, he began giving public lectures in chemistry and mineralogy at his laboratory, until increased attendance required the use of a larger hall.[17] Accum's skill as both a teacher and public lecturer was recognized in 1809, when he was appointed Professor of Chemistry at the Surrey Institution, where he gave lectures on chemistry, mineralogy, and pharmacy, until his return to Germany in 1821. His lectures again proved extremely popular with the London public and were attended by persons of all ages.[18]

The importance of his private "school" was considerable, because it was perhaps the first laboratory in England, indeed among the earliest in Europe, where students could gain practical experience in chemistry. His students included many men of high rank, adding a fashionable element; his school was also the early training ground of students from the United States, including such figures as Benjamin Silliman, Sr. (1770–1864) of Yale, William Dandridge Peck (1763–1822) of Harvard, and James Freeman Dana (1793–1827). These men were responsible for Accum's role in equipping the laboratories of early American colleges such as Yale.[19]

Early recognition of Accum's abilities as an analyst and industrial chemist was supported by his important contributions as a consulting chemist to both private manufacturers and the government. The work in this field varied and included such things as the investigation of the chemical and medicinal properties of mineral springs (important to the establishment of water-cure establishments), the invention of a welding compound for iron, the invention of an explosive for use against the French navy, an investigation of the production of soda, and research on new minerals for manufacturing earthenware. In addition, he frequently testified as a chemical expert at hearings and trials.[20] Accum's most memorable and extensive contribution in this field was undoubtedly his part in the introduction of gas lighting between 1812 and 1815. Accum's considerable persua-

sive skills in popular writing served an admirable end in dispelling
public prejudices against gas lighting, which had been condemned as
unsafe by Davy and other scientists.[21] Browne remarked that "in
Accum's various books upon gas lighting, we see him occupied not
only as a chemist, but also as a most skillful propagandist." [22]

Accum's numerous books and articles for scientific publications
were written in excellent English and precise scientific style, which
may have been as important a factor in his success as his ability to
capitalize upon the utilitarian appeal of chemistry to the public.
Many of his twenty or so books were translated into other languages
and passed through countless editions. Some were of an inferior
"scissors-and-paste" variety, a technique probably learned from
Nicholson. Nevertheless, his understanding of the public's wants was
almost intuitive and his success unqualified.[23]

Although Accum's direct contributions to chemistry were not
great, he carried on considerable research that influenced later developments in chemistry.[24] His first book, *System of Theoretical and
Practical Chemistry* (1803), was one of the earliest English chemis-
tries based on Lavoisier's new concepts and was intended as a textbook for students and the lay public. It differed considerably from
contemporary treatises written essentially for fellow chemists and
had added appeal for the lay reader in its content of everyday
kitchen-variety chemistry.

Accum's tour de force, and at the same time his coup de grâce, was
undoubtedly his *Treatise on Adulterations*, published in 1820.
Browne believed the work was "in all probability the most extensively
reviewed book upon chemistry ever written." [25] The popularity of the
work was attested by the appearance of a second edition the same
year, when the first printing of one thousand copies sold out within a
month. An American edition also appeared in 1820 and a German
translation in 1822, by which time a fourth English edition had been
printed.[26]

Although the *Treatise* dealt primarily with food, Accum devoted
some space to a plea for government action in the adulteration of
drugs and medicines, stating that "nine tenths of the most potent
drugs and chemical preparations used in pharmacy, are vended in a
sophisticated state by dealers who would be the last to be suspected." [27]

His remarks on drug grinders who supply cinchona powder "at a
much cheaper rate than the substance can be produced for in its
natural state" we have already noted, and he makes other comments
which give a general impression of the extent of drug adulteration:

Cheapness and not genuineness and excellence, is the grand desideratum with the unprincipled dealers in drugs and medicines.

. . . .

A great many of the essential oils obtained from the more expensive spices, are frequently so much adulterated, that it is not easy to meet with such as are at all fit for use; nor are these adulterations easily detectable.[28]

All these accusations appear plausible in the light of conditions existing prior to 1820 and for several decades afterward. Cinchona bark and the essential oils long remained heavily adulterated; powdered drugs were particularly susceptible, and drug grinders were universally blamed for many prevalent adulterations; and the rage for cheap drugs still proved bothersome to the Pharmaceutical Society and was the most common reason offered for the extent of the problem.

Accum pursued a bold policy of listing the names of the offenders (taken from the Minutes of Parliamentary Committees of Investiga-

Figure 12. Vignette from the titlepage of Accum's *Treatise on Adulterations* (fourth edition, 1822). This design appeared on the titlepage of the second and all succeeding editions of Fredrick Accum's *Treatise on Adulterations*. (Reproduced from a copy of the *Treatise* now in the University of Wisconsin Memorial Library, probably originally in the library of Alfred S. Taylor, Professor of Medical Jurisprudence and Chemistry, Guy's Hospital, London.)

tion), regardless of their position.[29] The antagonism this engendered undoubtedly increased when in the second edition he declared his refusal to be intimidated and his intention to continue his exposés.[30]

A charge of "robbery" was made against Accum in December, 1820, for tearing pages out of books in the library of the Royal Institution, of which he was still a member. When the case was dismissed, the managers changed the charge to one of "mutilating books." The publicity arising from the affair proved overwhelming for the man who had once been referred to as the Londoners' "pet chemist." [31] Accum did not appear at the trial and shortly thereafter returned to his native Germany, crushed by his sudden fall from popularity, of which he had been "by nature intensely fond." [32]

The seriousness of his work on adulterations may have been obscured by its rather folksy style and wit. His appeal to popular imagination is obvious from his opening remarks:

[I] confined myself to the task of pointing out such operations only as may be performed by persons unacquainted with chemical science; . . . express[ed] all necessary rules and instructions in the plainest language, divested of those recondite terms of science, which would be out of place in a work intended for general perusal.

The design of the Treatise will be fully answered if the views here given should induce a single reader to pursue the object for which it is published; or if it should tend to impress on the mind of the Public the magnitude of an evil, which, in many cases, prevails to an [alarming] extent . . . .

For the abolition of such nefarious practices it is the interest of all classes of the community to co-operate.[33]

However, if all Accum wanted was popularity he scarcely would have created the antagonism he knew would be caused by publishing names and making derogatory remarks against business interests and against lack of sufficient government surveillance. He counted upon his reputation and his popularity to gain support for a cause he considered worthy. His German background may have led him to regard the proposed government control as more natural than would most of his English readers; yet, Accum was acutely aware of the strong laissez faire attitude of the English government. It was incomprehensible to him that for the sake of the revenues the law should be relaxed to favor business, apparently in proportion to its extent.[34] He found it "astonishing that the penal law is not more effectually enforced against practices so inimical to the public welfare"; and commented scathingly upon the business and public morals of the time: "The practice of sophisticating the necessaries of life, being reduced to systematic regularity, is ranked by public opinion among other mercantile pursuits; and is not only regarded with less disgust than formerly, but is almost generally esteemed as a justifiable way to wealth." [35] Accum also recognized the demoralizing effect of the Napoleonic Wars as one contributing factor in the rise of adulteration; and he was perceptive concerning the ill effects of industrialization:

> It is a painful reflection, that the division in labour which has been so instrumental in bringing the manufactures of this country to the present flourishing state, should have also tended to conceal and facilitate the fraudulent practices in question; and that from a correspondent ramification of commerce into a multitude of distinct branches, particularly in the metropolis and the large towns of the empire, the traffic in adulterated commodities should find its way through so many circuitous channels, as to defy the most scrutinizing endeavour to trace it to its source.[36]

What about the torn library books? Whether it was cause, symptom, or pretext for the real reason of his ignominious departure from England, it effectively ended the most useful part of his colorful career.

Accum's fight for pure foods and drugs did not gain immediate success. His approach may have been still too much that of a muckraker and not enough that of a scientist to obtain a full hearing from his contemporaries. The distressing conditions he fought remained effectively undisturbed until the British physician, Arthur Hill Hassall, under the sponsorship of the *Lancet*, revived the issue in 1851. The interest Accum stimulated, however, moved in the direction leading toward the subsequent passage of food and drug legislation in Great Britain and, ultimately, in the United States and Canada.

LESSER FIGURES

The period between 1820 and 1850 was not entirely bereft of serious efforts to cope with drug adulteration. Few of these individual efforts, however, had the popular appeal of Accum and his successors, nor the professional and scientific support enjoyed by Hassall. We recall the activities of the pharmacist-chemist Richard Phillips (1777–1851) well known for the purity tests he introduced into the last nineteenth-century editions of the *London Pharmacopoeia* (1824, 1836, 1851). His testimony upon the extent of adulteration practices to an 1834 Parliamentary Select Committee investigating the urgent need for medical reform, was notable, as were also his earlier reports upon the state of pharmacopeial preparations then (1842–43) dispensed by London pharmacists.[37]

Aside from the work of Phillips, and the more general treatises of

Alphonse Normandy and John Mitchell,[38] English publications on the subject of adulteration following Accum and preceding Hassall were predominantly of the "scare" variety, and anonymously published. In this category fall *Deadly Adulteration and Slow Poisoning; or Disease and Death in the Pot* (1830?), attributed to John Dingwall Williams; *The Domestic Chemist* (1831); and *The Tricks of Trade in the Adulterations of Food and Physic* (1856). These popular little treatises stand in marked contrast to the publications of Arthur Hill Hassall.

ARTHUR HILL HASSALL (1817–1894)

> *I have never claimed to be the originator of the Analytical Sanitary Commission of* The Lancet. . . . *What I do claim is, that I was the first to apply on a large scale the microscope to the detection of adulteration; that I was the chief labourer in the work of the Analytical Sanitary Commission; that I was the author of the Reports* [*of the* Lancet *Commission*].[39]

These were the words of the greatest single figure in the English movement for pure foods and drugs, Arthur Hill Hassall—comparable only with Harvey Washington Wiley (1844–1930) in the United States.[40] The words reflect an unabashed pride of accomplishment and an understandable claim for recognition of that accomplishment.

In discussing application of the microscope to the detection of adulteration (see Chapter 5) it was unavoidable that we should hit upon the pivotal contributions of this man. It was equally unavoidable that we should have referred to his opinions on the definitions of adulteration and on appropriate modes of punishment (see Chapters 10 and 11); and we shall have to come back to his thoughts concerning the administration of government controls of adulteration. The present context asks for a still different viewpoint—an interpretation of the basis for his success.

The recognition of his work is clear from the volume of his testimony before several Parliamentary Select Committees on adulteration, notably those of 1855 and 1856.[41] Equally significant is the recognized influence his observations had upon the work of others concerned with adulteration problems in Great Britain and on the Continent, throughout the second half of the nineteenth and into the twentieth century.[42] As we shall see, there was considerable controversy over how much credit he deserved for the reports of the *Lancet's* "Analytical Sanitary Commission," over the caliber of his chemical knowledge, and over his personal interpretations of the extent of adulteration practices. But no serious questions ever arose, as far as we know, over his skill and competence as a microscopist. Hassall brought to the almost unexplored subject of food and drug analysis in England a high degree of specialized knowledge developed through his keen, life-long interest in biology.[43]

But at first glance it is not easy to understand why Hassall, unlike the many other able microscopists and noted biologists of his time, turned his special talents to the problem of adulteration; what circumstances determined that he was to make more than an isolated contribution as had his contemporaries; and why he pursued the subject after his paper on the adulteration of coffee. After all, Hassall was then, at 33, a physician and remained so until his death.[44] It is important that we remember this to allow a true evaluation of his accomplishments and a better interpretation of the reactions of his contemporaries, particularly his critics. Hassall himself wrote to this effect in the preface of his autobiography:

> It should be borne in mind, that of more than seventy years over which this narrative extends, during fifty I have been and happily still am occupied in medical practice, this indeed being of necessity the main object and purpose of my life; the periods devoted to natural history, chemistry and other kindred subjects, were for the most part interludes.
>
> The great and foremost pleasure of my life has consisted in my work, selected for the most part because of its congenial character, in natural history, microscopical and chemical investigations.[45]

We can perhaps trace Hassall's interest in public health and welfare to his microscopical investigations of London drinking water just prior to 1850. In his *Narrative* Hassall told that about 1850 he settled in St. James, where he "fitted up a commodious laboratory, adapted alike for chemical and microscopical research." He went on to say that he now had a little time to think about his future and on his trips through London streets he was struck by the apparently wide disparity between the food exhibited in many shop windows and the accompanying advertisements describing it. At the same time he saw frequent newspaper accounts concerning the quality and genuineness of ground coffee then sold in London. His decision to investigate the latter situation resulted in his 1850 paper, "On the Adulteration of Coffee." [46]

Up to this point, Hassall's significance looms no greater than that of any of his immediate predecessors writing on adulteration and the microscope. The sequence of events surrounding the report on coffee determined Hassall's course in the immediate future, we are convinced, and this led in turn to the Parliamentary investigations of 1855 and 1856 and the Adulteration of Food Act of 1860. The circumstances determining initial events fell together partly out of happy chance.

Among the fortunate circumstances surrounding Hassall's first investigation of adulteration was the public attention it attracted. Hassall had pointed out the extent of the adulteration and also the fact that none of the processes of roasting or charring destroyed the characteristic structure of coffee, or its adulterants. A notice of this fact appeared in the London *Times,* but more than ordinary interest was created because Hassall's observations flatly contradicted a statement made about the same time in the House of Commons by the Chancellor of the Exchequer, Sir Charles Wood. For in response to intensive questioning concerning the losses in revenue occasioned by heavy adulteration of coffee with chicory, Sir Charles announced that, according to the Commissioners of the Inland Revenue, "neither by chemical nor by any other mode could it be ascertained with any degree of certainty whether a mixture [of coffee] contained chicory or not." [47]

But the most fortunate development from the publicity Hassall received came when Thomas Wakley, founder and editor of the medical journal *Lancet,* approached Hassall.[48] As we shall see in our discussion of Wakley and the *Lancet* Commission, Wakley had an earlier interest in the problem of adulteration, but this produced no result. It seems not overly dramatic to say that the significant movement against adulteration in England began with the meeting of Hassall and Wakley. Wakley offered his important journal as a medium for publicizing the findings, complete with the names and addresses of offenders, unearthed by Hassall, who was to be "Chief Analyst" of the *Lancet's* so-called "Analytical Sanitary Commission." [49] Wakley assumed complete responsibility for legal risks and expenses, and Hassall was left free to pursue his project in any manner he saw fit. Hassall's name was not made known until the end of the initial series of reports, yet he considered that he incurred considerable risk himself from possible loss of his "scientific and professional reputation." [50] The importance of the association between Hassall and Wakley lay in the technical skill and scientific knowledge of the one, and the influence (through his journal), courage, and foresight of the other. The value of publicity to make socially effective even the most convincing scientific evidence became clear also a half-century later to Hassall's counterpart in the United States, Harvey W. Wiley.

Hassall carried out the greater part of the investigations for the Analytical Sanitary Commission, assisted by an artistic microscopist (specially trained by Hassall), who accompanied Hassall on his purchasing trips. Careful examinations of samples, in their pure and adulterated states, and of the adulterants themselves were followed by illustrations made with the camera lucida, by the preparation of wood engravings, and finally by written reports.[51] Most of the reports appeared between 1851 and 1854 in the *Lancet*, then in book form in 1855 (Hassall, *Food and Its Adulterations*) and subsequently.[52] The accuracy of Hassall's observations is clear, for during the whole time (1851–1854) his series of publications appeared in the *Lancet*, legal action was threatened in but one case, and this was dropped before it reached court.[53]

One of the most valuable contributions Hassall made in his *Lancet* reports and subsequently in his books probably lay in the generous use of microscopic illustrations. Hassall's microscopy apparently was entirely qualitative. Consequently the illustrations took on additional significance and constituted an important reference tool for others who applied microscopy to the detection of adulteration, or who elaborated upon his investigations.

From Hassall's scientific contributions toward the control of adulteration, we move to a brief examination of some of his ideas for social controls. Aside from legislative means to control adulteration and the dissemination of information to the public—a need he thought filled with his *Adulterations Detected* (1857)—Hassall suggested several ways in which the public might protect themselves against adulteration. Some of these, like his suggestion for the formation of co-operative consumer organizations, still seem timely, perhaps indeed were then in advance of their time. In disappointment over the Adulteration Act then proposed, Hassall wrote:

[One] means of affording great additional protection, [is by means of] an organization originating with and supported by consumers. It should consist of members paying a small annual fee, and have for its object the analyzation, free of any further charge, of such articles as are forwarded for analyses by the members.[54]

Even though Hassall felt this would do more good than the emasculated 1860 Adulteration Act, experience proved that the public did not avail themselves of the right—incorporated into all the nineteenth-century Food and Drug Acts—to have analyses made of suspected samples. For example, *Local Government Board Reports* show that in 1887 private purchasers submitted only 148 of 23,956 samples examined; in 1906, only 256 of 90,504. As the editor of the

British Medical Journal observed: "Imagine a poor wretch . . . going to a private analyst, and incurring the expense of examining any article of food he may suspect of being adulterated!" [55]

On the question of warranties Hassall proposed that packaged goods have a guarantee of purity printed on their wrappers, perhaps certified by reputable scientists.[56] Some years later (in 1881) Hassall co-operated in the formation of a "Pure Food Company," which guaranteed the purity of the products it manufactured. Unfortunately, perhaps because the problem of adulteration had largely abated by then, the venture failed.[57] Hassall thus put into practice, unsuccessfully, an idea he put forward many years earlier, but which had never previously been carried out by others.[58]

It seems doubtful whether the reports (1851–1854) of the *Lancet* Analytical Sanitary Commission alone would have led to the Parliamentary Select Committee investigations (1855, 1856), or to subsequent legislation (1860), had not both Wakley and Hassall been militant. Wakley contributed most in this respect until the end of the major series of *Lancet* reports, when Hassall's name first appeared; Hassall rose in significance from this time and established a powerful, separate influence as the result of his first books (1855, 1857) and his participation in the Select Committee hearings.[59] The relative significance of Hassall in the whole early anti-adulteration movement came into sharp focus just at this time, partly as the result of petty jealousies arising out of convictions that Hassall was attempting to pre-empt a disproportionate share of the credit.

In spite of Hassall's clear statement to the contrary, a feeling arose that he made "extravagant claims" before the 1855 and 1856 Select Committees on Adulteration, with the result that the credit for the *Lancet* inquiry was mainly attributed to him.[60] A public controversy, waged in 1855 in the columns of the London *Times* and reprinted in the *Lancet* and in the *Pharmaceutical Journal*, seems to have centered mainly about petty jealousies over who deserved the greatest credit for investigations that paved the way for legislation. Hassall never denied the part played by Thomas Wakley, editor of the *Lancet* and chief protagonist in this quarrel, although he felt undue claims were made by Henry Letheby, a noted chemist who had conducted some of the chemical analyses for Hassall.[61] In an elaborate attempt to clear his name, Hassall even published a pamphlet that reported the investigation of the issues involved by a barrister, a member of the clergy, and others.[62]

We shall discuss Wakley separately, but it seems doubtful that the true picture of exactly what transpired can be reconstructed. The actors in this emotion-charged drama were lined too neatly into sharply divided camps. John Postgate, the Birmingham surgeon who initiated legislative action against adulteration and whom we shall meet separately, seems also to have become somewhat sensitive about his role in the movement, and "observed a disposition to filch credit from Birmingham by taking it from the originator and workers of this question." [63] Others not directly involved in the issue, such as Jacob Bell and Theophilus Redwood, prime movers of the Pharmaceutical Society, watched with obvious relish this dissension, for they had not approved the methods employed by the *Lancet's* Commission and had suspected the motives of both Wakley and Hassall. Besides, this provided apparent proof of certain inadequacies on the part of Hassall, the moving power behind the *Lancet* survey.[64]

In spite of this bitter controversy over the real part played by Hassall in bringing to some concrete realization the control of adulteration, he received wide credit for his specific contributions. This included special recognition given him by the Select Committee *Report* (1856), numerous tributes in the press, and official recognition of his services in a public testimonial to him.[65]

The *Analyst* evaluated Hassall in these words:

[Hassall] became for a time the chemical oracle of the public, and this upon the basis of his microscopic work, which part of his work was in every way excellent. To him public analysts owe most of their knowledge of the microscopic structure of food and some drug substances. His activity gave articulate form to the outcry against adulteration; he was truly the father of public analysis. . . . To the end of his life he remained what he essentially was, a microscopist, not a chemist, or an analyst in the modern sense of the word. His merits are none the less for the fact, and his name will be long and gratefully remembered by the members of the analytical profession.[66]

Controversy has obscured the real part Hassall played in bringing government control of adulteration into practical reality. A complete re-evaluation of the voluminous record of the period is needed; but it already seems clear that Hassall was first to realize full and systematic application of microscopy to the detection of adulteration. This application opened to analytical science a whole area of organic substances, and particularly drugs, that had necessarily remained previously unexplored in the light of existing chemical knowledge. Hassall, therefore, first provided a certain means of detecting adulteration, detection having previously been limited largely to inor-

ganic chemical compounds. This meant that legal controls of adulteration could be applied effectively for the first time. Although Thomas
Wakley conceived the idea of the *Lancet* Analytical Sanitary Commission, Hassall's skill as a microscopist unquestionably accounted
for its success and for the wide attention it attracted to existing
problems of adulteration and to the possibility of a solution. John
Postgate carried the matter to Parliament's attention, but Hassall
obviously was the key witness in the Select Committee hearings that
preceded legislation. It seems doubtful that Postgate would have
succeeded as well as he did without the firm scientific foundation
Hassall provided and the wide publicity the *Lancet* gave to demands
for social reform.

JOHN POSTGATE (1820–1881)
> *For twenty-five years of his life, without reward, and under*
> *heavy discouragement, he laboured to protect the health*
> *and to purify the commerce of this people.*[67]

Born in the very year that Accum startled his contemporaries with
his *Treatise on Adulterations*, John Postgate began his career as a
grocer's boy, then served as an apprentice and later assistant to a
surgeon-apothecary in Scarborough. After studying at the Leeds
School of Medicine, he became an assistant apothecary to the Leeds
Public Dispensary and a licentiate (1843) of the Society of Apothecaries of London. In 1854, the year he began his crusade for pure
foods and drugs in Birmingham, he became a Fellow of the Royal
College of Surgeons; and in 1860, the year of the first Adulteration
Act, he was appointed professor of medical jurisprudence and toxicology at Queen's College, Birmingham.

Perhaps tracing back to his early grocer's work, but more likely
growing out of his observations as an apprentice and assistant apothecary and of conditions in the great industrial center of Birmingham,
where he had moved in 1853, Postgate began in 1854 to agitate
against existing adulteration practices. From the first, he had the co-
operation of the Birmingham members of Parliament, William
Scholefield and George Frederick Muntz.[68]

Public meetings held in Birmingham and nearby towns presented
the picture of adulteration and the need for legislation. Postgate and
Scholefield participated actively in these meetings at which samples
were publicly exhibited and analyzed.[69] Early in 1854 Birmingham
appointed a new local official, "a public analyzer, charged with the
examination and suppression of adulterations in all articles of consumption." [70] By April, sufficient progress had been made to recom-

mend the appointment of examiners by the government to prevent importation of adulterated goods, the appointment of public analysts, the establishment of a system of fines, and a request that Scholefield and Muntz bring the question before the House of Commons. Scholefield "expressed his readiness to bring the subject under the notice of Parliament with a view of applying the necessary remedial measures." [71] In December, 1854, Postgate asked Wakley's co-operation in publicizing a circular letter being sent to members of the medical profession, in an effort to stimulate local interest through the formation of committees and to support, via petitions, Scholefield's proposed efforts in the Commons.[72] Postgate's experiences in Birmingham no doubt permitted him to make the following observations at first hand:

> That the evils resulting from these causes, which are alarmingly on the increase, press more directly and injuriously upon the young children and the working classes, the alimentary constituents of the main articles of their consumption . . . being, by the adulterations employed, materially reduced in quantity and deteriorated in quality.
> That the whole subject demands the serious consideration of the community, as a question deeply concerning the public health, and urgently requires the interference of the Legislature to suppress practices which involves gross impositions on society, and especially the poorer classes.[73]

Scholefield moved for the appointment of a Select Committee in the House of Commons, in June, 1855. On the strength of the evidence assembled by the Committees (1855 and 1856) under Scholefield, and after nine bills promoted by Postgate, the Adulteration of Food and Drink Act passed in 1860.

That Postgate considered himself the father of the 1860 Adulteration Act is clear from his comments that "he was happy in having been instrumental in obtaining an Act of Parliament"; that "The Act is not all I desired or asked for"; and the following:

> As is well known, this agitation had its rise in Birmingham; and that my object in commencing it, and carrying it on in conjunction with Mr. Scholefield, was to benefit the public. . . . It was a source of gratification, six years ago, to find that I suggested a scheme for the suppression of adulteration which met with the approval of Mr. Scholefield—a scheme unanimously adopted at the town's meeting . . . and now forming the base of the Act of Parliament.[74]

Postgate's part in this and subsequent legislation is clear, but he scarcely could have succeeded without the supporting evidence contained in Hassall's *Lancet* reports and Hassall's testimony before parliamentary committees.[75]

THOMAS WAKLEY (1795–1862)

> *Though he aroused strenuous opposition and bitter ill will among his contemporaries, time has proved his contentions in every instance of importance to be just. But no feeling of personal malice entered into his controversies; he spoke or wrote solely with a view to portraying clearly injustice or wrong-doing, and never with the purpose of paining or humiliating an enemy.*[76]

Wakley's contemporaries, who felt his sharp barbs, found it difficult to feel so understanding of his intentions as the biographer quoted above. Jacob Bell and Theophilus Redwood exchanged bitter jibes with Wakley, and Wakley's great protégé, Hassall, likewise suffered certain unkindnesses from his associate. Although Hassall's able research provided the scientific basis supporting the appeal for legislative controls, and Postgate's efforts precipitated the enactment of these controls, the courage and zeal of Wakley accounted for the success of both—just at this time (mid-nineteenth century) and in this way (through legislation).

Wakley was the crusading editor of the *Lancet*, which he founded in 1823. He had been apprenticed to an apothecary at fifteen and by 1817 had become a member of the Royal College of Surgeons. Between 1835 and 1852 he served an active tenure as a member of Parliament and was vitally concerned with problems touching medical reform, a live issue at this time.[77]

Wakley's interest in the issues centering about adulteration trace back to the early days of the *Lancet* and indicate some of the legitimacy of his later claims of priority. Articles and letters on adulteration appeared in the *Lancet* even before W. B. O'Shaugnessy's paper on "Poisoned Confectionary"[78] that Wakley mentioned as the first evidence of the projected Analytical Sanitary Commission. O'Shaugnessy's departure for India, we are told, prevented further accomplishments in that direction.[79] However, there is no evidence that the chemist T. H. Henry was approached in 1836 to continue the earlier plan, or that a journal devoted entirely to the subject had been projected, except for the letters reproduced by Wakley.[80] There seems no reason to doubt his integrity or his statement that "one of the obstacles to the execution of my design at a much earlier period arose from some apprehensions which I entertained, in consequence of the opinions expressed by my legal friends and advisers, that I might be involved in ruinous expenses if I published the names and addresses of the falsifiers of food."[81]

In spite of the early attention given adulteration by Wakley in the *Lancet*, we cannot trace any serious beginnings of projects before the years 1850 and 1851. For it was just at this time that Wakley first approached Hassall, whose paper on detecting the adulteration of coffee by means of the microscope had received notice in the *Times*.[82] And this point we may regard as the beginning of a significant movement against adulteration.

When the first reports of the Commission appeared in the *Lancet* of January, 1851, Wakley clearly felt he was "re-enter[ing] upon the labour . . . which we actually commenced in 1831." [83] He considered the special features of these enquiries to be their basis upon actual observations and experiments, the use of accurate illustrations, and the publication of the names and addresses of offenders.[84] This latter feature found graphic expression in the epigram that later appeared preceding each report. It read: "To attack vice in the abstract, without attacking persons, may be safe fighting indeed, but it is fighting with shadows." [85]

This same feature (publicity), considered so important by Hassall and others in their testimony before parliamentary committees, was severely criticized by the *Pharmaceutical Journal* and later by the *British Medical Journal*. Both seemed to feel that the *Lancet* unfairly singled out individuals for attack.[86] The latter journal sarcastically questioned Wakley's motives in originating the Analytical Sanitary Commission:

. . . one of the most hazardous, and, we believe, one of the most successful schemes, ever devised for increasing the circulation of a periodical. During the appearance of these Reports, a copy of the Lancet was to be met with on the club table, in the gentleman's library, and frequently in the grocer's little back parlour—an increased circulation developed by this peculiar stimulant, and ceasing with its disuse.[87]

The reaction to the reports was immediate and varied, and prompted Wakley to comment:

We are encouraged to believe, by information received from a multitude of persons and places, that the labours of our Commission will be productive of immense public benefit; and that those labours will be continued with unbated vigour, all classes of adulterators will have our most positive and determined assurance. A few threats have already been transmitted to us. The trouble of sending others may be spared, as all denunciations of the course we are pursuing will prove utterly unavailing.

Although only one report . . . has been published . . . the utility of the undertaking which we have engaged to execute has been acknowledged by thousands.[88]

Appeals for an investigation of the adulteration of drugs which "concerns the medical profession, if possible, more than the tampering with articles of food," [89] also came within a short time. The reply stated simply, "The reports of the Commission on the Analyses of Drugs and Chemical Preparations will be published at no distant period. The work is already in progress." [90] Although, of course, the reports concerned themselves primarily with food, some drugs were included, as we have seen.

The great service rendered by Wakley and the Analytical Sanitary Commission investigations was on the whole freely and widely acknowledged, but a negative view again found expression in the pages of the *British Medical Journal*. As early as 1855, in a somewhat critical review (already referred to) of Hassall's *Food and Its Adulterations,* it expressed the opinion that although the *Lancet* reports "excited interest and made some noise in their day . . . the effect . . . has already disappeared." The reviewer further doubted that any permanent check upon adulteration practices was to be expected.[91] Some years later (1861) when a report in the *Lancet* still indicated a rather high percentage of adulteration, the writer repeated the thought that the *Lancet* Commission did little more than to point out evils everyone was already fully aware of. "The *Lancet* has done good in pointing out scientifically these abominations," concluded the article, "but the remedy for their removal has clearly to be sought elsewhere than in the revelations of the *soi-disant* Commission." [92]

In spite of these few misgivings about Wakley's motives and about the long-range good resulting from the *Lancet* investigations, Wakley stands out as one of the important individuals responsible for the development of social controls of adulteration. He accomplished this through the press, which thirty years earlier, in more popular form, had served Accum, and found many of the less intrepid of those following Accum publishing anonymously. Without Hassall and the newly applied microscope, Wakley would have had little scientific basis for his attacks, and perhaps this is essentially why he had to abandon his proposed Commission twenty years earlier.

14.

THE ROLE
OF THE GOVERNMENT

While the British government tried to control adulteration before 1860, earlier statutes for the most part touched only upon the purity of particular foods or beverages and they aimed primarily at preventing fraud against the revenue. This development can be properly understood only in the light of our previous discussion of the economic, political, and social background to this period and in the problems centering about satisfactory definitions of adulteration and provisions for adequate penalties against the practice.

In spite of the government's willingness to pass the 1860 Act prohibiting the adulteration of food and drink, the testimony to progress made by the Pharmaceutical Society in controlling drug adulteration delayed the placing of drugs under legal control until 1872. The fact that the 1860 Act was ineffective does not change the significance of the willingness to let pharmacy try on its own to solve the problems of drug adulteration.

In spite of the great interest aroused in pure food and drug legislation, the first measures of 1860 and 1872 probably did little more than appease immediate demands for government protection of the consumer. It remained entirely the prerogative of local governing boards and councils whether they wished to appoint analysts and inspectors to administer the Acts. Even though these early forms of legislation touching adulteration were of little more than token character, some deterrent effect was felt. The 1875 Act, repealing those preceding it, made the appointment of analysts and inspectors compulsory.

Just as the British legislators and administrators had to learn from experience what form adulteration laws had to take in order to be effective and administered with minimum difficulty, so foreign countries—such as Germany,[1] the United States, and Canada—watched with interest the progress of British legislation and profited from British experience. British legislative controls might have operated more smoothly had Parliament heeded the advice of expert witnesses and special groups interested in adulteration problems. Difficulties centering about inadequate definitions and standards of purity plagued the administration of the 1875 Act and its amendments throughout the nineteenth century. The Society of Public Analysts had foreseen these problems while the law was still passing through Parliament, and had suggested concrete solutions. Ironically, these remained unheeded at home, while adopted by Canada and the United States.

Some important factors bringing to fruition proposals for control that had been ignored for a half century past were: the development and application of scientific analytical techniques, particularly microscopy in the hands of Hassall; the conviction and zeal of Hassall, Wakley, and Postgate, supported by science and an enterprising medical journal, willing to risk the ire of laissez faire industry and business; and the interest of a Member of Parliament noted for his support of liberal legislation.

ADMINISTRATION OF THE LAW AND SOME LEGAL PROBLEMS

Witnesses before the Select Committee hearings of 1855 and 1856 presented diverse views of how adulteration laws could best be enforced. Some, like Hassall, felt existing government departments could properly be expanded for effective operation of proposed official controls. Others disagreed concerning the capability of existing agencies to adapt themselves to such specialized functions. The principal issues, then and later, centered about the powers of local authority, as opposed to some central authority, to guide the operation and ensure uniformity of action. The need for some approved central authority to rule upon the qualifications of analysts and the definition of adulteration and limits of purity, and to act as an independent court of reference in cases of disputed analyses, began to find an official recognition only toward the end of the nineteenth century. The sound advice of expert witnesses and of bodies such as the Society of Public Analysts remained largely unheeded.

Hassall favored a central board or commission, composed of scientific experts, competent in analytical chemistry and microscopy. The board's function would entail directing the purchase and analysis of samples and the publication of periodic reports. Inspectors were to watch for and purchase suspected articles and forward them to the board. He also thought the board should publish a cheap, illustrated treatise on adulteration (a need he later thought he himself filled in his *Adulterations Detected* [1857]). Hassall felt the public should be encouraged to submit suspected samples for analysis and strongly recommended the value of inspecting imported drugs, following the example of Europe and the United States. Hassall envisaged the existing Excise (i.e., all branches of the Civil Service involved with collection of taxes and/or customs duties) with enlarged "detective and analytical departments" as fulfilling the functions of such a central board.[2] John Postgate, the Birmingham surgeon, also stressed the necessity of some central power and suggested the Board of Health, but was not so explicit in the details of such a body as was Hassall. The *Lancet's* editor, Thomas Wakley, also favored a system including the General Board of Health.[3]

Among those greatly opposed to Hassall's plan were Richard Archer Wallington, solicitor and Chairman of the Leamington Local Board of Health, and John Simon, London health officer. Wallington felt that the Board of Trade, the Treasury, or some other official department should periodically ban the sale of certain articles judged to be adulterated. Wallington also felt it best to overcome the difficulties encountered by having inspectors who could not be expected to be universally competent and knowledgeable. His plan was to get expert opinions on different articles from various authorities. Simon favored administration of the law by the local boards of health.[4] Wallington felt the problem would largely resolve itself if the trade were left to prohibit fraudulent and injurious adulterations. This was also the opinion of some members of the Pharmaceutical Society of Great Britain, such as Redwood, as far as drugs were concerned.[5]

The Select Committee Report suggested leaving the greater part of the execution of the law in the hands of local authorities, who were to appoint officers as they saw fit, and either to act upon complaints or to take samples in cases of suspected adulteration. The committee apparently considered it sufficient to appoint "one or more scientific analysers" under the authority of the General Board of Health to answer any queries of local authorities.[6] Hassall considered the latter provisions quite insufficient and held to the idea of utilizing the existing facilities of the Excise.[7]

The Select Committee also recognized the accomplishments of the Pharmaceutical Society in controlling drug adulteration; saw the need for licensing qualified pharmacists; suggested the need for a unified British pharmacopeia; and doubted the value of an inspection system for imported drugs, although it recognized the possible value of a more strict system of domestic inspection.[8] As Hassall pointed out, the Committee made no special recommendations with respect to drugs; furthermore, he disagreed with their minimizing the value of import inspections.[9]

The comprehensive, official control of adulterated drugs first began with the amending Act of 1872. This measure suffered in its administration from inadequacies similar to those of the earlier Act. The proof of guilty knowledge remained a serious legal stumbling block, as did the relative inexperience of many analysts. But the most serious problems centered about who was to administer the law. The power to appoint analysts or not, as they wished, remained the prerogative of local governments, although the Local Government Board could require such appointments where it considered them necessary.[10] However, Inspectors of Nuisances or other local officers were to procure suspected samples for analysis. A satisfactory court of reference for disputed analyses was still lacking.

The complaints arising out of the apparent harassment that the administration of the 1872 Act represented for the trade led to the appointment of another Select Committee in 1874 (and subsequently to the Act of 1875, which was to remain in effect for more than fifty years). The Committee recognized that the 1872 Act was clearly defective, stressing that "considerable injury, and . . . heavy and undeserved penalties [were imposed] upon some respectable trades-men." [11] The Committee also recognized the difficulties imposed by the lack of a clear definition of adulteration, by the lack of under-standing on the part of the courts, and by the inexperience of analysts. But neither the Committee nor the legislators recognized the need for some central body to co-ordinate the administration of adulteration law by local authorities, to decide upon questions involv-ing standards and definitions, or to settle disputed analyses. The Society of Public Analysts, founded partly in response to criticisms by the Select Committee of conflicting reports by practicing analysts, clearly recognized this need, but its suggestions remained unheeded.

Under the new Act, the Local Government Board remained the central power—though hardly in the spirit intended by Hassall or by the public analysts—and the laboratory of the Department of Inland Revenue at Somerset House became the court of reference for some of the conflicting analytical reports.

The delegation of special referee powers to Somerset House re-sulted in a repetition, during the rest of the century, of the very difficulties this move hoped to solve. Somerset House repeatedly contradicted the best reputed analytical reports. In spite of the fact that it operated under unsatisfactory conditions and used rudimentary and outmoded methods, its decisions were accepted as final by the courts in cases of disputed decisions. Commenting upon the wasteful duplication of efforts between this government laboratory and the Society of Public Analysts, Dyer explained: ". . . its officers were more or less swathed in an entanglement of red tape, which was, unfortunately, knotted by legal advisers of the department in such a way as to limit their freedom of intercourse with those whom they might otherwise have regarded as their outside colleagues." [12]

Although relations between members of the Society and the director of Somerset House remained cordial, open enmity broke out between certain members of both camps.[13] The situation remained essentially unchanged until 1894, when the chemist and former public analyst, Edward Thorpe, became the new director of Somerset House. Co-operation with the Society of Public Analysts began after the passage of the 1899 Act; and in 1911 the laboratory received independent departmental status.[14]

In spite of the efforts to establish a more representative and acceptable board of reference than Somerset House, and especially during the proceedings leading up to the 1899 amendment of the 1875 Act, no satisfactory measures were taken during the period under consideration. The laboratory of the Board of Inland Revenue became increasingly more scientific in character at the end of the century and the 1899 Act did empower the Board of Agriculture to make some rulings with regard to the acceptable standards of certain dairy products. But this legislation, like that preceding, ignored the need of a representative body to deal with definitions and standards of purity. Largely through the efforts of the Society of Public Analysts and the recommendations of the Select Committees (1894, 1895, and 1896), an 1899 amendment of the 1875 Act proposed that the Board of Trade appoint a standing committee to include representatives from the Local Government Board, the Board of Agriculture, the Society of Public Analysts, the General Medical Council, the Institute of Chemistry, and the Pharmaceutical Society of Great Britain.[15] As we have already noted, these provisions had disappeared from the 1899 Act when it finally emerged.

In spite of the fact that the 1875 Sale of Food and Drugs Act is usually considered to have required the appointment of analysts and inspectors, the specific language of the Act is much the same as that of the preceding Act of 1872. Local authorities *"may,* as soon as convenient after the passing of this Act, where no appointment has hitherto been made, and in all cases as and when vacancies in the office occur, or when required so to do by the Local Government Board, *shall* . . . appoint . . . analysts." [16] The local authorities specified included: for London, the Commissioners of Sewers, and the vestries and district boards; for counties, the courts of quarter sessions; and for boroughs, with separate courts of quarter sessions or separate police establishments, the town council.[17] According to this Act, samples for analysis could be procured by:

Any medical officer of health, inspector of nuisances, or inspector of weights and measures, or any inspector of a market, or any police constable . . . and if he suspect the same to have been sold to him contrary to any provision of this Act, shall submit the same to be analysed.[18]

The Local Government Board had the power to require the appointment of analysts where it felt this necessary, and it reserved the right to approve the appointment or removal of analysts. The law also stipulated that the Board "may require satisfactory proof of competency to be supplied to them, and may give their approval absolute or with modifications as to the period of the appointment and removal, or otherwise." [19] The nature of the proof of competency was not spelled out, as we shall see, until the end of the century. Repeated complaints, culminating in the proceedings of the Select Committees of 1894–1896, suggest that the power of the Board remained rather limited; for the execution of the Act continued to be uneven, and in some districts few or only infrequent analyses were made.[20] This seems to have been especially true as far as drugs were concerned, for the 1892 report of the Local Government Board reported prosecutions for only 44 samples, and the aggregate fines inflicted amounted to only £26.0.6.[21]

Not until the enactment of the 1899 Sale of Food and Drugs Act did the Board (and the Board of Agriculture, with respect to agricultural matters) receive power to delegate analysts and inspectors to check upon the uniform operation of the Act throughout the country. The expenses of such operations were charged to the local authorities, who could subsequently be forced satisfactorily to carry out the provisions of the Act where this had not been previously done.[22] For the first time, it seems, the law explicitly stated the obligation of local authorities to carry out the stipulations of the Act:

It shall be the duty of every local authority entrusted with the execution of the laws relating to the sale of food and drugs to appoint a public analyst, and put in force from time to time, as the occasion may arise, the powers with which they are invested, so as to provide proper securities for the sale of food and drugs in a pure and genuine condition, and in particular to direct their officers to take samples for analysis.[23]

It is indeed curious and perplexing that while drugs were specifically mentioned, along with foods, in the section making enforcement a duty of local authorities, foods alone were mentioned in the clauses outlining how the Local Government Board might ensure the uniform administration of the laws.[24]

In spite of good effects from the adulteration laws during the nineteenth century, to speak of effective official control seems premature until the twentieth century. This could not be otherwise until the government vested sufficient power in a central authority, the Local Government Board (1899), to see to it that laws were indeed enforced. Even so, the legislature failed to give concrete official recognition to the need for an equally powerful, yet representative body to ensure the smooth and efficient operation of the laws, by setting official standards of purity where these were lacking and by deciding questions of conflicting analytical reports. Yet for the first time, it was taking positive steps to ensure the competency of analysts appointed under the laws and so to give added effectiveness to now enforced regulations.

Caliber of Analysts.—At least part of the difficulties under the Acts of 1860 and 1872, as we have seen, were blamed upon the conflicting decisions and inexperience of the public analysts. The Select Committee Report of 1874 pointed out "a decided want of chemical knowledge [on the part of some analysts], but no more than was to be expected from the sudden call made for the services of the adepts in a branch of chemistry which had not previously been very highly valued." [25] The Committee suggested that one way of overcoming this defect was for the Local Government Board to require of analysts a certificate of competency from the School of Chemistry at South Kensington.[26]

Shortly after the report of the Select Committee appeared in 1874, the Society of Public Analysts came into being, partly to refute the "unjust imputation" that the imperfect functioning of the 1872 Act might be thrown upon the public analysts and to repudiate the "proposed measures of interference with our professional position and independence." [27] The formation of the Society, as we have seen, was not merely a reaction against criticism and in fear of government restriction. They hoped to overcome some of the difficulties encountered previously by devoting their concerted efforts to investigating and systematizing the best methods for detecting adulteration, by promoting the smooth operation of adulteration laws, and by promoting the appointment of competent analysts.[28]

In fact, one of their first acts was to criticize the unsatisfactory qualifications for a public analyst specified in the Act of 1872, which asked for "competent medical, chemical, and microscopical knowledge." [29] The Society's first president, Theophilus Redwood, had a strong feeling against this requirement, possibly fostered by his association with the Pharmaceutical Society. Some members of the Pharmaceutical Society considered pharmaceutical chemists eminently qualified to act as analysts under the Adulteration Acts. But the order in which the qualifications for analysts were set forth implied that medical practitioners might receive preference in these appointments. When the point was pursued by the Pharmaceutical Society, the Attorney-General and the Solicitor-General concurred that all that was meant was competency to analyze, without any intended restrictive meaning being attached to the term "medical." [30]

At least part of the answer to the question of who was most qualified to be a public analyst lies in the question—what class of individuals were practicing chemical analysis when British law first created a demand for public analysts? Those most qualified seem, for the most part, to have had academic roots, as professors of chemistry connected with university laboratories, or as lecturers in medical colleges associated with hospitals.[31] Even the relatively small group of commercial analysts then practicing usually came originally from this class.[32] But the number of chemists qualified, or capable of qualifying, for this work was small indeed, as local authorities realized when they tried to comply with government directives for the appointment of public analysts. Medical officers of health received many appointments as analysts, particularly as a result of the apparent preference for medical knowledge read into the Act of 1872, though many of them possessed scant training for the chemical work required.[33] A small number of physicians, such as Hassall, Letheby, and others, possessed sufficient chemical, or other analytical knowledge to pioneer in food and drug chemistry.

Still, in 1874 some public analysts lacked the qualifications necessary to fulfill their duties, and food and drug chemistry remained largely unexplored. Recall that the first textbook in English on organic analysis was Prescott's *Outlines of Proximate Organic Analysis* (1875), followed by Allen's *Commercial Organic Analysis* (1879 et. seq.). No wonder then that the Select Committee Report upon the operation of the 1872 Adulteration Act pointed to the conflicting decisions and inexperience of analysts, as one problem that demanded correction. The question of qualifications for analysts was widely raised at about this time.[34]

According to the 1875 Act, the local governments were to appoint analysts "possessing competent knowledge, and skill, and experience, as analysts of all articles of food and drugs sold within the said city, metropolitan districts, counties, or boroughs." Approval of such appointments was, however, as we have seen, subject to the approval of the Local Government Board. This section (10) of the Sale of Food and Drugs Act, 1875, also forbade the appointment of analysts "engaged directly or indirectly in any trade or business connected with the sale of food or drugs in such place." [35]

If we may rely upon various reports following this Act, the requirement of competency meant little until the end of the century. Some appointments remained sinecures, and in some districts few or infrequent analyses were being made by as late as the time of the 1894–1896 Select Committee hearings. The Local Government Board possessed relatively little power until the 1899 amendment, and, so far as we are aware, the first clear pronouncement concerning qualifications for analysts was not issued until 1900.[36]

Most of these requirements probably came as a result of the efforts of the Society of Public Analysts, which had taken its task seriously indeed. During the early years of its existence, several analysts showing incompetency were either publicly expelled, or their resignations were otherwise forced.[37] At least ten years before the Local Government Board finally took, or indeed was able to take action, the Society's Council suggested to the president of the Local Government Board that the time had come when "higher and more definite standards of qualification should be required from candidates for the post of Public Analyst as a condition of the ratification of their appointments by the Board." [38] The Society suggested that in addition to a science degree, fellowship in the Institute of Chemistry, or some analogous qualification, an appointee should have spent at least a year in the laboratory of a public analyst or of someone professionally engaged in food and drug analysis. The Council recognized that too often a candidate's only qualifications were medical experience, or testimonials of experience, whose value was extremely difficult to assess.

Several years later (1892) when a Bill amending the 1875 Act was introduced into Parliament, the Society's Council again pursued the question of satisfactory qualification, suggesting that consideration be given to instituting a qualifying examination and diploma of efficiency for candidates seeking appointment. The Council subsequently dropped the issue, believing that they were trespassing upon the rights of the Institute of Chemistry.[39]

Power to carry out some of these suggestions was given to the Local Government Board by the 1899 Food and Drugs Act amendment. The Board (and the Board of Agriculture) received power to have analyses made anywhere throughout the country, to check upon the uniform operation of the Act, and further, to force local authorities to carry out the Act where this had not been done. The Local Government Board also received the power to frame regulations setting forth the requirements of competency for analysts.[40] Such pronouncements first appeared in 1900, when appointees were required to furnish proof of "competent skill in the knowledge of (a) analytical chemistry, (b) therapeutics, and (c) microscopy," supported by appropriate "documentary evidence." [41] The Board accepted as documentary evidence the diploma of fellowship or associateship of the Institute of Chemistry, together with the certificate granted by the Institute after an examination conducted by them according to specifications of the Board, in therapeutics, pharmacology, and microscopy. A medical diploma was considered acceptable as fulfilling the requirements for microscopy and therapeutics, but additional proof of competency in analytical chemistry was needed. Furthermore, the Board required all statements of competency coming from individuals to be from recognized authorities "as to proficiency in the particular qualification in question." [42] The requirement of a special certificate from the Institute of Chemistry seems obviously a carry-over from a proposal of the Society of Public Analysts almost a decade previously. In spite of these official requirements, the Institute of Chemistry, as late as 1905, deprecated the analysis of samples under the Sale of Food and Drugs Acts by persons whose qualifications had not been approved by the Local Government Board.[43]

Although food and drug legislation had controlled adulteration practices for more than a quarter of a century, not until the end of the nineteenth century did the official central administrative body receive recognized powers for ensuring the efficient execution of the laws, particularly as this depended upon the competency of analysts appointed under the Adulteration Acts. The Society of Public Analysts not only promoted such official recognition of requisite qualifications, but maintained high requirements for admission to its own ranks, and expanded the scope of membership according to the best interests of the profession.[44]

Legal Difficulties.—Perhaps the most difficult legal problem [45] to arise in the administration of the 1860 and 1872 Acts was the responsibility these statutes thrust upon the prosecutor to prove guilty knowledge of willful intent to adulterate detrimentally (and in 1872 also fraudulently) on the part of the accused. The general concept of adulteration is so closely linked with ideas of intent, neglect, or knowledge, that it seemed natural that early adulteration laws should incorporate this qualification, just as most of the preceding statutes dealing with individual foods had done. The Pharmacy Act of 1868, which incorporated the law of 1860 and applied it to drugs, wisely avoided the problem by considering every admixture injurious to health, and by assuming that "any Person registered under this Act who sells any such Article adulterated shall, unless the contrary be proved, be deemed to have Knowledge of such Adulteration." [46] As we indicated previously, this section of the Pharmacy Act was apparently never used.

The 1872 Food and Drug Act incorporated the whole of the 1868 Pharmacy Act, without repealing section 24. It is interesting to speculate to what extent this clause (sec. 24) nullified sections in the 1872 Act dealing with drugs, but limited to willful adulteration. The first three sections of the 1872 Act clearly connect offenses under this law with intent and knowledge, on the part of:

Every person who shall *wilfully* admix, and every person who shall *order* any other person or persons to admix . . . any ingredient or material with any drug to adulterate the same for sale . . . . and every person who shall sell as unadulterated any . . . drug which is adulterated . . . . [and] any person who shall sell . . . any drug, *knowing* the same to have been mixed with any other substance with *intent* fraudulently to increase its weight or bulk, and who shall not declare such admixture.[47]

The 1875 Sale of Food and Drugs Act avoided all the pitfalls of the earlier measures connected with proving intent or knowledge on the part of the accused, for it (sec. 5),

provided that no person shall be liable to be convicted under either of the two last foregoing sections of this Act in respect of the Sale of any . . . drug, if he *shows to the satisfaction of the justice or court* before whom he is charged *that he did not know* of the . . . drug sold by him being so mixed, coloured, stained, or powdered as in either of those sections mentioned, *and that he could not with reasonable diligence have obtained that knowledge*.[48]

The offense was still defined to include intent and knowledge, of course, but it now rested with the defendant to prove lack of guilty knowledge "with reasonable diligence." [49]

This was the only section of the Act to include the connotation "knowingly." Absence of guilty knowledge was no defense under those sections (6, 7, 24) that made punishable the sale of a drug to the "prejudice" of the purchaser because it was "not of the nature, substance, and quality of the article demanded"—nor compounded "in accordance with the demand of the purchaser." It rested on the defendant to prove himself protected by the exceptions under these.[50] Intentional fraud formed the basis of offenses involving harmless and undeclared admixture, and of false labelling.[51]

Closely associated with the problem of guilty knowledge and intent was the responsibility of an individual for the guilty actions of his servants. Just as lack of knowledge proved no defense under section 6 of the Act, so ignorance of the actions of a servant, even when such actions were contrary to explicit orders of the master, proved no defense; but a servant could also be convicted under this section of the Act as the actual seller.[52]

Some members of the Pharmaceutical Society recognized that proof of guilty knowledge made adulteration legislation virtually impossible to enforce,[53] yet endorsed—as a reflection of the whole basis of British, indeed Anglo-American justice—the idea that "the laws are made for the protection of the innocent, and it were better that rogues sometimes escape, if their punishment could only be effected by including the guilty and the innocent in the same category." [54] While possibly the Pharmaceutical Society's deputation was partly responsible for insertion of the "knowingly . . . and fraudulently" clauses in the 1872 Act,[55] these had been opposed by some members of the Pharmaceutical Society and the Society of Public Analysts.[56]

In the 1875 Act the phrase concerning the sale of substances to the "prejudice of the purchaser" was almost as much a block to effective functioning of the new Act as the proof-of-guilt clauses were in the earlier measures. The clause was used to hinder completely proceedings under this section of the Act, because it was argued that sales to inspectors for purposes of analysis could not be considered prejudicial to the purchaser. Within four years (1879), Parliament passed an amendment making it indefensible under this section to claim that a sale for analytical purposes was not to the prejudice of the buyer.[57]

The majority of the early charges involving drugs brought under this section of the 1872 Act hinged partly on the problem of an official standard for drugs, but more so upon questions of acceptable trade practice. The confusion resulted partly from the fact that the courts considered it to the prejudice of the purchaser if he asked for any drug—such as mercurial ointment—by a name recognized in the

British Pharmacopoeia, but instead received one differing at all from the standards set forth therein.[58] Some commercial standards differed from the *British Pharmacopoeia,* those of the latter being poor or untenable in some cases. Some trade practices made respectable by public acceptance, as we shall see presently, promoted names that bore no relation to the product itself, or else harked back to former editions of the *London Pharmacopoeia* or *British Pharmacopoeia.* Not only did this confuse analysts and the courts, but it divided pharmacists amongst themselves, and perhaps it explains some of the later charges of indifference to trade questions, which were leveled by chemists and druggists' organizations against the Pharmaceutical Society of Great Britain. The courts did not recognize claims of commercial standards differing from *British Pharmacopoeia* standards; but in cases where only the formula or method of preparing a drug—as opposed to the composition—was given by the *Pharmacopoeia,* the courts did not consider this a standard.[59]

The unfortunate part of this situation, aside from the conflict it engendered within the ranks of pharmacy, was the disparaging light it tended to throw upon the profession and upon the administration of the food and drug laws. As we saw in our discussion of the extent and nature of adulteration, analysts tended to concentrate their attention upon these products involving "trade questions" (partly because they promised positive results), and so perhaps missed others more deserving of their attention or created an unbalanced picture of the actual nature and extent of adulteration practices.

Some pharmacists considered slightly tyrannical these proceedings against custom-honored practices, but the plea of commercial trade standards and customs was probably abused. Others, such as some members of the Pharmaceutical Society, believed the proper solution was to call drug preparations by their proper generic names. The Pharmaceutical Society viewed fanciful or non-descriptive drug titles as a trade practice it did not wish to appear to defend by becoming involved in any legal cases. Among pharmaceutical preparations involved in these controversies were the sale of effervescent citro-tartrate of soda under the name "citrate of magnesia," "milk of sulphur" in place of precipitated sulfur of the *British Pharmacopoeia,* "sweet spirit of nitre" in place of spirit of nitrous ether of the *Pharmacopoeia,* and "castor oil pills" containing no castor oil.[60]

The general reaction of the pharmaceutical and medical press was that it was questionable to treat some of these cases as examples of adulteration and that prosecutions might better concentrate upon products of more immediate concern to public health and welfare. A problem lay in the fact that the public had been accustomed to expect certain products under names not, or no longer, rationally applicable. In the "citrate of magnesia" controversy, the editor of the *Pharmaceutical Journal* commented that it lay outside the Pharmaceutical Society's domain to suggest names for drugs and that all that was needed was representative labelling. The British Pharmaceutical Conference formally condemned non-descriptive trade names.[61]

Another problem encountered in the section referring to sales "to the prejudice of the purchaser," but likewise corrected by the 1879 amendment, was the clause linking such prejudice to the sale of drugs "not of the nature, substance, and quality of the article demanded." [62] The 1879 Act made it plain that it was not a "good defence to prove that the article of food or drug in question, though defective in nature or in substance or in quality, was not defective in all three respects." [63]

Some difficulties centered about the meaning of the terms "prejudice" and "deleterious." The 1872 Act had already avoided using the terms injurious or poisonous in connection with the adulteration of drugs, and the 1875 Act likewise did not require proof of direct injury to health, where drugs were concerned. It was necessary merely to show deficiency of quality or potency. The 1868 Pharmacy Act had of course considered all admixtures with drugs injurious to health.[64] The term "prejudice" was taken to mean more than pecuniary prejudice, and it was not necessary to prove that a purchaser had actually sustained prejudice or damage.[65]

To protect the innocent seller and to acknowledge the public demand for certain mixtures, the 1875 Sale of Food and Drugs Act allowed the sale of drugs under a warranty of purity from the manufacturer and the sale of admixtures if the buyer were made aware of such mixture. (The only exceptions to this were injurious practices, according to section 4 of the Act.[66]) To avoid abuse of the warranty clause, a dealer had to obtain a written warranty at the time of the purchase, and be able to prove that the drug covered by the guarantee had been resold in the same state in which received. In addition, where such a warranty applied to foreign drugs, it became necessary for the dealer to take reasonable steps to prove the accuracy of the guarantee. To avoid selling to the "prejudice" of the purchaser, a seller might give either clear, written (including a label) or verbal notice of harmless mixtures, at the time of the sale. Neither the warranty nor the notice of mixture was considered admissible defense in the case of fraudulent adulteration.[67]

In the absence of standards, how did the courts determine the extent of admixture that might be considered fraudulent? Personal judgment was the rule in cases in which the quantity of diluent exceeded that of the main ingredient. The 1875 Food and Drug Act clearly stated that a label giving notice of admixture had to be "distinctly and legibly written or printed," although it did not require —much to the chagrin of some—that either the nature or the degree of the mixture be mentioned.[68]

At least two sections of the 1875 Act referring to compounded drugs proved entirely inoperative. These clauses made an exception to the offense of selling to the "prejudice" of the buyer in cases "where the . . . drug is compounded as in this Act mentioned" and specified that "no person shall sell any compounded . . . drug which is not composed of ingredients in accordance with the demand of the purchaser." [69] In one case (sec. 6, subsec. 3), the clause had no meaning because the Act contained no definition of "compounded drugs." A similar exception allowed in section 4 was equally meaningless; section 7, intended to apply to prescriptions or recipes, medical or otherwise, remained little used, because prosecutions for the same offense could be brought, and usually were, under section 6 of the Act ("not of the nature, substance, or quality of the article demanded").[70]

The inadequacies of many provisions under the nineteenth-century adulteration laws created problems of administration. In some instances these deficiencies were quickly recognized and corrected. Other basic problems of effective administration, stemming from inadequacies recognized even before the passage of the 1875 Act, remained uncorrected still at the end of the nineteenth century. Aside from the need for clearer definitions of adulteration, one of the most serious handicaps attached to the 1875 Food and Drugs Act revolved about the question of legal standards for drugs.

OFFICIAL STANDARDS

> *Where there is no statutory standard for the articles demanded, it is the duty of the justices to fix for themselves a standard based on the evidence before them.*[71]

In discussing the changing concepts of the definition of adulteration and of the problems of administering the adulteration laws, we have often referred to the question of official drug standards. Without guides of some sort it would have been impossible to say when and to what extent adulteration occurred. What standards were "official" or legally enforceable under the English Food and Drugs Acts?

Briefly, the *British Pharmacopoeia* was an official standard for all pharmacists registered according to the 1868 Pharmacy Act, which specified that pharmacists "who shall compound any Medicines of the British Pharmacopoeia except according to the Formularies of the said Pharmacopoeia, shall for every such Offence be liable to pay a Penalty or Sum of Five Pounds." [72] This clause remained in effect up to 1906. Between 1868 and 1875 the *Pharmacopoeia* was the official standard for drugs under the adulteration laws; from 1875 until 1906, it was not so recognized. Its very brief official status came, as we have seen, as a result of the incorporation of the 1860 Act into the Pharmacy Act, and subsequently the inclusion of drugs, as well as the incorporation of the Pharmacy Act, into the 1872 Adulteration Act.[73] The 1875 Sale of Food and Drugs Act neither recognized the *British Pharmacopoeia* nor incorporated the 1868 Pharmacy Act. Furthermore, it repealed section 24 of the Pharmacy Act, which had originally extended the 1860 Adulteration Act to drugs.[74]

If there was no official standard for drugs under the Food and Drugs Acts after 1875, what guide did courts and analysts use in deciding whether adulteration had been committed under the provisions of adulteration laws? In practice and by necessity, prosecutions under the pertinent sections of the 1875 statute were brought upon the basis of the standards of purity set down in the *Pharmacopoeia*. We have seen that Bartley interpreted the Act as meaning that "where there is no statutory standard for the article demanded, it is the duty of the justices to fix for themselves a standard based on the evidence before them." [75] Except in the case of certain substances coming under the jurisdiction of the Excise—alcohol, for instance— no specific standards were fixed by adulteration statutes until the 1899 amendment of the Food and Drugs Act, when the Board of Agriculture set limits for certain dairy products.

Even though the quantitative standards given by the *British Pharmacopoeia* remained small in number until very late in the century, and in spite of *Pharmacopoeial* deficiencies, some guide of purity was essential to the operation of the Act. For without such a guide, how were analysts and the courts to decide when the "quality or potency" of a drug were "injuriously" affected? Without a standard how could they determine when a drug had been sold "to the prejudice of the purchaser," or was "not of the nature, substance, and quality of the article demanded by the purchaser"? They could not, and did not. The only possible exception to the general reliance upon the *Pharmacopoeia* to determine the relative purity of suspected samples was in those cases in which the *British Pharmacopoeia* gave only processes for preparation, with no methods for determining strength or purity.[76] "The standard of the British Pharmacopoeia," concluded Bell, "is not conclusive, but . . . very strong evidence is necessary to displace it." [77]

Why did Parliament hesitate to designate the *British Pharmacopoeia* or some other official standard for drugs? Part of the reason may have lain in the very practical reason that few discriminating standards existed for most animal and vegetable drugs until the end of the nineteenth century or later. This was a reflection of the state of analytical science in its special application to foods and drugs, as noted in detail in our discussion of scientific and technological methods of detecting adulteration. This explains in part why the *British Pharmacopoeia* remained such an uncertain guide until the end of the century, although it does not explain why it should have been noticeably behind the *Pharmacopeia* of the United States in this respect—a circumstance we shall examine later. Here we note a more probable reason for the deficiency of legal standards in the Adulteration Acts: the pronounced laissez faire attitude of the English government toward trade and commerce. By enforcing a set of imperfect standards the government may have hampered trade, not only because trade practices followed commercial standards different from the *British Pharmacopoeia*, but also because the wholesale dealer remained relatively immune to the operation of the laws, much to the disadvantage of the retail dispenser. And if specifications for each drug, other than those of the *British Pharmacopoeia*, had to be drawn up, it would have created an impossible task for the limited forces engaged in administering the laws, and for the less than adequate facilities of the official court of reference, Somerset House.

The need for following some standard, usually the *British Pharmacopoeia*, is clearly indicated by the testimony of some witnesses before Parliamentary Select Committees, by the definitions of drug adulteration drawn up by the Society of Public Analysts within the first few months of its existence, and by Wigner's model Adulteration Act. We have already seen that these latter definitions of adulteration based upon variation from the standards in the official pharmacopeia, or some other recognized standard, entered the early adulteration laws of Canada and the United States. These definitions were ignored by British legislators in spite of their British origin and strong efforts for their adoption.

The Select Committee Report of 1856 recognized the need for uniform drug standards throughout Great Britain, but this referred rather to the confusion resulting from three separate pharmacopeias than to any single legal standard.[78] The Report called upon medical authorities to remedy the situation, but the exclusion of drugs in the 1860 Act rendered the task of no immediate concern to the profession. The Society of Public Analysts strongly urged the adoption of official standards while the Food and Drugs Act (1875) was still passing through Parliament.

The question of official standards came up again a few years later, while the 1879 amendment was before Parliament. In testimony before the Select Committee (1879), Herbert P. Thomas, a clerk of the Sanitary Department of the Local Government Office, strongly urged reincorporating section 15 of the 1868 Pharmacy Act to make the *British Pharmacopoeia* a standard for all drugs contained therein. He based his recommendation partly upon the reports of difficulties made to him by the analysts under the Act.[79] Thomas was strongly opposed by the influential figure of James Bell, chief of the Somerset House laboratory. We have already discussed Bell's views on the *Pharmacopoeia* as a legal standard. Bell, as we have seen, was more a civil servant than a scientist, but the legislature was apparently more impressed with his line of reasoning (not without merit) than with that of Thomas, or the chemist Charles Graham.[80]

How satisfactory was the *British Pharmacopoeia* as an official standard? In discussing the growth of scientific and technological means of detecting adulteration we noted repeatedly that serious deficiencies existed in the *British Pharmacopoeia* and its predecessor, the *London Pharmacopoeia,* in the light of existing knowledge of drugs and such European standards as the Wurttemberg (1771) and Prussian (1798) pharmacopeias. Chemists and pharmacists, such as Fredrick Accum and Richard Phillips, criticized severely the lack of purity tests in the current editions of the *London Pharmacopoeia.* Criticism of the *British Pharmacopoeia's* failure to keep abreast of the latest pharmaceutical and chemical knowledge, and its consequent inadequacies as a standard, continued to be voiced throughout the century. These comments became particularly sharp by the turn of the century. For just at this time the whole subject of carefully standardized drugs became a lively issue and a practical reality in the case of many drugs and drug preparations.[81] The activity in this respect was reflected especially in the publication of C. G. Moor's *Suggested Standards of Purity for Foods and Drugs* (1902); William Chattaway's *Digest of Researches and Criticisms . . . of the British Pharmacopoeia, 1898* (1903); and H. Mansfield Robinson and Cecil H. Cribb's *Law and Chemistry of Food and Drugs* (1895).

Robinson and Cribb discussed in detail why "excepting a limited number of *chemical* drugs . . . the whole pharmacopoeia is a dark continent to the chemist," and explained how this has greatly limited the action taken against adulterated drugs. They rightly concluded that the *British Pharmacopoeia* was then still a recipe book, useful primarily for chemicals and a few "organic" substances, including the vegetable alkaloids, but not for most of the drugs of vegetable and animal origin that formed the bulk of the official materia medica. They also believed that the sheer number and variety of drugs, by far outnumbering foods and drinks, precluded the public analysts from examining more than a small proportion for which well defined tests existed. In keeping with more recent custom, they considered a variation of plus or minus 10 per cent of the required drug strength to be a reasonable allowance of variation from the stated standard.[82]

Such allowance of variation would probably have quieted the fears of some individuals, such as James Bell, that the *British Pharmacopoeia* was too "harsh" a criterion for the Food and Drugs Act, because it failed to take into account minor deviations that often developed soon after compounding.[83] Variations ensuing as the result of deterioration through neglect could also be ruled out as indefensible in such cases.

The *United States Pharmacopeia* was recognized as being vastly superior to the *British Pharmacopoeia*. "The American standards," remarked one chemist, "were much more exact than the British, and it often happened that when a [British] pharmacist was in a fog with the British Pharmacopoeia that the fog was illuminated or dispersed by reference to the United States Pharmacopoeia." [84] We have seen that beginning with the sixth revision (seventh edition, 1883), which Urdang called the "first modern *United States Pharmacopoeia*," the *United States Pharmacopeia* contained detailed purity and identity tests and assay procedures. The 1885 and 1898 editions of the *British Pharmacopoeia* began to show the same modern spirit, but the 1914 edition most strikingly deserves the appelation "modern."

Pharmacists played a minor role in revision work, which seems to have been too limited in view of the major role played by American pharmacists in the *United States Pharmacopeia* from 1877 onward. This situation gradually changed in Great Britain at the end of the nineteenth century, which may help explain the increasingly scientific flavor of the *British Pharmacopoeia* and greater acceptance of the *British Pharmacopoeia* by pharmacists.

What efforts were made to correct the deficiencies of the *British Pharmacopoeia*? The *London Pharmacopoeia* appeared under the sponsorship of the College of Physicians; the *British Pharmacopoeia*, under the sponsorship of the General Council of Medical Education and Registration of the United Kingdom. Pharmacy had no direct representation in either of these bodies up to 1906. But individual pharmacists, and later the Pharmaceutical Society, contributed to various revisions upon invitation. We have already spoken of the part the chemist and pharmacist Richard Phillips played in the *London Pharmacopoeia*. The chemical tests for purity and, indeed, the general form the work assumed during the time he was associated with it carried over into the *British Pharmacopoeia* and resembled the form that *Pharmacopoeial* monographs still take.

Participation of members of the Pharmaceutical Society in *Pharmacopoeial* revisions began slowly. Theophilus Redwood edited the *Pharmacopoeias* of 1867 and 1885. He was associated in the first instance with Robert Warington of Apothecaries' Hall, and in the second with John Attfield, closely connected with the Pharmaceutical Society. A long step was taken with the *British Pharmacopoeia, 1898*, when "assistance of great value . . . [was] rendered" by a special committee of the Pharmaceutical Society. John Attfield, professor of chemistry, director of the laboratories of the Pharmaceutical Society, and president of the British Pharmaceutical Conference, acted as editor for this edition; and a number of outstanding pharmacists acted as "referees" in special fields, e.g., the noted botanist Edward Morrell Holmes (1843–1930) in botany, and the expert in essential oils, William A. Tilden (1842–1926), in chemistry.[85]

Pharmacy's increased role in the 1914 *Pharmacopoeia* is evident from generous credits given in the preface to that work and from accounts in the *Pharmaceutical Journal*.[86] Many pharmacists also came to feel that complaining about having to comply with a deficient book of standards was not enough. They realized that, whether they received official recognition from the General Medical Council or not, it was their task to help develop better standards.[87]

Following proposals made in 1885, special arrangements had been made by the Society's council for pharmaceutical research touching primarily upon preparations of the *Pharmacopoeia*. The work was carried out in the laboratories of the Pharmaceutical Society, under the direction of the professor of chemistry and the professor of pharmaceutics, who periodically reported to a Research Committee of the Society's Council.

Two members of the Society had been asked to confer with the Medical Council after the 1885 *British Pharmacopoeia* appeared, and by 1900 work had already begun, at the request of the Medical Council, upon revision of the *British Pharmacopoeia, 1898*. They had been requested specifically to check: 1) to what extent the standardization of potent drugs could be carried out with accuracy and success; 2) the boiling points of certain substances; 3) the percentage of ash in certain drugs; and 4) the solubilities of the chemical salts in the *British Pharmacopoeia*.

The extent to which pharmacy contributed to the improvement of the *British Pharmacopoeia* and the number of these improvements that first appeared in the *Pharmaceutical Journal* or the *Chemist and Druggist* may be seen from an examination of Moor's *Suggested Standards* and Chattaway's *Digest* of the *British Pharmacopoeia* of 1898. The names of E. M. Holmes, J. C. Umney, J. Barclay, and H. G. Greenish are outstanding. In these works we note equally great contributions, which appeared first in the *Analyst,* coming from prominent members of the Society of Public Analysts, such as C. G. Moor himself, T. H. Pearmain, E. J. Parry, and Martin Priest.

Members of the Pharmaceutical Society and of the Society of Public Analysts agreed on the desirability of establishing some official central board of reference to decide questions of standards, to ensure the uniform administration of the food and drug laws. The government, as we have seen, did not act upon these proposals during the period under consideration, and the laboratory of the Department of Inland Revenue remained the court of reference. It was hoped that such a board of reference would consist of representatives from the Society of Public Analysts, the Pharmaceutical Society, the Institute of Chemistry, the General Council of Medical Education and Registration, the laboratory of the Department of Inland Revenue, and the Local Government Board.[88]

At the end of the century organized pharmacists and physicians seldom remained aloof, as they once had done, from the pressing need for scientific pharmacopeial work. The former now demanded equal recognition while the latter characteristically questioned its propriety.[89] Even those who clearly saw the urgent need for making the *British Pharmacopoeia* an acceptable legal standard recognized that the original intent had never been to guide chemical analysts.[90] A few individuals even considered by-passing the *British Pharmacopoeia* and began privately to compile sets of standards.[91]

How did pharmacists see their obligations to the *Pharmacopoeia*? On the whole, pharmacists felt little responsibility to use the *British Pharmacopoeia* as far as the Food and Drugs Acts were concerned, but many of them felt a moral obligation to follow it.[92] The fact that they were obligated to use the *Pharmacopoeia* under the 1868 Pharmacy

Act was rarely mentioned. One pharmacist even explicitly contended he could vary from the *Pharmacopoeia* at his own discretion, quoting in defense the Medical Act of 1858 to the effect that: "Nothing in this Act contained shall extend or be construed to extend to prejudice or in any way to affect the lawful occupation, trade, or business of chemists and druggists." [93] As might be expected, his opinion found little support.[94]

In spite of a generally recognized moral obligation to follow the *British Pharmacopoeia,* the indications are that a number of pharmacists did not do so. Aside from convictions under the Adulteration Acts, there were the reports of the pharmacist Richard Phillips, which appeared in the early volumes of the *Pharmaceutical Journal* (1842–1843), Hassall's *Lancet* reports (1851–1854), and an interesting (if prone to exaggeration) little publication by the pharmacist William Bastick entitled *The Pharmacopoeia a Dead Letter* (1845).[95] Bastick perhaps saw the problem and its solution in terms of his experiences as a student in Germany, at the University of Giessen; but his remarks were directed both at pharmacists for transgressing, and at physicians for allowing the transgression. The general tenor of Bastick's little tract is conveyed in the following excerpt:

In short the Pharmacopoeia is a dead letter—an obsolete code of medical legislation; for it is tacitly permitted, and justly so, to deviate from the direction laid down therein, in the preparation of chemical compounds whose constitutions are the same, independently of the processes followed in their manufacture; and it is also notoriously the custom amongst Pharmaceutists almost invariably to depart from the instructions given, in the preparation of those bodies which do not possess a definite constitution, and which are mostly of animal and vegetable origin.[96]

The impression that standards were followed more in the spirit than the letter of *Pharmacopoeial* specifications seems confirmed by continuous references to so-called commercial standards and "trade" customs. Bastick, especially, complained of this practice, and purported to give formulas from private recipe books of some "of the most influential houses in London. In fact, so accustomed are the public, and even some of the profession, to these frauds, that they often mistake the genuine article for the adulterated, and *vice versa.*" [97] More than fifty years later a writer in the *Pharmaceutical Journal* satirically called upon wholesale druggists to manufacture a line of pure drugs as well as one of substandard drugs, on the grounds that there was a market for such preparations! He proposed a company that would specialize in nothing but *British Pharmaco-*

poeia products, to the great advantage of the retail dealers. (Prosecutions under the Food and Drugs Acts seldom touched the wholesaler, and consequently, were considered to bear unusually harshly upon the retailer.) [98]

How were drug standards to be enforced, once established? Two significantly different views are typified by the solutions offered by Bastick and Henry Wippell Gadd, an Exeter chemist and druggist especially interested in the question. Bastick suggested a "detective medical police," periodic visitations, government intervention to improve "this unhealthy condition of the body Pharmaceutical," government supervision and control, government separation of medicine and pharmacy.[99] Wippell Gadd's suggestions are more in keeping with the traditional ideas of the Pharmaceutical Society upon the subject; namely, better education of pharmacists, "a new prophet to preach that cheap drugs are nasty," "only in the last resort should standards be maintained by penal proceedings," and "technical breaches of the law should not be treated as criminal offences." [100]

The problem of pharmacopeial standards remained unsolved until the end of the nineteenth century, when it became possible scientifically to develop precise standards of purity for many drugs of vegetable and animal origin for the first time. From this time stems closer co-operation by organized pharmacy with the work of pharmacopeial revisions. The dearth of adequate standards, official or otherwise, combined with the socio-legal situation, perhaps accounts for the relatively minor attention paid to drug adulteration by enforcing officials, and also for some of the administrative difficulties encountered with drugs. The *British Pharmacopoeia* was in many ways a poor standard, compared to European and American official compendia, but it was nevertheless a standard. That it remained unrecognized in the Sale of Food and Drug Acts can perhaps be explained best in terms of the general political and social philosophy of the times.

In the same light, we perceive most clearly the manner in which the English government answered demands for adulteration controls, administered these controls, and met the administrative difficulties encountered. The first Parliamentary Select Committee pointed the way when it maintained,

it is impossible to frame an enactment on this subject which shall rely on strict definitions. The object of the law is to strike at fraud, and wherever a fraudulent intention can be proved, there to inflict a penalty. [But] what constitutes fraud must be left to the interpretation of the administrators of the law.[101]

15.

THE EMERGENCE
OF SPECIAL SOCIETIES
AND PUBLICATIONS

The voluntary efforts of certain members of the medical profession, perhaps regarded as among the most qualified to judge the problem, first excited interest in the seriousness of existing adulteration practices. The government answered demands for protection with legislative controls, after weighing ample—if sometimes contradictory—evidence given by expert witnesses. But the successful operation of legislative controls depended upon the rise of specialized groups that evolved to solve, in a systematic and scientific manner, the many problems raised by the enforcement of controls.

Analytical techniques had developed to a considerable degree of accuracy before the passage of the Sale of Food and Drugs Act of 1875, but the most spectacular advances did not come until the last quarter of the nineteenth century. Besides, relatively few persons in England were actually qualified to apply these techniques to food and drug analysis. And those who were so equipped early realized the necessity of pooling their knowledge and collective experiences for an organized attack upon the special problems raised by the scientific application of their skills to detecting adulteration. Just such necessity, sharpened by criticisms directed from all sides, led the then practicing public analysts to form, in 1874, the Society of Public Analysts.

THE SOCIETY OF PUBLIC ANALYSTS

Public analysts appointed by direction of the Adulteration Acts of 1860 and 1872 came from several groups, had varying qualifications, and fulfilled their obligations to equally varying degrees. A combination of circumstances led to the founding of the Society of Public Analysts, which was dedicated to several objectives, but mainly directed toward increasing the effectiveness of government efforts against drug adulteration.

Bernard Dyer and C. Ainsworth Mitchell, both intimately associated with the Society of Public Analysts, give some pertinent facts about its growth and development.[1] These are reinforced by other evidence touching upon the same questions.

We saw that most of the early analysts came from academic circles and from the ranks of medicine. Many were poorly qualified for their positions, but the burden of their functions was increased by difficulties created by the laws themselves, by the lack of adequate and accurate standards of reference, and by the absence of textbooks in English on the subject of organic analysis touching foods and drugs. Consequently, conflicting decisions of analysts were not uncommon, as the 1874 Select Committee Report upon the operation of the 1872 Adulteration Act pointed out. The public analysts themselves eventually called for some such compulsory qualifications, but in 1874 they saw these as only a criticism of their competency and a threat to their independence. Their immediate reaction against both directly stimulated the founding of the Society of Public Analysts.

Twenty-seven public analysts—physicians and academicians prominent among them—met under the chairmanship of Theophilus Redwood, professor of chemistry at the Pharmaceutical Society of Great Britain, in answer to the summons sent out by two prominent London public analysts, C. Heisch and C. W. Wigner. Redwood became the Society's first president; Heisch and Wigner, secretaries; Arthur Hill Hassall and J. A. Wanklyn, both prominent food and drug analysts, vice-presidents. Among the members of the Society's Council, Alfred Henry Allen stood out as the member who was to contribute more to the special field of the Society's interests than any other single person.

The association of this group of public analysts in actual practice,[2] "for the purpose of mutual assistance and co-operation," was from the first more than merely a mutual defense association. It proceeded immediately to draft definitions of adulteration and to suggest limits of purity or standards.[3] It strongly opposed the government's plan to make the laboratory of the Department of Inland Revenue a court of reference for disputed cases, contending the laboratory to be scientifically unfit for the task. It suggested that all admixtures should be declared by label. It faced the question of the training and qualifications that public analysts should possess. These same problems occupied them during the rest of the century; for the British legislature, as we have seen, remained particularly deaf to their suggestions.

Between the time of the new Society's first two general meetings in February and May of 1875, a new Food and Drugs Bill was before Parliament. The Society's Council pressed for desirable amendments during the bill's passage. On several vital issues—such as definitions, standards, and a court of reference—their pleas were ignored in the Sale of Food and Drugs Act that emerged.[4] But in spite of this, and the repeated discouragement the Society suffered in its frustrated attempts to make English adulteration laws precise and operative, the Society strove continuously to live up to its early aspirations and objectives:

1. To promote and maintain the efficiency of the laws relating to adulteration.
2. To promote, and as far as possible to secure, the appointment of competent public analysts.
3. To improve the processes for the detection and quantitative estimation of adulterations, and to secure uniformity in the statement of the results by holding periodical meetings for the reading and discussion of original papers on chemical and microscopical analysis, especially with reference to the detection of adulteration.[5]

We have already seen how the Society attempted to fulfill, and largely succeeded in fulfilling, all of these objectives.

"To promote and maintain the efficiency of the laws relating to adulteration"? Beginning with the 1875 Sale of Food and Drugs Act, still passing through Parliament as the Society came into being, and continuing through the subsequent amending Acts of 1879 and 1899, the Society exerted constant and ever growing influence upon the form of law. Only small portions of its definitions entered the 1875 Act; and in 1899 its hopes for a representative central board to decide questions of standards and definitions still remained unfulfilled. But the 1899 Act gave increased powers to the Local Government Board, including the prerogative of enforcing the operation of the Act in areas where it had been neglected. Moreover, the Board of Agriculture had been empowered to set certain standards dealing with dairy products; and the laboratory of the Department of Inland Revenue was becoming increasingly scientific. Individual members of the Society, such as Otto Hehner and A. H. Allen, represented the Society's views at Select Committee Hearings on the laws. Largely unappreciated by the English government, the Society's work was recognized within a few years of its founding when it was consulted by the German government; and was indirectly influential upon early American adulteration laws.[6] Wigner's model law (1880) reflected its ties with the Society's thinking on the subject. We have seen that Wigner's definitions of drug adulteration, taken from the Society's definitions of 1874, carried over into the early state laws of New York (1881), New Jersey (1881), and Massachusetts (1882), and into the Canadian federal statute (1884).

Aside from such specific influence upon other nations, the Society provided invaluable information on the administration and problems of the food and drug laws, through the medium of its journal, the *Analyst*.[7] The *Analyst* published Police Court proceedings under the 1875 Act (after 1885, only Appeal cases), and otherwise helped to clarify many of the legal problems in connection with legislation that largely occupied the Society during the first two or more decades of its existence. It also helped by collecting and collating information on the composition of foods and drugs, and on the best analytical methods for these substances. The Society further contributed to the smooth operation of the law by discovering, circumventing, and publicizing current "tricks of the trade." The value of its scientific contributions to the administration of the Food and Drugs Acts increased after 1902 with the broader scope of its membership.

"To promote, and as far as possible to secure, the appointment of competent public analysts"? In this area, too, we saw that the Society's efforts began to bear fruit at the end of the century. According to the 1875 Act, the Local Government Board theoretically could approve or disapprove the appointment of analysts, and require proof of competency. But not until the 1899 amendment did it actually receive official power to frame the regulations governing competency of appointees under the Act. The Board made its first pronouncement on the subject in 1900, requiring proof of knowledge and skill in analytical chemistry, therapeutics, and microscopy. It recognized a medical certificate as fulfilling only the latter two requirements and made arrangements with the Institute of Chemistry to conduct examinations to prove competency in the former. The marked increase in required qualifications for public analysts came as a direct result of the Society's representations on the subject.[8] This was a far cry from a quarter century earlier, when chemically unlearned medical officers of health commonly received appointments, and when such appointments often became sinecures, with few or no actual analyses conducted.

The qualities the Society looked for in official appointees, it also demanded of its members. Closed to all but practicing analysts until 1902, membership was limited to individuals nominated by four members, and personally certified by at least two of them. During the early years of its existence, several analysts showing incompetency were either publicly expelled from the Society, or their resignations were otherwise forced.[9]

In discussing the evolution of scientific and technologic methods of detecting adulteration, we referred repeatedly to the work of individual members of the Society and to that of the Society as a whole. A. H. Allen, C. G. Moor, E. J. Parry, C. H. Cribb, A. Wynter Blyth, George Jarmain, John Attfield are the names of only a few of those members who published important works on food and drug analysis and standards. Through its journal, the *Analyst,* and through other professional and scientific journals—such as the *Pharmaceutical Journal,* the *Chemist and Druggist,* the *Journal of the Chemical Society,* and the *Yearbook of Pharmacy* (of the British Pharmaceutical Conference)— the Society spread its findings among English and foreign analysts.

During its first two decades the Society was largely occupied with legal and technical problems of administering the food and drug laws; and its official organ, the *Analyst,* reflected a personal flavor resulting from its private ownership (until 1891). While scientific activities of members were noteworthy from the first, they tended to become more obvious after 1891. Between 1875 and 1885 the problems in connection with drugs centered largely about "trade" questions—"milk of sulphur," "paregoric substitute" without paregoric, "castor oil pills" without castor oil. However, they also reported upon various tests for the alkaloids, such as quinine and morphine; upon a colorimetric determination of salicylic acid; and upon the saponification of fats.[10] During the following decade, members devoted much attention to the analysis of fats and oils—to the Maumené test, bromine thermal value, iodine value, optical dispersion, and spectrometric examination. The names of Hehner, Mitchell, Muter, Liverseege, Chattaway, Pearmain, Moor, and Allen stood out in connection with this research.[11] The attention to systematic analysis of fats and oils became even more pronounced in the third decade of the Society's existence, along with alkaloidal and other analysis.

It appears that after 1905, just at the end of the period here examined, the Society reached its full maturity. This seems apparent from the nature of its specific research, from the special organized investigations undertaken under its sponsorship (Analytical Investigation Scheme), from the increased attention it could give to standardizing methods and equipment, and from its invited participation in international meetings, such as the first International Conference on Food Analysis (1911).

Thus although the fruits of its labors became fully apparent only in the twentieth century as the Society matured along with analytical science, the foundations had been laid carefully, patiently, if sometimes necessarily slowly. And side by side with this maturation and recognition, there developed, still more slowly, more satisfactory relations with the British government, with the legislature, with the Local Government Board, and with the Department of Inland Revenue.[12]

THE ANTI-ADULTERATION ASSOCIATION AND "REVIEW"

The Anti-Adulteration Association [13] came into being in February, 1871, and existed until at least 1898; its organ, the *Anti-Adulteration Review* (1871 to 1886),[14] was apparently succeeded by *Health News,* which seems to have ceased in 1898.[15] At its inception, the Association's primary object was "to secure the introduction of a *compulsory* Bill against adulteration of Food, Drink and Drugs. And, further, to aid such measures by eliciting a large amount of public support by petition and otherwise." [16] Because it considered existing laws to be "permissive and inadequate," it also saw an obligation to seek out proof of the necessity of legislation, to get laboratory reports from eminent chemists, and to seek out and prosecute injurious adulteration and fraud.[17]

These objectives remained largely unchanged. It also offered to make its laboratory services available to any of its subscribers who gave one guinea or more toward its support. The Association's leaders clearly considered that without "outside pressure" even existing legislation would not be enforced.[18] The customary line of attack was to collect samples privately and analyze them in the Association's laboratory; when circumstances demanded, they alerted the authorities.[19]

How successful was the Association? Within a few months of its founding it claimed the approval and support of "over Four Thousand of the most influential classes, together with a considerable amount of assistance in donations and subscriptions"; and by one year later this number had reportedly increased to 10,000.[20] Just how many of these lent actual financial support is not clear, for on the one occasion when an annual report of the organization was printed they disclosed an income for the first two years of about £500 and £600, respectively, with expenses about equal to income. The lists of members—heavy with prominent members of society, the clergy, and bankers—do not indicate which provided only moral support and which financial as well.

In terms of fulfilling some of its stated objectives, the Association later boasted of "having framed and passed two Acts in Parliament, also of being the instrument of many convictions, directly and otherwise." [21] If this was true, and particularly the claimed effect on legislation, it is curious that nowhere in the proceedings or reports of the Select Committees is the Association mentioned, nor do its officers appear to have testified. Nor do the many persons connected with the pure food movement refer to the Anti-Adulteration Association or its publication. Thus, while its influence may have been subtle it does not appear to have been overt. Another claim, which may be more readily refuted, is origination of a proposed definition of adulteration that is identical with one proposed publicly nearly twenty years earlier by Arthur Hill Hassall. [22]

Whatever its influence, the Association's *Review* did concentrate upon those causes espoused by the organization. Thus the *Review* regularly published articles on legislation, reported the results of analyses carried out in the Association's laboratory, commented upon the working of the Acts and convictions in various parts of the country, and discussed the relative effectiveness of inspectors and analysts. Drugs found little or no place in the contents of the journal. [23] Within a few years of its founding, the *Review* editors claimed that 80,000 copies had been given away without charge, and that an additional 35,000 were purchased and then given away by "private firms and parties who appreciated the importance of the movement." [24]

While proposing to elicit public support and understanding for their objectives, the Anti-Adulteration Association, through its organ, the *Review*, seems to have recognized repeatedly that the public generally was apathetic on questions of education. Moreover, they felt the public, through its demand for cheap goods, had to accept the blame for adulteration practices. [25] This realization of the public's indifference to its own welfare may, however, be considered to have been the chief *raison d'être* of the Association.

The "British Food Journal" and International Ramifications

At just about the time (1898) the Anti-Adulteration Association and its publication faded into oblivion, there emerged yet another publication that had similar objectives, the *British Food Journal*. [26] The hope of enlisting the aid of the public was perhaps even more apparent in this journal's intentions to make itself "neither too obtruse or technical, nor too popular," but to make its contents such as can be "understanded by the people." [27] In spite of these intentions, which remind us somewhat of Accum, the British Food Journal rapidly became and has remained a scientific periodical of some consequence, with some of the leading public analysts of the time on its editorial staff. As its name implies, it concerned itself primarily with foods and only occasionally with drugs.

As a means of achieving some of its objectives the journal promoted the "British Analytical Control." Under the system, any manufacturer could submit his products for examination. If the products proved satisfactory, the manufacturer could furnish his customers a convincing proof of guaranteed purity as attested by the Control's certification.[28] To ensure continued purity, goods were re-examined periodically. The scheme is vaguely reminiscent of Arthur Hill Hassall's ill-fated "Pure Food Company."

The British Food Journal began as and long remained the official organ of the International Commission on Adulteration.[29] While there is no mention of it in the British Food Journal and while there is no similarity in style, format, etc., the British journal may have been intended as the British counterpart of the Revue internationale des falsifications, as envisioned and edited by Van Hamel Roos of the Netherlands.[30] Van Hamel Roos, who also edited a similar journal in the Netherlands,[31] had proposed such a publication at the 1885 meeting in Brussels of the 6th International Congress of Pharmacy.[32] Apparently discouraged by slow acceptance of his idea, he began issuing the Revue on his own initiative in September 1887;[33] but with the second number of the journal, the editor proudly announced that the Revue had been designated the official organ of the "International Commission for the Repression of Falsifications" (Commission internationale pour la répression des falsifications), just founded at the Vienna meeting of the VIth International Congress of Hygiene and Demography.[34] The Revue was superseded in November, 1908, by the Annales des falsifications,[35] at first published under the patronage of the White Cross Society (Société Universelle de la Croix Blanche) of Geneva, and beginning in 1912 the official organ of the Société des Experts-chimistes de France.[36] The Revue, like the British Food Journal, directed most of its attention to foods, rather than to drugs, and gradually became a journal of applied analytical chemistry.

Like the British Food Journal, the Revue maintained a laboratory that guaranteed to the public the purity of various foods offered for sale by firms that placed themselves under the surveillance of the laboratory. The firms listed were located mainly in the Netherlands.[37]

THE PUBLIC AND ITS PRESS

Reacting to the *Lancet's* reports on adulteration, the editor of the *Pharmaceutical Journal* observed in 1855 that "the press generally joined in the cry, the public became alarmed." As far as the public was concerned this contradicts the general experience, already referred to, of the Local Government Boards, Anti-Adulteration Association, and others, concerning the public's apathy on the subject. But what of the public press?

If we check three popular magazines of the time, we find that *Gentleman's Magazine* remained silent, *Cornhill Magazine* published a single article, and *Punch* ran a few caricatures and satirical commentaries. The London *Times* restricted itself primarily to news reports and seldom editorialized.

The lengthy article, "Adulteration and Its Remedy," in *Cornhill Magazine*, was authored anonymously by Arthur Hill Hassall.[38] It began with dramatic declamations reminiscent of the scare techniques of Accum and the "death" series: "There is a certain ugly little monster of most insidious habits, and endowed with the power of rendering himself invisible, of assuming a variety of forms and shapes, and of being almost ubiquitous." [39] Only at the end of the fifth such paragraph did Hassall reveal it was "ADULTERATION" he was talking about, although this was apparent from the title. In some detail he discussed the inadequacy of most means of dealing with the adulterator, the various forms of adulteration, and the chief scientific means of detecting it. But the heart of the article pointed out, again in detail, the serious flaws of the Bill then passing through Parliament. In a lengthy metaphor, he described the Bill as "weak, diluted, and itself adulterated . . . a Placebo," rather than an effective medicine, but expressed hope that it was merely "a first prescription, embracing the preliminary treatment." [40]

Because this article was aimed at the public, Hassall offered suggestions for two means the public might take for protecting itself. The first was to demand a warranty for every article purchased; the second was a consumer organization, whose members could have samples analyzed for them without charge and who would receive regular reports on all forms of adulteration. Hassall considered such an organization would do more good than the proposed legislation.[41] His first idea was put into practice of course by his own ill-fated Pure

Food Company, and more successfully by the British Analytical Control; the second was espoused by the Anti-Adulteration Association and its publications. Hassall made only a single reference to adulterated drugs in this article, but it was a telling one, placed emphatically in the closing sentences, which pointed out that even drugs were valueless.[42]

Figure 13. "A Chemical Preventive Force Wanted." Initial letter *K* for a satirical article (see below) on adulteration in *Punch, 21* (Nov. 1, 1851), 196.

Probing *Punch* turned surprisingly little of its biting satirical prose and few of its incisive caricatures (see Plate X and Figures 13 and 14) against adulteration, considering the ripe field it must have provided. Its first jab came in reaction against the revelations of the *Lancet* Commission concerning the adulteration of tea. It chided the government for having been lax and for driving the population to drink. A cleverly designed decorative initial "K" (see Figure 13) directed attention to the article, "A Chemical Preventive Force Wanted," that began with the words "Keenly alive to the welfare of our country. . . ."[43]

THE USE OF ADULTERATION.

Little Girl. "IF YOU PLEASE, SIR, MOTHER SAYS, WILL YOU LET HER HAVE A QUARTER OF A POUND OF YOUR BEST TEA TO KILL THE RATS WITH, AND A OUNCE OF CHOCOLATE AS WOULD GET RID OF THE BLACK BEADLES?"

Punch returned to the subject during the deliberations of the Select Committee of 1855. "Such is the extent to which adulteration is carried," it complained, "that we cannot get even our drugs in a pure state, and it is almost as difficult to get an honest black dose, as an honest glass of port. It is horrible to think that we cannot even make sure of a 'cup of cold pison' in a sound condition, for our prussic acid is diluted, and our laudanum is deprived of a large percentage of its strength." [44]

Drugs were referred to again a few weeks later in a satirical poem, "The Adulterator's Alphabet":

> D is the Druggist—the Lancet explains
> How he poses each drug,
>   and increases your pains.[45]

Still another poem, "Adulteration is Artful Aid," was published in reaction to the Parliamentary Committee of 1874, but made no reference to drugs.[46]

As telling perhaps as the satire or caricature that involves the recognizable subject in its own setting is that which uses it as leaven for political or social commentary. One such example in *Punch* was a clever political satire on the Whig and Tory government, "Adulteration of Government," that used drug adulteration as its pervading element. A sample will suffice:

Lord John Russell, Political Druggist, late of Vienna, stated that he had considerable experience in the practice of adulteration, more particularly in political drugs. Had examined several samples of Whig Government, and found them all perfectly pure. Absolute purity in most cases was unattainable, but the articles he had exercised his microscopic skill upon were as free from deleterious matter as they could be, and he doubted strongly, if they were made any purer, whether the people would like them half as well.[47]

The important London *Times* diligently reported activities surrounding adulteration for the news it was. Thus factual accounts of the reports of the *Lancet* Commission appeared, as did lengthy proceedings of the Parliamentary Select Committees and Acts, but little or no space was occupied by the subject during periods when there was no such activity. Only seldom did the *Times* raise its majestic editorial voice to comment upon adulteration. It did so to take exception with the Select Committee Report of 1856 that assumed the public was perfectly aware, from the very price they paid, that they had bought a mixture rather than a pure article. The *Times* editorial

---

Figure 14 (*facing page*). "The Use of Adulteration." A caricature from *Punch*, 29 (Aug. 4, 1855), 47. The two articles requested by the young customer were both, and especially tea, adulterated to varying degrees. Thus tea was said sometimes to contain the drug catechu (terra japonica), green vitriol (iron sulfate), and verdigris (copper acetate); chocolate, to be colored with Venetian red (red iron oxide), itself liable to contain red lead (lead tetroxide). The various bags and containers visible under the counter contain adulterants said to be used in everyday food and drink. Armenian Bole is a red silicacious clay, said to have been used to color cocoa, anchovies, potted meats, and sauces; nux vomica (containing strychnine), to impart a bitter taste to beer and ale; red lead (lead tetroxide) to color annatto (cheese coloring) and curry powder; plaster of paris and sand, to increase the bulk and weight of flour and so bread.

strongly denied that the consumer had any such understanding or gave his consent to such practices. It considered the public largely at the mercy of the shopkeepers, for consumers "have no choice but to buy what is placed before them, and cannot change their chymist [i.e., pharmacist] or their grocer." [48] At the same time the editorial warned against expecting too much from legislation in the way of a cure and considered that more might actually be gained from continuing Hassall's investigations and regularly publishing the names of fraudulent dealers.

One other editorial reacted rather kindly to testimony concerning drug adulteration that had been given by Jacob Bell and a wholesale druggist and concluded: "The adulteration of our drugs is not to be laid exclusively at the door either of our drug-grinders or our chymists [i.e., pharmacists]. They come into the country adulterated." [49] While the editorial saw the answer in government inspection of imported drugs and fines, it also recognized the value of licensing qualified pharmacists and pointed to the noteworthy reforms from within that had already been carried out by the profession.

While the reading public could thus become fully informed about adulteration through the news and occasionally the editorial columns of the *Times,* it seems not to have reacted, at least through its prerogative of the letter to the editor. Although it is true that considerable space on the subject was given over to letters in late July and early August, 1855, this was devoted entirely to the vitriolic public exchange of accusations over due credit and priority (already referred to) by Hassall, Wakley, Letheby, and Henry.

FROM CAVEAT EMPTOR TO CAVEAT VENDITOR

The cursory survey in this chapter suggests that the public in general remained outside the battle for pure foods and drugs. And while some elements of the public press kept their readers informed of the battle in progress, they did not enter into the fray directly to any great extent. The responsibility thus remained in the hands of a small number of crusaders and some specialized organizations.

In 1820, Accum prematurely exposed prevailing adulteration practices to a commercially oriented society. Thirty years later Hassall fortunately found staunch and powerful support; and the government, forced to listen, passed increasingly stringent legislation to cope with existing problems. Many difficulties surrounded the administration of the early laws, but from 1874 onwards, the Society of Public Analysts devoted its full efforts to correcting them. In 1906, when the United States enacted its first federal statutes, many problems still remained unsolved. But almost a half-century of experience in administering the British laws and the enlightenment science brought made it merely a question of refining and extending the existing approach to controls rather than attempting any drastically new approach. Thus the shift from *caveat emptor* to *caveat venditor* came slowly in Britain. Of the many factors that contributed to this change during the nineteenth century, the advance and application of science to the detection and control of adulteration was one of the most important. But equally significant, or perhaps even more so, were the efforts exerted by society—by individuals and by groups of men who insisted that the adulteration of food and drugs should, in Hassall's words, "be branded a crime."

REFERENCE MATTER

NOTES

CHAPTER I
BEFORE 1820: DRUG ADULTERATION AND ITS DETECTION
OVER TWO MILLENNIA

1   For a more detailed discussion see Ernst W. Stieb, "Controlling Drug
Adulteration in England, 1820–1906" (unpub. Ph.D diss., Univ. of
Wis., 1959), 1–135. To our knowledge no other comprehensive
study from this particular viewpoint has been made of this early
period. A few facets have been published by Stieb: "Drug Adulteration and Its Detection in the Writings of Theophrastus, Dioscorides,
and Pliny," in *Journal Mondial de Pharmacie*, No. 2 (January
1958): 117–134; and "Robert Boyle's *Medicina Hydrostatica* and
the Detection of Adulteration," in *Actes, Xth International Congress of the History of Science* (Ithaca, N.Y., and Philadelphia, Pa.,
1963), 2:841–845.
    Brief discussions, treating mainly Pliny and Dioscorides, and
perfunctorily Galen, are offered by Alfred Schmidt, *Drogen und
Drogenhandel im Altertum* (Leipzig, 1924), 114–125; and Leon
Moulé, "Les Fraudes pharmaceutiques dans l'antiquité," in *Bulletin de la Société française d'histoire de la médecine*, 14(1920):
199–226. Charles Albert Browne, "Adulteration and the Conditions
of Analytical Chemistry among the Ancients," in *Science*, 29
(1909): 455–458, deals almost exclusively with Pliny. Browne was
familiar with the types of chemical and physical tests used by
Pliny, but did not document many of his examples and appears
quick to generalize, but his paper is one of the best on the subject.
For the Islamic period there is Eilhard Wiedemann's "Über Verfälschungen von Drogen u.s.w. nach Ibn Bassam und Nabarawi"
(Beiträge zur Geschichte der Naturwissenschaften, 40) in *Sitzungsberichte der physikalisch-medizinischen Sozietat in Erlangen*,
46(1914): 172–206; and B. Ben Yahia's "Falsification et contrôle
des médicaments pendant la période islamique," in *Actes du VII*

congrès international d'histoire des sciences (Jerusalem, August 4–12, 1953), 210–215. Yahia's study is uncritical.

2   Pliny, *Natural History*, XI.14 (3:13 of the translation by John Bostock and H. T. Riley, 6 vols. [London, 1855–57]; subsequent references to this work will cite the volume and page of this translation in parentheses).

3   Paul Walden, *Drei Jahrtausende Chemie* (Berlin, 1944), 116.

4   Theophrastus, *Enquiry into Plants*, I.12 and IX.13 (1:85–89; and 2:281–287 of Sir Arthur Hort's translation of Theophrastus, *Enquiry into Plants and Minor Works on Odours and Weather Signs*, 2 vols. [2nd printing; London, 1948, 1949]; subsequent references to this work will cite the volume and page of this translation in parentheses).

5   *Ibid.*, IX.4.10 (2:241).

6   *Ibid.*, IX.4.4–7; IX.5.1; IX.8.4; IX.7.4; IX.10.3–4; IX.15.6–8 (2:235–239; 2:243; 2:255–257; 2:251; 2:267–269; 2:293–295).

7   *Ibid.*, IX.16.3–4 (2:297–299); and Theophrastus, *On Odours*, IX. 37–41 (2:361–365).

8   Theophrastus, *Enquiry into Plants*, IX.8.3, 16.9, 17.1 (2:255, 305).

9   *Ibid.*, IX.6.2 (2:245–247).

10 Theophrastus, *History of Stones* (13–17 of John Hill, trans., *Theophrastus's History of Stones* [London, 1746]).

11 Alexander Wynter Blyth and Meredith Wynter Blyth, *Foods: Their Composition and Analysis. A Manual . . . with an introductory Essay on the History of Adulteration* (6th ed.; London, 1909). See also Browne, "Adulteration," *Science*, 29(1909): 456.

12 Dioscorides, *Materia medica*, I.77 (pages 42–43 of the edition by Robert T. Gunther, *The Greek Herbal of Dioscorides* [Oxford, 1934]; subsequent references to this work will cite the page number of this edition in parentheses). Similar observations may be made in the following cases: bitumen, I.99 (52); ebony, I.129 (68–69); aloe, III.25 (257); asafoetida, III.94 (328); copper sulfate, V.88 (628).

13 *Ibid.;* see the following: mastick, I.90 (49); castor, II.26 (99); crocodile dung, II.98 (123); wormwood, III.26 (259); sarcocolla, III.99 (333); elaterium, IV.155 (547).

14 *Ibid.*, I.18 (18–19).

15 *Ibid.*, I.18 (45–46).

16 *Ibid.*, V.129; II.84 (646; 113).

17 *Ibid.*, see the following: opium, IV.65 (458–460); calamine, V.34 (624); verdigris, V.92 (629–630); buckthorn, I.132 (71); galbanum, III.97 (330–331); pompholoyx, V.85 (625).

18 *Ibid.*, I.6, 7 (10, 11); II.93, 190 (118–119, 200); IV.1, 69, 104, 157 (399, 465, 501, 551).

19 *Ibid.*, I.1, 2, 4, 5, 6, 11 (6, 8, 10, 13); IV.69, 114, 151, 157, 161 (464, 507, 542, 551, 555); V.18, 84, 104, 112 (608, 623, 637, 638).

20 Pliny, *Natural History*, XXII.56 (4:439); XXIV (5:3); XXXIII.1 (6:69).

21 *Ibid.*, XXXII.42 (6:124–125).

22 *Ibid.*, XIV.8 (3:243); XVI.18 (3:357); XVIII.30 (4:43); XIX.15, 52 (4:145, 147, 195–196); XXXV.14 (6:237).

23 *Ibid.*, XXI.54 (3:151); XIX:15 (4:145); XXXIII.40 (6:122).

24 *Ibid.*, XII.20, 35, 43, 49, 55 (3:116, 131, 141, 145, 151); XXXIII.39, 58 (6:121, 143).

25 None of the various collectors of drugs, or those who handled or prepared them, during the Greco-Roman era have been considered equivalent to the modern pharmacist. *Kremers and Urdang's History of Pharmacy*, rev. by Glenn Sonnedecker (3rd ed.; Philadelphia, 1963), 408, listed the following designations: (by the Greeks) *migmatopoloi, myropoeoi, myrepsoi, pharmacopoeoi, pharmacopoloi,* and *rhizotomoi;* and (by the Romans) *circumforaneae pharmacopoei, pharmacotribae, pharmacotritae, pharmacopolae, pigmentarii, seullularii, seplasiarii,* and *unguentarii.*

26 Pliny, *Natural History*, XXXIV.25 (6:195). For references to *seplasiarii* elsewhere see *ibid., n.* i; XXXIII.58 (6:143); and XVI.18 (3:357).

27 *Ibid.*, XII.27 (3:121).

28 Browne, "Adulteration," *Science*, 29(1909): 457. The same interpretation was given by Paul Walden, *Chronologische Übersichstabellen zur Geschichte der Chemie von den ältesten Zeiten bis zur Gegenwart* (Berlin, 1952), 19, and in most histories of chemistry. The fact that it is the first reference to the use of test paper to come down to us, does not of course give any special priority to Pliny himself.

29 Pliny, *Natural History*, XII.37 (3:134); re: labdanum.

30 *Ibid.*, XII.54 (3:150–151).

31 *Ibid.*, XII.54 (3:151); XXIII.27 (4:478).

32 *Ibid.*, XXXV.52 (6:295). See Browne, "Adulteration," *Science*, 29(1909): 457.

33 Galen, *De compositione medicamentorum per genera*, III.2 (13:571 of the Carl Gottlob Kühn edition of *Medicorum graecorum opera quae exstant*, 20 vols. [Leipzig, 1833]). Our translations have been entirely from the Latin edition by Kühn, for which volume and page numbers will be cited in parentheses. The correctness of our interpretations has been corroborated by comparison with the Greek, in the Kühn edition. We are grateful to Miss Elizabeth Nash for checking the Greek text, with some assistance from Dr. Herbert M. Howe, Professor of Classics, University of Wisconsin.

34 Galen, *De simplicium medicamentorum temperamentis et facultatibus*, IX.35 (12:215).

35 *Ibid.* (12:216–217).

36 *Ibid.* (12:216); Galen, *De antidotis*, I.2 (14:7).

37 *Ibid.* (14:7–8).

38 *Ibid.*, I.11 (14:54–55).

39 Galen, *De compositione medicamentorum per genera*, III.2 (13:570 ff.); Galen, *De compositione pharmacorum localium*, I.4 (12:450 ff.); and Galen, *De theriaca ad Pisonem liber*, [Chap.].2(14:215).

40 Galen, *De compositione medicamentorum per genera*, III.2 (13.570).

41 *Ibid.* (19:721–747).

42 Sami K. Hamarneh, "Rise of Professional Pharmacy in Islam,"

Medical History, 6(1962): 59–66, gives a detailed account of the rise of privately owned, "public" pharmacy shops during the last quarter of the eighth century in Iraq, and the evolution during the first half of the ninth century of a class of educated, responsible pharmacists known as *ṣayādilah* (often transliterated as *sandalani*). The majority of the drug dealers were, however, spice and perfume sellers or herb dealers (*'aṭṭārīn*) or charlatans, and it was often difficult to distinguish these from the *ṣayādilah* on one side, or, for that matter, from the physicians on the other. A third class of vendor, sellers of juices and syrups (*sharrābīn*), also existed.

43 Sami Hamarneh, "Origin and Functions of the Ḥisbah System in Islam and Its Impact on the Health Professions," in *Sudhoffs Archiv für Geschichte der Medizin und der Naturwissenschaften*, 48(No. 2, June 1964): 157–173; and George Sarton, *Introduction to the History of Science*, 3 vols. (Baltimore, 1927–1948), 2(1931): 463. See also: Martin Levey, "Chemical Technology and Commercial Law in Early Islam," in *Chymia*, 9(1964): 19–22.

44 Yahia, "Falsification," *Actes du VIIe congrès international d'histoire des sciences* (1953): 211, 213–215.

45 Sarton, *Introduction*, 2:463–464; Wiedemann, "Über Verfälschungen," *Sitzungsberichte der physikalisch-medizinischen Sozietat in Erlangen*, 46(1914): 173–174; and Walter Behrnauer, "Memoire sur les institutions de police chez les Arabes, les Persans et les Turcs," *Journal Asiatique* [ser. 5], 15(1860): 463–464. Yahia, "Falsification," *Actes du VIIe congrès international d'histoire des sciences* (1953): 211, notes that a modern Arabic edition of Shayzarī's *Nihāyat* was published (Cairo, 1940) by Al-Sayd al-Bāz al-'Arīnī. Shayzarī is variously designated as "Abnabrāwi," "Annabrāwi," and "Nabrāwi." Behrnauer (15:463–464) and Wiedemann (173–174) indicate that a number of similar manuscripts, bearing slightly different titles or the names of different authors, may all be traceable to one work. Behrnauer, in subsequent volumes of *Journal Asiatique* [ser. 5], (16[1860]: 351–392; and 17[1861]: 5–76), publishes the text of one of these.

46 Wiedemann, "Über Verfälschungen," *Sitzungsberichte der physikalisch-medizinischen Sozietat in Erlangen*, 46(1914): 175–184, publishes a translation of chapters 38, 39, and 40, with notes and comments (184–201).

47 Behrnauer, "Memoire," *Journal Asiatique* [ser. 5], 16(1860): 364–367; and Wiedemann, "Über Verfälschungen," *Sitzungsberichte der physikalisch-medizinischen Sozietat in Erlangen*, 46(1914): 201–206.

48 Behrnauer, "Memoire," *Journal Asiatique* [ser. 5], 16(1860): 387, 391.

49 Wiedemann, "Über Verfälschungen," *Sitzungsberichte der physikalisch-medizinischen Sozietat in Erlangen*, 46(1914): 175–176.

50 Compare Shayzarī, XVII.18 (Yahia, "Falsification," *Actes du VIIe congrès international d'histoire des sciences* [1953]: 213), or Ibn Bassām, XXXVIII.18 (Wiedemann, "Über Verfälschungen,"

Sitzungsberichte der physikalisch-medizinischen Sozietat in Erlangen, 46[1914]: 177–178, 190), with Dioscorides, *Materia medica,* V.92 (629–630); Shayzarī, XVII (Yahia, 213–214; or Behrnauer, "Memoire," *Journal Asiatique* [ser. 5], 16[1860]: 391); or Ibn Bassām, XXXVIII.24 (Wiedemann, 178), with Dioscorides, I.18 (18–19); and Shayzarī, XVII (Yahia, 214; or Behrnauer, 16:387–388) or Ibn Bassām, XXXVIII.1 (Wiedemann, 176, 185–186), with Dioscorides, IV.65 (458–460). In the monograph on balsam, the Arab author added one test not found in Dioscorides, the flammability of pure balsam upon the ignition of a head of grain dipped in the test sample. While similiarities may also be drawn to Pliny, there are enough differences to rule him out (compare the monographs for the same drugs in the *Natural History,* XXXIV.26, XII.54, and XX.76 [6:196, 3:150–151, and 4:277]).

Yahia's unbridled admiration of the tests given by Shayzarī and others as "ancestors" of the assays of modern pharmacopeias (213) overlooks the fact that these procedures trace back at least to Dioscorides and Pliny. Certain comparisons of Yahia and Behrnauer create doubt whether Yahia was using an edition of Shayzarī or the augmented version of Ibn Bassām.

51 Paul Dorveaux, *Livre des simples médecines* (French trans. [Paris, 1913] of thirteenth-century manuscript of Platearius, *Liber de simplici medicina dictus Circa instans*), xvi; future references to this work will give the page number of this translation in parentheses. See also Charles Singer, "Herbals," in *Edinburgh Review,* 237 (1923): 107; and Sarton, *Introduction,* 2:50, *n.* 55. The ultimate sources of Constantine, through Haly Abbas, were Greek.

52 Dorveaux, *Livre des simples,* xvi–xxi. See also Agnes Arber, *Herbals, Their Origin and Evolution: A Chapter in the History of Botany, 1470–1670* (Cambridge, 1938), 22, 25, 26; and Eleanour Sinclair Rohde, *The Old English Herbals* (London, 1922), 66–67.

53 Dorveaux, *Livre des simples,* x, *nn.* 1, 2.

54 *Ibid.,* xi. See also Sarton, *Introduction,* 2:241. The Dorveaux edition belongs to the latter type. This undoubtedly explains why of the twenty-five specific references to adulteration in the *Grete Herball,* ten are not mentioned in this edition of the *Circa instans,* in spite of the strong connection between the two works. With the corresponding chapter numbers taken from *The Grete Herball . . .* (Peter Treveris, London, 1526), shown in parentheses, these include the following: Aloes (1), Aloes ligno (2), Galbanum (188), Gomme Elempni (201), Hartshorn (319), Pearls (276), Cloves (185), Crocus (103), Galyngale (187) and Sarcocolla (388).

55 *Circa instans,* 121 (23); where Shayzarī directed the use of a head of grain to test the flammability of balsam, the *Circa instans* suggested the tip of a sword. Since this test is one not traceable to Dioscorides, who was obviously a source for Shayzarī, it is possible it was of Arabic origin and passed into the *Circa instans* by way of the Arabic sources of Constantinus Africanus.

56 *Ibid.,* 749 (129); see chapter 286 of *Grete Herball.*

57 *Circa instans,* 120, 671 (23, 114); chapters 55, 267 of *Grete Herball.*

Circa instans, 142, 314, 587 (28, 56, 102). In the case of lapis
lazuli, the *Grete Herball* (230) adds "Bycause moche is founde in
Armeny."

58 *Circa instans,* 575, 535 (100, 94).

59 *Ibid.,* 212, 296, 770, 854, 1065 (39, 53, 134, 147–148, 182). See also
ibid., 137, 529, 908 (26, 93, 156). These appear in the *Grete
Herball* as chapters 83, 97, 287, 322, 382; and 60, 194, 337.

60 Arber, *Herbals,* 44–51; Rohde, *Old English Herbals,* 65–73. An untenable remark by Arber (*Herbals,* 50) in connection with the
Grete Herball, due perhaps to a confusion of terms and a lack of
clear definition, is her opinion that: "One of the most noticeable
features of the herbal [*Grete Herball*] is the exposure of methods of
'faking' drugs, for the protection of the public. . . . This is a great
step in advance from the days of the old Greek herbalists, when
secrecy was part of the stock-in-trade of a druggist." Although
elsewhere (7) Arber defined herbalists as "root diggers, or herb
gatherers" and druggists as "drug sellers," she appears to have used
these terms interchangeably in this passage and would probably
have been well-advised to retain the designations "root diggers" and
"drug sellers" to avoid confusion. The implication that the *Grete
Herball* was somehow unique in its revelation of adulteration practices is entirely unsupported, in view of the wealth of similar
literature which precedes the *Grete Herball* through at least fifteen
centuries.

61 *Grete Herball,* 319. See also, *ibid.,* 84, 276.

62 *Ibid.,* 201.

63 London, 1690. Second titlepage reads: "Experiments and Observations Relating to the Materia Medica." A Latin translation appeared
in 1693. Our discussion is adapted, with permission of the publisher
(Hermann, Paris), from Stieb, "Robert Boyle's *Medicina Hydrostatica* . . . ," *Actes, Xth Internat. Cong. Hist. of Sc.* (1963),
2:841–845.

64 J. F. Fulton, "A Bibliography of the Honourable Robert Boyle, Fellow
of the Royal Society," *Oxford Bibliographical Society Proceedings
and Papers,* 3(1931–1933): 118, questions Boyle's use of the term
"medicina" to title his treatise. The medical slant of the work seems
pronounced enough to counter such a criticism, as do Boyle's own
comments throughout.

65 Boyle did not, as we shall see, view specific gravity as a constant
according to our understanding of the term.

66 Boyle, *Medicina Hydrostatica,* 11–12, 20. Boyle also refers frequently to Mersenne's *Hydraulica* in *Cogitata physico-mathematica*
. . . (Paris, 1644). For the importance of Boyle's work on specific
gravity to chemistry and physics see: Fulton, "Bibliography," *Oxford Bibliographical Society Proceedings and Papers,* 3(1931–
1933): 118; and Marie Boas, *Robert Boyle and Seventeenth-Century Chemistry* (Cambridge, 1958), 228.

67 Specific gravity, along with solubility, remained one of the few
physical tests of drug purity or identity that found even occasional
application before the early part of the nineteenth century.

68   Boyle, *Medicina Hydrostatica*, 36.
69   *Ibid.*, 39.
70   *Ibid.*, page i of unnumbered appendix. Antimony is shown to have a
     weight of 391 grains in air and 295 grains in water. By our
     methods this would mean a S.G. of 4.07, i.e., $\dfrac{391}{391 - 295}$. See also,
     ibid., 100: "Proportion . . . of the Solid to the Liquor, or between
     Bodies of the same Denomination."
71   *Ibid.*, 34.
72   *Ibid.*, 97.
73   *Ibid.*, 100–105, *passim*. See also Preface (unnumbered pp. ix–x).
74   *Two Essays, Concerning the Unsuccessfulness of Experiments, Con-
     taining Divers Admonitions and Observations (chiefly Chymical)
     touching that Subject* (London, 1661), published as part (pages
     37–105) of *Certain Physiological Essays, Written at distant Times,
     and on several Occasions* (London, 1661; "Printed for *Henry Her-
     ringman* at the *Anchor* in the Lower walk in the New-Exchange").
     See *Certain Physiological Essays*, 39–41.
75   Boas, *Boyle*, 126–141 *passim*, but particularly 126, 127, 130, 213,
     and 214, provides convincing evidence that Robert Boyle provided
     those concerned with the problem of adulteration a wide variety of
     qualitative tests, capable of detecting adulteration in chemical
     drugs, two centuries before Fredrick Accum's crusade (1820) in
     England.
76   Ward Benjamin White, "Adulteration," in *Encyclopaedia Britannica*,
     1(New York, 1952): 188.
77   A Paris edition of 1694–95, published by the author himself, carries
     two titlepages. The first (dated 1695) gives: *Le Marchand sincère
     ou traité générale des drogues simples et composées*. . . . The
     second (dated 1694) gives the more common title: *Histoire géné-
     rale des drogues, traitant des plantes, des animaux, et des mineraux
     . . . .* White, "Adulteration," *Encyl. Brit.*, 1:188, erroneously gives
     the publication date as 1650, which is most unlikely, considering
     that Pomet's life span was 1658–1699. A second French edition
     appeared in 1735, supervised by Pomet's son, Joseph, a hospital
     pharmacist. An English edition, augmented by material from Lem-
     ery and Tournefort, first appeared in 1712 as *A Compleat History
     of Druggs* . . . , 2 vols. in 1(London). For a biographical account
     see "Pierre Pomet," in *Nouvelle Biographie Générale*, 40(Paris,
     1862): 690–691.
78   Pomet, *History of Druggs*, dedication.
79   *Ibid.*, 2:330.
80   *Ibid.*, 282 (re: alum); and 391–392 (re: sulfur).
81   *Ibid.*, 1, preface. To avoid confusion with modern terms, we have
     chosen to use the word "pharmacist" where an "apothecary" is
     referred to by the author; "non-pharmacist dealer in drugs," where
     a "druggist" is referred to; and "herbalist," where a "dealer in
     herbs" is referred to.
82   *Ibid.*, 1:215.
83   For brief characterizations of these works see Henry A. Schuette,

"Death in the Pot," *Wisconsin Academy of Sciences, Arts and Letters, Trans.,* 35(1943): 283; and Blyth and Blyth, *Foods,* 30, n. 1.

84 We do not consider the numerous polemic tracts which appeared during the sixteenth century as a manifestation of the quarrels between physicians and apothecaries to be in the same category. These include, in abbreviated titles: Symphorien Champier, *Myrouel des apothicaires et pharmacopoles* (1532); Sebastien Colin (under pseudonymn Lisset Benancio), *Déclaration des abuz et tromperies que font les Apoticaires* (Tours, 1553), edited by Paul Dorveaux (Paris, 1901); Pierre Braillier, *Déclaration des abus et ignorances des médecins* (Lyon, 1557); Jean Surrelh, *Apologie des médecins contre les calomnies et grands abus de certains apothicaires* (Lyon, 1558); Pierre Braillier, *Sur l'apologie de Jean Surrelh* (Lyon, 1558). Dorveaux (vii) believes Colin's work was copied by Giovanni Lodetti (1569)—of which Thomas Bartholin made a Latin translation, appended to his Latin translation of Lisset Benancio (1671)—and Christopher Merrett (1669, 1670). These tracts often mentioned drug adulteration, but their exaggerated style precludes value as reliable evidence of the extent or nature of adulteration practices, or as tools for detection and control.

85 J. E. Gilibert, *Anarchie médicinale,* 3 vols. (rev. and cor. ed.; Paris, 1776).

86 Gilibert seems to use the terms *apothicaire* and *pharmacien* interchangeably, and indeed, it was just at this time that the use of the latter term was being encouraged. The term *droguiste* appears to have been intended, as in England, for the drug wholesalers, concerned mainly with the trade in imported drugs. The *herboristes* appear to have been more restricted to trade in indigenous drugs. Gilibert was a doctor of medicine of the Faculté de Montpellier, and Professor of Botany, Anatomy, and Surgery at the Collège Médecins de Lyon.

87 Gilibert, *Anarchie médicinale,* 1:287–288.

88 *Ibid.,* 1:281–414, and *passim,* but especially, 1:276–278, 288–290, 293, 393, 398–400, 404.

89 *Ibid.,* 1:409. Just a year after this work appeared, in 1777, the Collège de Pharmacie came into being as an administrative as well as educational institution of French pharmacy.

90 J. B. Vanden Sande, *La Falsification des médicaments* (The Hauge and Brussels, 1784). Joseph Defrecheux, "Jean-Baptiste-Augustin Vanden Sande," in *Biographie Nationale de Belgique,* 21 (Brussels, 1911–1913): 290, notes that this work made the author's reputation, and that a German translation by Samuel Hahnemann appeared as early as 1787 (Dresden). The same source (290) notes a small (20 pp.) earlier publication (Amsterdam, 1781) by Vanden Sande on a related topic, *Lettre sur la sophistication des vins.*

91 Vanden Sande, *Falsification des médicaments,* i–ii, viii–ix, 205. In using the term *marchands* it is possible that Vanden Sande meant spicers and non-pharmacist dealers, whom he referred to variously as *marchands epiciers,* or *marchands de drogues* (*ibid.,* i, viii, 4, 118, 119, 205, 418).

92 *Ibid.*, x.
93 *Ibid.*, vii–viii, xii–xiii, xix, 205.
94 *Ibid.*, xiv–xix. See also *ibid.*, xx–xxii.
95 *Ibid.*, 413 (syrups), 425 (jalap resin), 402–404 (essential oils), 418 (powders).
96 Blyth and Blyth, *Foods*, 26.
97 Vanden Sande, *Falsification des médicaments*, 93 (cinchona), 102 (safran), 118–119 (cloves), 143–144 (white pepper), 202 (opium), 205 (scammony), 208 (storax), 216 (galbanum), 218 (myrrh), 222 (sagapenum), 257 (white wax), 255 (castoreum).
98 *Ibid.*, 144 (white pepper), 166–167 (balsam of Peru), 181 (dragon's blood), 250 (bezoar).
99 *Ibid.*, 163. The tests dismissed as imaginary include coagulation of milk; inducement of nasal bleeding upon inspiration; disappearance through the pores, when held in the hand; non-staining action upon linen.
100 *Ibid.*, 305.
101 We have made use here of the translation from the German, *Police judiciaire pharmaco-chimique . . .* , by E. J. B. Bouillon-Lagrange and A. Vogel (Paris, 1816). Second and third German editions appeared in 1811 and 1827. An indication of the work's stature is the flattering appraisal by Guyton-Morveau, which was reprinted at the beginning of the French edition, preceding Remer's own preface.
102 Remer, *Police judiciaire*, 145–179.
103 *Ibid.*, 142–146.
104 *Ibid.*, 146.
105 *Ibid.*, 144, *n.* 1 [translators' note?].
106 *Ibid.*, 406.
107 *Ibid.*, 167.
108 *Ibid.*, 163–164; compare with Vanden Sande, *Falsification des médicaments*, 402–404.
109 Favre, *Sophistication*, vi. At the time this book appeared, Favre was pharmacist to a certain Cardinal Fesch, and a member of the School of Pharmacy, the Society of the School of Medicine, and the Medical Society *d'emulation* of Paris; previously, he had been professor of pharmaceutical chemistry, materia medica, and botany at Brussels and Secretary of the Society of Medicine, Surgery and Pharmacy of Brussels. For details see *ibid.*, i–ii, iv.
110 *Ibid.*, vii–xi.
111 *Ibid.*, x–xi. Cf. Gilibert, *Anarchie médicinale*, 1:287–288.
112 Favre, *Sophistication*, 67, 152, 182, 216.
113 *Ibid.*, xi–xxii. Favre acknowledged Gilibert among those who had dealt with the serious consequences of the so-called *anarchie pharmaceutique*.
114 *Ibid.*, 67, 94, 96, 104, 106, 108, 152, 160, 216.

CHAPTER 2
AN OVERVIEW

1 The books by the English physician and food and drug reformer, Arthur Hill Hassall (1817–1894), concentrated largely upon the

single technique of microscopy and predominantly on its application to foods. Slightly earlier works by Alphonse Normandy (1850) and John Mitchell (1848) fall before the application of the microscope and also concentrate primarily upon foods. Otherwise, analytical methods applicable to drug adulteration appeared primarily in textbooks of pharmaceutical chemistry or of materia medica; and even here, English literature remained sparse in comparison to continental materials.

2   Bernard Dyer and C. Ainsworth Mitchell, *The Society of Public Analysts and other Analytical Chemists: Some Reminiscences of Its First Fifty Years, and a Review of Its Activities* (Cambridge, 1932), 6, remarked of Prescott's *Outlines:* "What was known relating to general commercial organic analysis had been put together by Professor Prescott of Michigan in a little book . . . which including its index, extended to less than 200 pages." Prescott (1832–1905) pioneered in scientifically based pharmaceutical education as the first head of the first department of pharmacy in an American state university (Michigan).

3   Alexander Wynter Blyth, *A Manual of Practical Chemistry: The Analysis of Foods and The Detection of Poisons* (London, 1879). The two divisions of the book later appeared separately—the first as *Foods: Their Composition and Analysis; A Manual for the Use of Analytical Chemists and Others, with an Introductory Essay on the History of Adulteration* (London, 1882), and in many subsequent editions, the sixth in 1909.

Alfred Henry Allen, *An Introduction to the Practice of Commercial Organic Analysis; A Treatise on the Properties, Proximate Analytical Examination, and Modes of Assaying of Various Organic Chemicals and Products Employed in the Arts, Manufactures, Medicine, with Concise Methods for the Detection and Determination of Their Impurities, Adulterations, and Products of Decomposition.* There have been numerous, multi-volume, and occasionally non-consecutive editions of *Commercial Organic Analysis.* Since frequent reference is made to virtually all of these editions throughout this work, subsequent citations throughout will carry title, volume number, and place and date of publication of the given volume. For the further guidance of the reader, listed below is a general description of the principal editions used: 1st, 2 vols. (London, 1879–1882); an identical edition, printed in Philadelphia, referred to herein as 1st American ed.; 2nd, 3 vols. in 6 parts (London, 1885–1896); 2nd American, 4 vols. in 6 parts (Philadelphia, 1885–1898); 3rd, 4 vols. in 8 parts (London, 1898–1907); an identical edition, printed in Philadelphia, referred to herein as 3rd American ed. All of these editions graphically illustrate the current research in areas of food and drug analysis; and the increasing proportion of this research by English chemists and pharmacists.

Some idea of the increase in the literature on adulteration and its detection that apppeared about this same time in England and elsewhere, may be gained from the bibliographic appendix (particularly the chronologically arranged bibliography of general works) in Jesse P. Battershall, *Food Adulteration and Its Detection; with Photomicrographic Plates and a Bibliographical Appendix* (New York, 1887), 258–267. There are numerous errors and omissions in this bibliography, but it is one of only two of its kind we are aware of. It gives a good over-all impression of the activity in this field, in spite of its deficiencies. A close examination suggests that Battershall may have taken some of these references from a similar bibliography given by Blyth, *Foods* (1882): 43–46. The similarities in errors suggest at least a common source. Blyth's bibliography is only about one-fourth the length of Battershall's, but his citations (especially author and subject) are more detailed, and partially annotated. Battershall covers a longer period (1690–1887) than Blyth (1690–1880), and includes numerous American works.

4   The sixth revision (7th ed.; 1883) of the *United States Pharmacopeia*, notably under the influence of American pharmacists, had assumed a modern scientific form. The pharmacopeia included detailed tests for identity and purity, and detailed alkaloidal essays. The *British Pharmacopoeia* of 1914, in many ways, might be considered the first to achieve this distinction, although signs of impending change were already apparent in the editions of 1885 and 1898.

CHAPTER 3
ORGANOLEPTIC TESTS

1   Fredrick Accum, *A Treatise on Adulterations of Food, and Culinary Poisons* . . . (London, 1820), 18.

2   *Ibid.,* 26–27. The whole sentence, of which a portion is quoted, was, we discover, taken verbatim from the German pharmacist Kaspar Neumann, *Chemical Works,* William Lewis, trans. (London, 1759), 273, *n.* "p."

3   Accum, *Treatise on Adulterations* (4th ed.; London, 1822), 23. Compare this with the first edition, 24.

4   Accum, *Treatise on Adulterations* (4th ed.), 17, 18. These important qualifications did not appear in the first edition. Quinine had been isolated by the French pharmacists Pelletier and Caventou in 1820. Had Accum known this, he might have suggested judging the purity of cinchona on the basis of its quinine content, variable as this might be. Considering Accum's reputation as an analytical chemist, it is difficult to imagine that he remained unaware of this important discovery. An explanation may be that Accum intended his *Treatise* primarily for "persons unacquainted with chemical science." (See 1st ed., v.)

5   N. J. B. G. Guibourt, *Histoire abrégée des drogues simples,* 2 vols. (Paris, 1820), 1:370, mentioned Pelletier's intensive research on cinchona; and also referred (2:234) to strychnine, isolated in 1818 by Pelletier and Caventou; morphine, isolated by Sertürner in 1804 (2:74); Trommsdorff's analysis of cloves in 1815 (2:74); Vauquelin's analysis of belladonna, and (1:340) his analysis of cinnamon. Guibourt was a member of the Paris Société des Phar-

maciens and at one time deputy head clerk of the Pharmacie
Centrale des Hôpitaux Civils, where, he tells us (1:xi), he came
under the guiding influence of Henry, also influential upon Favre
(see 23–24 of the present work).

6 Richard Powell, trans., *Pharmacopoeia of the Royal College of Physicians of London, 1809* (2nd ed.; London, 1809), 8.

7 Phillips' sharp criticisms of the 1809 edition, and its corrected reprint of 1815, resulted in his being commissioned to translate the 1824 edition, and subsequently to edit and translate the editions of 1836 and 1851.

8 These tests first appeared in Phillips' 1824 translation of the *Pharmacopoeia,* but were made part (a separate section) of the 1836 edition. Phillips, in turn, added further comments in his own translation of this edition.

9 Richard Phillips, *A Translation of the Pharmacopoeia of the Royal College of Physicians of London, 1836* (3rd ed.; London, 1838), 21.

10 *The British Pharmacopoeia, 1914* was the first, to our knowledge, to refer to refractive indices and optical rotation. It also first referred to "acid value," "saponification value," "iodine value," and other constants. The microscope seems also to have made its first appearance in the *Pharmacopoeia* in this edition.

11 Charles James Payne, "Address [of the Vice-President]," *Pharm. J.,* 2(1842–43): 324.

12 Jonathan Pereira, "Introductory Lecture on Materia Medica, Delivered at the Establishment of the Pharmaceutical Society, March 30," *Pharm. J.,* 1(1841–42): 575. See also Jacob Bell, "On the Adulteration of Senna," *Pharm. J.,* 2(1842–43): 65. Pereira served the Pharmaceutical Society as professor of materia medica from 1843–1851/2. The Society also benefited from the gift of his large collection of specimens, some of which carried extra significance through their association with Pereira's book *Elements of Materia Medica.* (See, Anon., "Memoir of the Life of the Late Jonathan Pereira, M.D., F.R.S., F.S.S.," *Pharm. J.,* 12[1852–53]: 415; see also the extended correspondence between Pereira and Editor Bell of the *Pharmaceutical Journal,* edited by Cecil Cloughly, in collaboration with Glenn Sonnedecker, publication pending.)

13 Bell, "On the Adulteration of Senna," *Pharm. J.,* 2(1842–43): 64–65; Jonathan Pereira, "On the Adulteration of Scammony," *Pharm. J.,* 4(1844–45): 269; Daniel Hanbury, "On an Article Imported as Calumba Wood, Supposed to be the Produce of a Menisperum," *Pharm. J.,* 10(1850–51): 323.

14 "Regulations Adopted and Confirmed by the Council, for the Examination and Registration of Members, Associates, and Apprentices," *Pharm. J.,* 3(1843–44): 339–340; "Class of Materia Medica," *Pharm. J.,* 6(1846–47): 19; "Questions for Examination in Materia Medica," *ibid.,* 507–508.

15 [Jacob Bell?], "On Competition in the Drug Trade," *Pharm. J.,* 2(1842–43): 557; Jacob Bell, "On the Adulteration of Drugs," *Pharm. J.,* 1(1841–42): 260.

16   Alfred Henry Allen, *Commercial Organic Analysis* . . . , 1(1st ed.;
      London, 1879), 3. Though Allen intended these preliminary ob-
      servations for organic substances of unknown nature, one could
      infer their usefulness for determining the purity of known organic
      compounds. In addition to these, Allen (*ibid.*, 4) mentioned micro-
      scopic appearance, crystalline form, and the effect of heat.
17   *Ibid.*, 3.

CHAPTER 4
PHYSICS AND INCREASING CERTAINTY

1   C. Sigalas, "La Physique appliquée à la Pharmacie; Leçon d'ouver-
     ture du cours de physique pharmaceutique (10 April 1902)," in
     Bulletin des Travaux de la Société de Pharmacie de Bordeaux,
     42(1902): 139–159, 175–188, 208–213, covers a wide variety of
     physical test methods applicable to detection of drug adulteration.
2   For the history of the balance, we have relied, in addition to Jo-
     sef Anton Häfliger, *Pharmazeutische Altertumskunde, und die
     Schweizerische Sammlung für Historisches Apotheken Wesen an
     der Universität Basel* (Zurich, 1931), 101–102, upon the following
     sources: Ernest Child, *The Tools of the Chemist: Their Ancestry
     and American Evolution* (New York, 1940), 75–91, little or no
     documentation, but authoritatively written, especially well illus-
     trated, and a good source for growth of European antecedents of
     American developments; Maurice Daumas, *Les Instruments scien-
     tifiques aux XVIIe et XVIIIe siècles* (Paris, 1953), 290; Friedrich
     Klemm, *Technik; eine Geschichte ihrer Probleme* (Munich, 1954),
     400; Armand Machabey, *Mémoire sur l'histoire de la balance et de
     la balancerie* (Paris, 1949), a particularly definitive study of devel-
     opments in France but also useful for terms used by various
     cultures to designate the balance, iconography of the balance (an-
     tiquity to the Middle Ages), and comprehensive bibliography (125–
     128). Maurice Daumas, "Precision Mechanics," in Charles Singer,
     et al., *History of Technology*, 5 vols. (Oxford, 1954–1958),
     4: 403–407, along with Child, is especially useful, and well illus-
     trated, while George Griffenhagen, *Tools of the Apothecary* (Wash-
     ington, D.C., 1957, reprinted from *J. Amer. Pharm. Assoc., Practi-
     cal Pharm. Ed.*), 8–9, presents a useful, illustrated capsule sum-
     mary. I. W. Brandel and Edward Kremers, "The Balance," in
     Pharmaceutical Review, 23(1905): 351–354, 384–388, and
     24(1906): 49–60, 75–83, 105–111, 151–154, 166–174, provide a
     broad survey of every imaginable type or form of balance, with
     many illustrations, and a bibliography (24[1906]: 171–174). Al-
     though only the first few pages of the Brandel and Kremers study
     are historical in approach, the entire series is of historical inter-
     est. See also: Robert P. Multhauf, "On the Use of the Balance in
     Chemistry," *Proc. Amer. Chem. Soc.*, 106(1962): 210–218.
     A comprehensive history of the balance has yet to appear. Up to
     the present time attention seems to have focused primarily upon
     the theory and technology of the balance in antiquity and the
     Middle Ages. A more detailed study of the period (late eighteenth

and early nineteenth century) treated briefly by Child and Smith would form a valuable addition to the history of science and technology. Actually, aside from the microscope, few analytical instruments have received the detailed historical investigations they merit.

3   Among the books devoted to the history of weights and measures are: Algemon E. Berriman, *Historical Metrology* (New York, 1953); W. Hallock and H. T. Wade, *Outline of the Evolution of Weights and Measures and the Metric System* (New York, 1906); John Perry, *The Story of Standards* (New York, 1955); W. M. F. Petrie, *Weights and Measures* (London, 1934); and K. M. C. Zevenboom and D. A. Wittop Konig, *Nederlandse Gewichten Stensels, Ijkwesen, Vormen, Makers en Merken* (Leiden, Holland, 1953). We found Berriman and Perry most useful, along with pertinent sections in Häfliger, *Pharmazeutische Altertumskunde*, 101–102; E. Fullerton Cook and Eric W. Martin, eds., *Remington's Practice of Pharmacy* . . . (9th ed.; Easton, Pa., 1948), 41–44; and Cyril Stanley Smith, "Metallurgy and Assaying" in Singer, et al., *History of Technology*, 3:61.

    In addition to these, we have found the following particularly helpful: "Weights and Measures in History," *Chemist and Druggist* (1929): 816–830; Fr. Berger, "Kürze Notizen zur Geschichte des pharmazeutischen Handwerkzeuges und des pharmazeutischen Gebrauchsgegenstände," *Zentralblatt für Pharmazie*, 25(1929): 169–171, a useful chronology; Brockenhaus, *Apothekergewicht* (n.p., n.d.), useful with respect to the evolution of Apothecary weights; and Griffenhagen, *Tools of the Apothecary*, 10–11, brief summary, with select bibliography.

4   Edmund C. von Lippmann, *Abhandlungen und Vorträge zur Geschichte der Naturwissenschaften*, 2 vols. (Leipzig, 1906–1913), 2:168–184, makes a comprehensive survey of the history of the application of specific gravity. Four papers comprise the series, and these include: "Die Spezifische Gewichtsbestimmung bei Archimedes"; and "Zur Geschichte des Saccharometers und der Senkspindel," with two supplements to the latter. Lippmann's study on the hydrometer, as one would expect, is more up to date than that of John Beckmann, *A History of Inventions, Discoveries, and Origins*, William Johnston, trans., 2 vols. (4th ed.; rev. & enlarg. by William Francis and J. W. Griffith, London, 1846), 2:171. Both accounts are well documented. Fritz Ferchl, "Zur Geschichte der Hydromechanik," *Geschichtliche Beilage der Deutsche Apotheker-Zeitung*, No. 9 (July 1936): 33–36, gives an excellent brief summary, is divided chronologically and topically (pycnometer. hvdrometer, and balance), and well illustrated. Paul Walden, *Mass, Zahl und Gewicht in der Chemie der Vergangenheit: Ein Kapitel aus der Vorgeschichte des sogenannten quantitativen Zeitalters der Chemie* (in *Sammlung chemischer und chemisch-technischer Vorträge*, series 2, No. 8 [Stuttgart, 1931], 24–31), brings a valuable table (29–30), comparing modern (1931) specific gravity values with those of al-Bīrūnī (*ca.* 1000 A.D.), Lewis (1746), etc. Freder-

ick A. Filby, *A History of Food Adulteration and Analysis* (London, 1934), 162–170, deals with various types of hydrometers, though principally in their application to excise purposes; Häfliger, *Pharmazeutische Altertumskunde*, 100–101, discusses briefly the history of hydrometers, pycnometers, and hydrostatic balances; Berger, "Kürze Notizen . . . ," *Zentralblatt für Pharmazie*, 25(1929): 169–171, includes in his chronology, various instruments used to determine specific gravity. Azor Thurston, *Pharmaceutical and Food Analysis: A Manual of Standard Methods for the Analysis of Oils, Fats and Waxes, and Substances in which they Exist; together with allied Products* (New York, 1922), 24–52 (Chap. III on "Specific Gravity") gives some references for the historical development of certain procedures, and (39–40) a supplementary bibliography.

Theophilus Redwood, "Abstract of a Lecture on the Determination of Specific Gravities and the Construction and Application of Hydrometers," in *Pharm. J.*, 4(1844–45): 394–404, discusses a variety of hydrometers and their specific applications. Alfred Henry Allen, *An Introduction to the Practice of Commercial Organic Analysis* . . . , 1(1st ed.; London, 1879), 5–7, discusses various hydrometers then in current use, along with some of their limitations. The remarks of Redwood and Allen are of historical interest, rather than as accurate historical accounts.

Brief discussions upon various early applications of specific gravity are included in R. J. Forbes, "Metallurgy and Assaying," in Singer, et al., *History of Technology*, 3:12, 22; Cyril Stanley Smith, "Metallurgy and Assaying," *ibid.*, 66–67; Abraham Wolf (with the co-operation of F. Danneman and A. Armitage), *A History of Science, Technology, and Philosophy, in the 16th and 17th centuries*, Douglas McKie, ed. (2nd ed.; London, 1950), 48–49, 87, 119–120.

5   Beyond the application of specific gravity merely to test adulterated drugs, Boyle showed other scientists of his time the importance of specific gravity. We cannot, therefore, support the opinion that the German-Russian pharmacist Lowitz (1757–1804) first applied specific gravity as a test for purity (Edward Kremers and George Urdang, *History of Pharmacy: A Guide and Survey* [2nd ed.; Philadelphia, 1951], 468.) Ferchl, "Zur Geschichte der Hydromechanik," *Beilage Deutsche Apotheker-Zeitung*, No. 9 (July 1936): 34, credits both the so-called Geber and Nicolaus de Cusa (1401–1464) with the knowledge that specific gravity served to confirm the purity of substances, and could be used for analysis. Alexander Wynter Blyth and Meredith Wynter Blyth, *Foods: Their Composition and Analysis* . . . *with an Introductory Essay on the History of Adulteration* (6th ed.; London, 1909), 25, *n.* 4, erroneously attributed the oldest specific gravity tables to Francis Bacon, in his *Historia Densis et Rari* (London, 1638, as part of *Operum moralium;* London, 1658, as part of *Opuscula varia*), for al-Khāzinī and al-Bīrūnī both anticipated Bacon. Indeed if we take the 1741 folio cited by Blyth and Blyth (*Foods*, 25, n. 4), Boyle may also be considered to have preceded Bacon as far as actual *publication* is concerned.

6   Fredrick Accum, "An Attempt to Discover the Genuineness and

Purity of Drugs and Medical Preparations," *Journal of Natural Philosophy, Chemistry, and the Arts* (William Nicholson's Journal), 2(1798): 119, 121 (acids, such as nitrous, muriatic, and acetous); *ibid.*, 4(1800): 35, 36 (alkaline preparations, such as "Water of Ammonia, Ph.L." and "Volatile Liquor of Hartshorn, Ph.L."); *ibid.*, 2(1798): 121 (boric acid); and *ibid.*, 4(1800): 36 (ammonium carbonate). These papers and Accum's introductory letter were forerunners of the sharp criticisms of pharmacopeial preparations made during the first quarter of the nineteenth century by Richard Phillips. Unlike Accum's *Treatise on Adulterations . . .* (London, 1820), these papers were written in serious scientific style, and only the introduction hints at the popular style that became Accum's forte.

7   Richard Powell, trans., *Pharmacopoeia of the Royal College of Physicians of London, 1809* (2nd ed.; London, 1809), 70, reproduces a table from Davy, listing the specific gravity of solution of ammonia in one column and the corresponding quantities of ammonia and water in other columns.

8   Richard Phillips, *An Experimental Examination of the Last Edition of the Pharmacopoeia Londinensis; with Remarks on Dr. Powell's Translation and Annotations* (London, 1811), 8–9, 10–12, 31–33, *et passim.* Phillips repeatedly noted that he had been unable to obtain a preparation from Apothecaries' Hall of the same strength as that directed by the College of Physicians. See, for example, pages 9 and 12.

9   Phillips changed this to 62°F in the 1836 edition. The *British Pharmacopoeia, 1898,* xii, first directed that specific gravity determinations be made at 60°F (15.5°C). Beginning with the *British Pharmacopoeia, 1963,* the temperature at which each individual determination is made is reported; there is no longer a required temperature indicated.

10   The *British Pharmacopoeia, 1914* (London, 1914), 526. This is the modern definition.

11   [John Dingwall Williams?], *Deadly Adulteration and Slow Poisoning Unmasked: or Disease and Death in the Pot . . .* (London, 1839[?]), 139. Edwy Godwin Clayton, *A Compendium of Food Microscopy . . .* (London, 1909), 401, attributes authorship to John Dingwall Williams. Filby, *History of Food Adulteration,* 256, cites Clayton, but elsewhere (193) refers to the anonymity of the authorship.

12   Anon., *The Domestic Chemist: Comprising Instructions for the Detection of Adulteration in Numerous Articles Employed in Domestic Economy, Medicine, and the Arts. To which are subjoined the Art of Detecting Poisons in Food and Organic Mixtures; and a Popular Introduction to the Principles of Chemical Analysis* (London, 1831), 255. The *Domestic Chemist* also reports (196) a specific gravity for olive oil, of 0.92. (The modern value is 0.910–0.913, at 20°C. Robert Boyle had given the value 0.913, in his *Medicina hydrostatica* [1690], and al-Bīrūnī [*ca.* 1000 A.D.] and al-Khāzinī [1121–22], 0.915.)

13 Kaspar Neumann, *Chemical Works* . . . , William Lewis, trans. (London, 1759), 271, *n.* "o" listed the specific gravities of a number of essential oils, as well as some expressed oils. Neumann doubted the application of these constants to distinguish adulterated from genuine oils, on the ground that the specific gravity of the same oil sometimes varied more from the beginning and end of its distillation, than that from a completely different source. He also considered a serious drawback the great similarity in specific gravities of several essential oils. This undoubtedly explains Neumann's stress (273, *n.* "p") upon organoleptic tests to distinguish between volatile oils. We are indebted to Filby, *History of Food Adulteration,* 228–229, for drawing this to our attention.

14 N. J. B. G. Guibourt, *Histoire abrégée des drogues simples,* 2 vols. (Paris, 1820), 1:15–18. *Ibid.* (2 vols., 3rd ed.; Paris, 1836), 1:621, recommends specific gravity and the hydrometer as a good way of recognizing the purity of essential oils in many cases. See also Guibourt, "Specific Gravity of Volatile Oils," *Amer. J. Pharm.,* 5(1833): 59–60.

15 E. R. Aschoff, *Anweisung zur Prüfung der Arzneymittel auf ihre Güte, Aechtheit und Verfälschung . . . zum Gebrauche für Physici, Aerzte, Apotheker und Drogisten* (2nd ed.; Lemgo, 1835), 20. The first edition had appeared in 1829; a Swedish edition, in 1831. *Ibid.,* 156–167 *passim,* gave the specific gravity of most oils in this work, along with the temperature (°R) in some cases.

16 H. Beasley, "Table of Densities of Alcoholic Liquids," *Pharm. J.,* 2(1842–43): 50. Using many sources, including Gay-Lussac, and the pharmacopeias of Edinburgh, Dublin, London, France, Austria, Sweden, Amsterdam, the author lists in five columns: the specific gravity at 60°F, along with the readings of the Gay-Lussac Alcoholometer at 59°F, the Sykes Hydrometer at 60°F, the Baumé Aerometer at 59°F, and Cartier Aerometer at 59°F, for alcohols of various strengths. In a footnote, Beasley notes: "The numbers on Gay Lussac's scale denote the percentage, by measure, of absolute alcohol; those of Sykes' hydrometer the excess or deficiency, per cent., of *proof spirit* in the sample. The Batavian scale is 10 less than Baumé's throughout, water being 0 instead of 10."

No wonder that Arthur Hill Hassall, *Adulterations Detected; or, Plain Instructions for the Discovery of Frauds of Food and Medicine* (London, 1857), 532–533, remarked: "It would be of the greatest possible advantage—would save immense time and trouble —if densimeters of all kinds were revised, and were reduced to one uniform centesimal scale, as is done in fact, in many of the instruments in use on the Continent." The Gay-Lussac Alcoholometer had a centesimal scale, intended for use at 15°C (59°F), as did the Brossard-Vidal Ebullition Alcoholometer, adapted by Lerebours and Secretan to use the Gay-Lussac Alcoholometer and a centesimally divided thermometer.

17 Redwood, "Abstract of a Lecture on the Determination of Specific Gravities, and the Construction and Application of Hydrometers," *Pharm. J.,* 4(1844–45): 394–404.

18   Anon., "To Correspondents ['Alpha']," *Pharm. J.*, 3(1843–44): 598.
19   Andrew Ure, "Potato Sugar," *Pharm. J.*, 2(1842–43): 12–15.
20   William Thomas Brande and John Thomas Cooper, "Abstract of Report on Dr. H. C. Jennings' Saccharometer," *Pharm. J.*, 7(1847–48); taken from Appendix No. 1, to the *Fourth Report from the Select Committee of the House of Commons on Sugar and Coffee Planting* (ordered to be printed 17 March 1848, Par. Mum. 184), entitled "Copy of the Report of Professors Brande and Cooper on a new kind of Saccharometer by Dr. Jennings." The Report is dated, London, 21 January 1847, and addressed to C. Scovell, Esq. Andrew Ure, "Observations on Jennings' Saccharometer," in *Pharm. J.*, 8(1848–49): 23–27. H. C. Jennings, "Dr. Jennings' Saccharometer," *ibid.*, 67–69.
        The saccharometer indicated directly the quantity of crystallizable and or uncrystallizable sugar in 100 parts of syrup.
21   H. Whippel Gadd, "Standards for Drugs," *Pharm. J.* [ser. 4], 15(1902): 213–215; discussion, 251–253.
22   John Mitchell, *Treatise on the Falsifications of Food, and the Chemical Means employed to detect them* (London, 1848), 260; Alphonse René le Mire de Normandy, *The Commercial Hand-Book of Chemical Analysis; or, Practical Instructions for the Determination of the Intrinsic or Commercial Value of Substances Used in Manufactures, in Trades, and in the Arts* (London, 1850), 208, 424–425, 432; Jean Baptiste Alphonse Chevallier, *Dictionnaire des altérations et falsifications des substances alimentaires, médicamenteuses, et commerciales: avec l'indication des moyens de les reconnaître*, 2 vols. (Paris, 1850, 1852), I: plates I (figs. 4–6), III (fig. 13), V (figs. 26, 28), II: plates I (figs. 2–4), III (figs. 21, 22); J. Léon Soubeiran, *Nouveau Dictionnaire des falsifications et des altérations des aliments, des médicaments et de quelques produits employés dans les arts, l'industrie et l'économie domestique; exposé des moyens scientifiques et pratiques d'en reconnaître le degré de pureté, l'état de conservation, de constater les fraudes dont ils sont l'objet* (Paris, 1874), 269–279, *et passim*.
23   Hassall, *Adulterations Detected*, 56–57.
24   *Ibid.*, 444, "Composition of the Clove."
25   *Ibid.*, 531–535.
26   Frank Wigglesworth Clarke, *Specific Gravities, Boiling and Melting Points and Chemical Formula*, Part I, *Constants of Nature*, 12 (*Smithsonian Miscellaneous Collections*, No. 255, Washington, 1873); First Supplement to Part I, 14 (No. 288, Washington, 1876); New Ed., 32 (No. 659, Washington, 1888). Albert Benjamin Prescott, *Outlines of Proximate Organic Analysis; for the Identification, Separation, and Quantitative Determination of the more Commonly Occurring Organic Compounds* (New York, 1875), 29, 72–73, 107–108.
27   British counterpart of the German Normaleichungskommission (later, Physikalische-Technische Reichsanstalt), founded in 1868, and the American National Bureau of Standards, 1901. Among the functions of these government bureaus, was the determination of

physical constants. The National Physical Laboratory evolved, beginning about 1871, out of Kew Observatory.

28   Alexander Wynter Blyth, *A Manual of Practical Chemistry: The Analysis of Foods and the Detection of Poisons* (London, 1879), 125, 205–207 (various essential oils used in the manufacture of gin), 218 (mustard), 223 (pepper), 231–235 (sweet and bitter almond). Of these, specific gravity was specifically mentioned as a means of detecting adulteration (aside from alcohols in general) only to discern nitro-benzine in essential oil of almonds.

29   Alexander Wynter Blyth, *Foods: Their Composition and Analysis* (London, 1882), 511.

30   Allen, *Commercial Organic Analysis*, 1(1st American ed.; Philadelphia, 1879), 4–6, described the Twaddell, Baumé, Cartier, and Beck hydrometers. Allen, *ibid.*, 1(2nd ed.; London, 1885), 6, *n.* 1, considered it a "serious misfortune" that the Baumé instrument ever came into use and "discreditable to both countries" that different scales developed in the United States and England.

31   Allen, *ibid.*, 1(2nd ed.; London, 1885), 62–68.

32   Allen, *ibid.*, 2, part 1 (3rd ed.; London, 1899), 28–34, 91–102; *ibid.*, 2, part 3 (3rd American ed.; Philadelphia, 1907), 243, 224; *ibid.* 3, part 1 (2nd ed.; London, 1889), 40–42.

33   The *British Pharmacopoeia* still expresses solubility in terms of parts of solvent at a specified temperature; the *U.S. Pharmacopeia* and *National Formulary* in terms of Gm. of solute, in the case of a solid, and ml. of solute, in the case of a liquid, per ml. of solvent. (By "parts" the present B.P. intends exactly the same units of measure as those explicitly expressed by the U.S.P.) Both continue to use relative terms when exact solubilities are not available. In the *British Pharmacopoeia, 1898*, some solubilities were expressed as Gm./cc.

34   Powell, trans., *Pharmacopoeia Londinensis, 1809*, 58, 55.

35   Allen in his *Commercial Organic Analysis*, 1(2nd ed.; London, 1885), 28–35, reported a detail upon extraction procedures, using a variety of solvents, and gave a table of solubilities for organic substances in cold and boiling water, and in rectified spirit, as well as in sodium hydroxide solution, amylic alcohol, ether, chloroform, carbon disulfide, benzene, and petroleum ether.

Lippmann, *Abhandlungen und Vorträge*, 2:182, 203–215, 216–225, questioned the generally accepted contention that the Arabs knew alcohol and discovered it. R. J. Forbes, *Short History of the Art of Distillation* (Leiden, 1948), 57, attributed the discovery of alcoholic distillation to the Salerno school of medicine, about the middle of the 12th century.

36   Accum, *Treatise on Adulterations* (1820), 299; [Williams?], *Deadly Adulteration* (1839[?]), 100· *Domestic Chemist* (1831), 202; Hassall, *Adulterations Detected* (1857), 367; Aschoff, *Anweisung* (1835), 170.

37   Guibourt, *Histoire abrégée des drogues simples* (1820), 2:293, indicated that the alcohol solubility of castor oil was first pointed out by Rose in Prussia and Planche in France, though we find it

difficult to attribute such a basic fact so specifically; Accum, *Treatise on Adulterations* (1820), 25; Aschoff, *Anweisung* (1835), 164; Allen, *Commercial Organic Analysis*, 2, part 1 (3rd ed.; London, 1899), 40.

38 Jonathan Pereira, "On the Alcohol-Test of the Purity of Castor and Croton Oils," *Pharm. J.*, 9(1849–50): 499–503.

39 Filby, *History of Food Adulteration*, 41–42, showed that the German pharmacist Kaspar Neumann (1683–1737), and the Dutch physician Hermann Boerhaave (1668–1738), both knew this test. See also Accum, *Treatise on Adulterations* (1820), 25; and Lewis C. Beck, *Adulterations of Various Substances used in Medicine and the Arts* . . . (New York, 1846), 154.

40 Gobley, "On the Adulteration of the Resin of Jalap," in *Pharm. J.*, 3(1843–44): 132–133 (extract from *Journal de Chimie Médicale*), pointed to the insolubility of jalap resin in ether, compared to its common adulterants, guaiac resin and colophony.

41 Anon., "On the Adulterations of Sulphate of Quinine, and the Means of Detection," *Pharm. J.*, 11(1851–52): 393–396.

42 Accum, *Treatise on Adulterations* (1820), 21.

43 *Ibid.*, 22. A precipitate of calcium sulfate or calcium carbonate, respectively, would ensue.

44 Allen, *Commercial Organic Analysis,* 3, part 1 (2nd ed.; London, 1889), 381–383. As we shall see, these same problems entered the exchange of opinion, by William Gilmour and Henry Pocklington in 1876, on the value of spectroscopy for detecting adulteration.

45 Andrew Ure, *A Dictionary of Chemistry on the Basis of Mr. Nicholson's* . . . (2nd ed.; London, 1823), 815–816 (Table XII, "Of the Solubility of some Solids in Water," at 60° and 212°); *Domestic Chemist* (1831), 155, detected adulterations of gums, resins and balsams, by solution in water; Jacob Bell, "On the Adulteration of Drugs," in *Pharm. J.*, 1(1841–42): 255, detected the adulteration of iodine and of benzoic acid by means of solubility; Anon., "To Correspondents," in *Pharm. J.*, 3(1843–44): 94, determined the purity of balsam of copaiba by its solubility in two parts of alcohol; Jonathan Pereira, "On the Adulteration of Scammony," in *Pharm. J.*, 4(1844–45): 271, determined the purity of scammony resin by its solubility in oil of turpentine and sulphuric ether; Prescott, *Outlines of Proximate Organic Analysis* (1875), 74 (general solubility of fixed oils), 103–104 (separation of resins according to solubility in different solvents), 108 (solubility of volatile oils in 90 per cent alcohol), 127–129 (solubility of alkaloids in 11 different solvents); Allen, *Commercial Organic Analysis*, 1 (2nd ed.; London, 1885), 28–35 (solubility of organic substances in 10 solvents, and the application of solubility to extraction procedures); *ibid.*, 2, part 1 (3rd American ed.; Philadelphia, 1899), 40–42 (solubility of fixed oils); ibid., 2, part 3 (3rd American ed.; Philadelphia, 1907), 247 (solubility of essential oils in alcohol); *ibid.*, 3, part 2 (2nd ed.; London, 1892), 301 (solubility of alkaloids).

46 Among the best accounts on the history of the thermometer, in English, are: Henry Carrington Bolton, *Evolution of the Ther-*

mometer, 1592–1743 (Easton, Pa., 1900), with useful "Table of Thirty Five Thermometer Scales" (88–89), "Chronological Epitome" (90–91), bibliography—mainly primary sources (92–96); Abraham Wolf, *A History of Science* (2nd ed.; London, 1950), 82–92, one of the best concise accounts, well documented, amply illustrated; and F. Sherwood Taylor, "The Origin of the Thermometer," in *Annals of Science*, 5(1942): 129–156.

For more particular emphasis upon the application of the thermometer—as of other instruments—to pharmacy, see: Fr. Berger, "Kürze Notizen," *Zentralblatt für Pharmazie*, 25(1929): 169–171, and Häfliger, *Pharmazeutische Altertumskunde*, 98.

47 Boerhaave was a contemporary, and possibly a friend of Fahrenheit, who did his most important work in Holland. Boerhaave discussed thermometry in his famous book on chemistry, *Elementa chemiae* (Leyden, 1732), "considered the best book on the subject in the first half of the eighteenth century," according to *Kremers and Urdang's History of Pharmacy*, rev. by Glenn Sonnedecker (3rd ed.; Philadelphia, 1963), 402. In his "Elements of Chemistry," Boerhaave described instruments made for him by Fahrenheit, and some of the difficulties encountered and resolved by their maker.

48 *Kremers and Urdang's History of Pharmacy*, 318–321, reviewed concisely the many contributions of pharmacists and non-pharmacists in the field of phytochemistry.

49 Accum, "An Attempt to Discover the Genuineness of Drugs and Medical Preparations," *J. Nat. Phil.*, 2(1798): 119. The only other instances in which he mentioned temperature in these publications was for the solubility of several chemicals and the volatility of "Prepared Ammonia Ph.L."

50 Accum, *Treatise on Adulterations* (1820), 334–335. The value of 38°F for the congealing point corresponds to the modern value.

51 *Ibid.*, 23, 25, 26.

52 *Ibid.*, 286–289, used distillation methods to determine the strength of alcoholic liquors.

53 Powell, trans., *Pharmacopoeia Londinensis, 1809* (2nd ed.; 1809), 337.

54 Richard Phillips, *A Translation of the Pharmacopoeia of the Royal College of Physicians of London, 1836* (3rd ed.; London, 1838), 80, 54, 383. None of these values appeared in the earlier Powell edition; but the boiling point of sulfuric acid was generally known earlier, for Accum cited it in 1798.

55 *British Pharmacopoeia, 1867*, xxi; *ibid., 1898*, xii–xiii; and *ibid., 1914*, 524–525.

56 Hassall, *Adulterations Detected* (1857), 57–61, 437, 449, 665, 675.

57 For example, his summary (72–73) of the properties of fixed oils, in which specific gravity is the only physical constant given, aside from congealing point.

58 Clarke, *Specific Gravities*, Part I, *Constants of Nature*, First Supplement; New Ed.

59 Arthur Angell, "A Method Determining the Fusing Points of Fats," *Chem. News*, 31 (1875): 226–227; Charles Heisch, "On a Method

of Taking the Melting Point of Fats," *ibid.*, 227–228; John Muter, "Methods and Apparatus in Use at the Laboratory of the Bourse de Commerce at Paris, for the Analysis of Certain Commercial Organic Products," *Analyst*, 15(1890): 85–89; Otto Hehner and C. A. Mitchell, "A New Thermal Method for the Examination of Oils," *Analyst*, 20(1895): 146–150; H. Droop Richmond, "Duclaux's Method for the Estimation of 'Volatile Fatty Acids,' the Laws Governing 'Volatility' Deduced Therefrom, and their Application to the Analysis of Butter," *ibid.*, 193–198; Otto Hehner and W. P. Skertchly, "The Estimation of Pentosans and Its Application to the Analysis of Foods," *Analyst*, 24(1899): 178–183.

60   Allen, *Commercial Organic Analysis*, 1(2nd ed.; London, 1885), 9–15. Allen (10) described a simple method of determining melting points, developed by T. Redwood, and pointed (12) to the great value of fractional distillation for the proximate analysis of mixed organic substances of differing boiling points.

61   Allen, *ibid.*, 2, part 1 (3rd ed.; London, 1899), 34–40, 32–34, 76–81. See also tables (91–102, *passim*), listing melting points and solidifying points, according to oil groups. The editor of this volume was Henry Leffmann, an American chemist.

62   Allen, *ibid.* 2, part 3 (3rd American ed.; Philadelphia, 1907), 226–227, 245–246, 241.

63   Blyth, *Manual of Practical Chemistry* (1879), 283–288.

64   Textbooks of pharmacy, such as Francis Mohr and Theophilus Redwood, *Practical Pharmacy: The Arrangements, Apparatus, and Manipulation, of the Pharmaceutical Shop and Laboratory* (London, 1849), dealt with distillation, sublimation and other processes in some detail. Redwood intended this free adaption of the noted German pharmacist's work mainly for the British pharmaceutical chemist, though he referred occasionally to the "chemist and druggist" as well.

65   George Urdang, "The Application of Science in Pharmacy," in *American Journal of Pharmaceutical Education*, 15(1951): 351, noted the required possession of distillation apparatus in German and French pharmacies. The official *British Pharmacopoeia* method for determining boiling points made use of distillation apparatus.

66   Thurston, *Pharmaceutical and Food Analysis,* 79–80, gave a comprehensive bibliography of the journal literature dealing with viscosity and the viscosimeter, for the period 1886 to 1920; Allen, *Commercial Organic Analysis*, 2, part 2 (3rd ed.; London, 1900), 116–128, discussed viscosimetry, primarily in connection with lubricating oils, with details concerning the various types of viscosimeters— Redwood, Engler, Allen, Torsion (Doolittle), Saybolt—and illustrations of these.

67   Johann Christoph Ebermaier, *Tabellarische Übersicht der Kennzeichen der Ächteheit und Güte, so wie der fehlerhaften Beschaffenheit, der Verwechselungen und Verfälschungen sämmtlicher bis jetzt gebräuchlichen einfachen zubereiteten und zusammengesetzten Arzneymittel* (4th ed.; Leipzig, 1820), 120. Ebermaier also mentioned the relative insolubility of almond oil in absolute alcohol, the standard test for the purity of castor oil.

68 Relative viscosity measure entered the *United States Pharmacopeia* only with the ninth revision (1916), and kinematic viscosity with the twelfth (1942). The *British Pharmacopoeia, 1914,* to which we have so often referred, apparently contained no references to viscosity; and Parry, *Foods and Drugs* (Vol. 1, 1911), likewise apparently ignored it.

69 Blyth, *Dictionary,* 412–413 (illustration). In later editions of *Foods* (e.g., 6th ed., 290), Blyth used viscosimetry to test the purity of butter, whereas in earlier editions (1882), he seemed to rely upon measure of surface tension.

70 Coleman's apparatus consisted of two glass tubes, one within the other, in which the test oil was timed in its flow through the inner tube, as the temperature of the outer tube was regulated by steam to 120°F. Coleman reported his results in minutes and seconds.

71 Boverton Redwood, "On the Viscosimetry, or Viscometry," in *J. Soc. Chem. Ind.,* 5(1886): 121–133, reported upon the variation in viscosity of different oils for every ten degree rise in temperature from 50°F to 300°F, and noted the comparable viscosity of water at 60°F.

72 Allen, *Commercial Organic Analysis,* 2 (1st American ed.; Philadelphia, 1882), 142–144, with illustration (142). In later editions of his work, Allen reserved his major discussion of viscosimetry for the chapters on lubricating oils that emphasized the need for standardized viscosimeters, including one of his own design. He expressed viscosity in terms of refined rape oil at 15.5°C (*ca.* 60°F), according to the Redwood standard viscosimeter and gave a formula for determining relative viscosity. (See *ibid.,* 2, part 1 [3rd ed.; London, 1899], 27; *ibid.,* 2, part 2 [1900], 116–128.)

73 Charles Tomlinson, "On the Verification of Castor Oil and Balsam of Copaiba by Means of their Cohesion Figures," in *Pharm. J.* [ser. 2], 5(1863–64): 387–393, presented originally at the 3 February 1864 meeting of Pharmaceutical Society of Great Britain. Tomlinson first presented his method before the 1861 Manchester meeting of the British Association (See Tomlinson, "Cohesion Figure of Liquids," in *Pharm. J.* [ser. 3], 5[1874–75]: 280.)

74 The "oleograph" sought permanently to capture the cohesion figure by placing over the figure for an instant a sheet of thin glazed paper, then blotted to remove excess oil and sometimes floated upon colored liquid for a moment before pressing to enhance the pattern. See *ibid.,* commenting upon a paper by an American pharmacist (University of Michigan), Kate Crane, reprinted from the *Amer. J. Pharm.,* 46(1874): 406–409, as "The Cohesion Figures of Oils as Tests for Their Identity and Purity," in *Pharm. J.* [ser. 3], 5(1874–75): 242–44.

Tomlinson found the thirty-six oleographs sent to him by Moffat "so much alike that they might fairly pass for variations of one oil," whereas from personal experience he found that a single oil might have two or more characteristic figures. He believed the oleograph could be of value only if one could capture faithfully that one "moment in the existence of every film when the characteristic figure is presented, by which the liquid can be recognised and its purity tested." See Tomlinson, "On the Verification of Castor Oil . . . ," *Pharm. J.* [ser. 3], 5(1874–75): 280.

75 Prescott, *Outlines of Proximate Organic Analysis,* 74–75, 105; Blyth, *Foods* (1882), 290–293, 511; Blyth, *Dictionary* (1876), 412; Allen, *Commercial Organic Analysis,* 2, part 1 (3rd ed.; London, 1899), 26.

76 See, for instance, Sigalas, "La Physique appliquée à la Pharmacie . . . ," *Bull. Trav. Soc. Pharm. Bordeaux,* 42(1902): 183.

77 In spite of the prominence given the method by Blyth in the first edition of his *Foods* (1879), it disappeared completely by the time of the sixth edition (in 1909), unquestionably a reflection of the intense activity centering about the analysis of fats and oils at the end of the nineteenth century. In fact between the time the first and third part (essential oils) of the second volume of the third edition of Allen's *Commercial Organic Analysis* were published (in 1899 and 1907), the method seems to have been dropped.

78 The modern Cenco-du Nouy surface tensiometer measures directly, by means of a torsion-balance type of arrangement, the force required for a platinum-iridium ring to break the resistance offered by surface or interfacial tension.

79 Sigalas, "La Physique appliqueé à la Pharmacie . . . ," *Bull. Trav. Soc. Pharm. Bourdeaux,* 42(1902): 182–183.

80 Gossart, Brunhes, Ostwald, Engler, Grobert, Demichel, Barbey, et al.

81 Max von Laue, *History of Physics,* Ralph Oesper, trans. (New York, 1950), 116–124, devoted an entire chapter to the "Physics of Crystals," of which pages 116–118 summed up the early history of crystallography. Alexander Wynter Blyth and Meredith Wynter Blyth, *Foods* (6th ed.; London, 1909), 25–27, presented some interesting material concerning early investigations of crystals by the Italian physician-chemist Francesco Redi (1626–1697) and the Dutch microscopist Antony von Leeuwenhoek (1632–1723), that merits more detailed historical study and evaluation.

We have chosen to consider the part played in adulteration detection by the identification of crystal structures under the head of "Crystallography." There is some reason to consider it also under optical methods, but the extent of our material on the measurement of angles (goniometry) does not warrant this.

The history of crystallography is also tied to the history of the polarization of light, and hence it will be mentioned separately when we consider the evolution of the polarimeter.

82 Thomas Thomson, *The History of Chemistry,* 2 vols. (London, 1830–31), 2:248, felt this invention allowed the "perfection" of crystallography.

83 Accum, "Attempt to Discover the Genuineness of Drugs . . . ," *Journal of Natural Philosophy, Chemistry, and the Arts,* 2(1798): 121; Powell, trans., *Pharmacopoeia Londinensis, 1809* (2nd ed.; 1809), 58; Phillips, trans., *Pharmacopoeia Londinensis, 1836* (3rd ed.; 1838), 31, 86.

84 Guibourt, *Histoire abrégée des drogues simples* (1820), 1:22–24.

85 Guibourt, *ibid.*, 1:vi, 2–11, explained the Haüy system, based upon
    his *Traité de minéralogie* (1801) and *Tableau comparatif des
    résultats de la cristallographie et de l'analyse* (1809). By the time
    Guibourt brought out the third edition of his *Histoire* in 1836, he
    had discarded the Haüy chemical classification in favor of the more
    modern one (1819) of Berzelius.
86 Thomson, *History of Chemistry*, 2:248.
87 Allen, *Commercial Organic Analysis*, 1(2nd ed.; London, 1885), 3,
    in a discussion of "Crystalline Form," as a method of preliminary
    examination.
88 Prescott, *Outlines of Proximate Organic Analysis* (1875), 125–127;
    Blyth, *Manual of Practical Chemistry* (1879), 286–288, 267–279
    passim.
89 See, for instance: R. D. Thompson, "Note by Dr. . . ." in *Pharm. J.*,
    4(1844): 33, taken from the *Lancet*[?], who reported detection of
    the adulterant sulfate of lime (calcium sulfate) in "milk of sul-
    phur" (precipitated sulfur prepared with calcium sulfate, but con-
    fused in some minds with pure precipitated sulfur), by means of
    the crystalline nature of the adulterant; Henry Deane and Henry B.
    Brady, "On Microscopical Research in Relation to Pharmacy," in
    Pharm. J. [ser. 2], 6(1864–65): 232–240, the ease of detecting
    crystalline bodies, in general, and various constituents of opium
    (including different types of opium), in particular; Blyth, *Manual
    of Practical Chemistry* (1879), 305, the various crystalline forms
    of strychnine.

CHAPTER 5
THE ADDED DIMENSION OF OPTICS

1 The colorimeter operated by adjusting the thickness of the column
   of one of a pair of solutions to match the other, by means of a
   reserve supply of the liquid, or by raising or lowering the prism
   through which the light passed. In each case, the light passing
   through both tubes was reflected into two halves of a circular field,
   viewed through an eyepiece. The concentration of the unknown
   might then be calculated by comparing the relative thickness of the
   two columns, and calculating the concentration. In some cases this
   concentration could read directly from the instrument.
2 According to Ernest Child, *The Tools of the Chemist: Their Ancestry
   and American Evolution* (New York, 1940), 162, Duboscq was the
   son-in-law of Soleil, himself a noted instrument maker (polariscopes), and worked for Soleil before joining Pellin, an equally
   noted French manufacturer of polariscopes, etc. The Jellet-Cornu
   polarimeter, in use during the last decades of the nineteenth century, was manufactured by Duboscq.
3 Normandy, *Commercial Hand-book of Chemical Analysis . . .*,
   (London, 1850), 281, 481.
4 J. Léon Soubeiran, *Nouveau Dictionnaire des falsifications . . .*
   (Paris, 1874), 285. Soubeiran included an illustration of the Colo-
   rimètre Houton de Labillardière (modified by J. Salleron). Equal

weights of a sample, in a convenient solvent, were compared in 10 cc. tubes. The color of the solutions was made equal by adding additional color from a graduated burette.

5 W. Walter Stoddart, "Report on the Purity of Sulphate of Quinine of Commerce," in *Pharm. J.* [ser. 2], 6(1864–65): 242, presented originally at the 1864 Bath meeting of the British Pharmaceutical Conference; Charles R. C. Tichborne, "Fluorescence as a Means of Detecting Adulteration," in *Pharm. J.* [ser. 3], 5(1874–75): 966, from the Proceedings of the Royal Irish Academy. Stoddart was an active member of the Conference, and an able microscopist; Tichborne, chemist to the Apothecaries' Hall of Ireland, president of the Pharmaceutical Society of Ireland, a member of the General Council of Medical Education and Registration of the United Kingdom, was a prolific contributor to the *Pharmaceutical Journal* during the 1870's on *British Pharmacopoeia* preparations, the detection of adulteration, and practical pharmacy.

6 John Muter, "Note on a Simple Method for Estimating the value of Commercial Samples of Salicylic Acid and Its Detection in Milk and Similar Organic Solutions," *Analyst*, 1(1877): 193–195.

7 Alexander Wynter Blyth, *A Manual of Practical Chemistry . . .* (London, 1879), 219–220; Blyth, *Foods: Their Composition and Analysis . . .* (London, 1882), 490. Blyth, *Manual of Practical Chemistry* (1879), 188–191 ff., gave different methods for detecting color in wines, including the penetration of dyes into jelly, and the dyeing of a piece of silk. The jelly-penetration test might be considered vaguely colorimetric, because pure wine penetrated slightly, whereas dyes such as cochineal and logwood readily dialysed. See also: Blyth, *Foods* (1882), 460–464 ff.; and 81–96, dealing largely with absorption spectroscopy of colored substances.

8 Alfred Henry Allen, *Commercial Organic Analysis*, 1(2nd ed.; London, 1885), 70.

9 *Ibid.*, 15–16.

10 *Ibid.*, 3, part 1 (2nd ed.; London, 1889), 383–384.

11 *Ibid.*, 312.

12 *Ibid.*, 351.

13 The single most fruitful guide to the history and development of spectroscopy to the end of the nineteenth century is the exhaustive and systematic bibliography of Alfred Tuckermann, *Index to the Literature of the Spectroscope* [–1887] (*Smithsonian Miscellaneous Collections*, No. 658, vol. 32, Washington, 1888); and the continuation [1887–1900] (No. 1312, vol. 41, 1902). Tuckermann divided his material topically, including sections on "History," "Apparatus," "Refraction," and individual substances such as morphine, or groups, such as the alkaloids. A general table of contents and author index completed the first publication (–1887). The section on "History" implies both histories of spectroscopy and publications on spectroscopy that have assumed historical significance, with special stress upon the latter. The topical subdivision according to individual substances makes it relatively easy to locate papers of particular interest for any subject. Tuckermann's bibliography is of

extra value because of the other bibliographies which it incorporates.

Among the brief histories of spectroscopy we have found most useful are: Tillman H. Pearson and Aaron J. Ihde, "Chemistry and the Spectrum Before Bunsen and Kirchhoff," in *J. Chem. Ed.*, 28(1951): 267–271, going beyond their title, indicated clearly the great contribution of Bunsen and Kirchhoff; Herbert Dingle, *A Hundred Years of Spectroscopy* (53rd Robert Boyle Lecture, Oxford University Scientific Club, Trinity Term, 1951, Oxford, 1951); Florian Cajori, *A History of Physics in its Elementary Branches, Including the Evolution of Physical Laboratories* (New York, 1924), 153–171. See also Herbert Dingle, "A Hundred Years of Spectroscopy," *British Journal for the History of Science*, 1(Part III, No. 3, June 1963): 199–216.

Blyth and Blyth, *Foods* (6th ed.; London, 1909), 55–59, 62–66, gave a good description, with illustrations, of various types of instruments then in use for food and drug analysis.

14 When the sixth edition (London, 1867) of *The Microscope* . . . by Jabez Hogg appeared, it included Sorby's work on spectro-microscopy. About ten years later, in a dispute as to who deserved credit for the first application of spectroscopy, Henry Pocklington, "The Spectroscopical Examination of Fixed Oils [correspondence]," in *Pharm. J.* [ser. 3], 7(1876–77): 19–20, mentioned Dr. Thudichum, writing (prior to 1867) in the 10th report of the Medical Officer of the Privy Council, 211 (appendix).

15 H. C. Sorby, "The Application of the Spectrum Microscope to the Detection of Adulteration," in *Pharm. J.* [ser. 2], 11(1869–70): 353, abstract of a paper read 10 November 1869, before the Sheffield Pharmaceutical and Chemical Association.

16 W. W. Stoddart, "The Application of Spectral Analysis to Pharmacy," *Pharm. J.* [ser. 2], 11(1869–70): 132–138. Stoddart used a microspectroscope, and recommended use of a small side-prism in order to observe the spectra of two solutions simultaneously.

17 *Ibid.*, 136.

18 H. C. Sorby, "On a Definite Method of Qualitative Analysis of Animal and Vegetable Colouring Matters by Means of the Spectrum Microscope," *Proc. Royal Soc.*, 15(1866–67): 433–455; William Gilmour, "The Spectroscope Applied to the Detection of Adulteration, etc., of Fixed Oils," *Pharm. J.* [ser. 3], 6(1875–76): 981–982; *ibid.*, 7(1876–77): 22–23, 110–112; Gilmour, "The Spectroscope in Pharmacy," *Pharm. J.* [ser. 3], 7(1876–77): 529–531, 569–571, 590–591; John Conroy, "Absorption Spectra of Iodine," *Pharm. J.* [ser. 3], 7(1876–77): 181–182.

19 Blyth, *Manual of Practical Chemistry* (1879), 50, 51, 259–261, 454, 188–189, 198.

20 Blyth, *Foods* (1882), 75–80, 84, 85, 82–93, *et passim*. See also, *ibid.*, 511, referring to the detection of cottonseed oil in olive oil, based upon the non-absorption of the adulterant.

21 *Ibid.*, 80.

22 *Ibid.* (6th ed.; 1909), 55–59, 62–66, 67–87.

23   We have chosen to do this with Allen because his scope is much
     broader than that of Blyth.
24   Allen, *Commercial Organic Analysis,* 1(2nd ed.; London, 1885), 15.
     He recommended the microspectroscope.
25   *Ibid., n.* 1.
26   *Ibid.,* 3, part 1 (2nd ed.; London, 1889), 381–383.
27   *Ibid.,* 2, part 1 (3rd ed.; London, 1899), 26–27.
28   *Ibid.,* 27, *n.* 1, referred to the studies on the absorption spectra of
     fixed vegetable oils by the French workers Doumer and Thibaut
     (Corps Gras Industriels), and briefly outlined their classification of
     oils on the basis of absorption.
29   Albert Benjamin Prescott, *Outlines of Proximate Organic Analysis*
     . . . (New York, 1875), 105.
30   Jesse P. Battershall, *Food Adulteration and Its Detection* . . . (New
     York, 1887).
31   Gilmour, "Spectroscope Applied to Detection of Adulteration,"
     Pharm. J. [ser. 3], 6 (1875–76): 982.
32   *Ibid.* [ser. 3], 7(1876–77): 529.
33   Henry Pocklington, "A Note on the Spectroscopic Examination of
     Fixed Oils [correspondence]," *Pharm. J.* [ser. 3], 6(1875–76): 1019;
     Pocklington, "The Spectroscopic Examination of Fixed Oils [corre-
     spondence]," *Pharm. J.* [ser. 3], 7(1876–77): 19–20.
34   Gilmour, "The Spectroscopic Examination of Fixed Oil [correspon-
     dence]," *Pharm. J.* [ser. 3], 6(1875–76): 1040. The microspectro-
     scope consists essentially of a microscope in which a spectroscopic
     ocular replaces the regular ocular.
35   William Hyde Wollaston (1766–1828), a London physician and
     chemist is also known for his investigations of electricity, emmis-
     sion and absorption spectra, multiple proportions, tables of equiva-
     lents; his invention of a process to render platinum malleable, and
     the camera lucida; and the discovery of palladium and rhodium.
36   Serious historical studies of the development of the refractometer
     are lacking. Abraham Wolf, *A History of Science, Technology and
     Philosophy in the 16th and 17th Centuries,* Douglas McKie, ed. (2nd
     ed.; London, 1950), 244–274 *passim* reviewed the history of refrac-
     tion of light. Azor Thurston, *Pharmaceutical and Food Analysis*
     . . . (New York, 1922), 22–23, gave a useful bibliography of
     journal literature (1893–1920) that dealt with the application
     of refractometers, at the end of his chapter on various types of
     refractometers. Most histories and some textbooks of chemistry or
     physics refer to the history of refraction briefly.
37   William Hyde Wollaston, "A Method of Examining Refractive and
     Dispersing Powers by Prismatic Reflection," *Philosophical Transac-
     tions,* 92(1802): 365–380.
38   Fresnel, Biot, and Arago developed early refractometers of the inter-
     ferometer type within a few years of the first appearance of Wol-
     laston's instrument; the Abbe refractometer (with improved dark
     and bright field boundaries, by means of color compensating
     prisms) appeared first in 1874, followed by the Abbe dipping
     refractometer (critical-angle prism fully immersed in test liquid).
     Instruments of the Abbe type still find wide use.

The names of these men recur repeatedly in the history of optical techniques and instruments. Fresnel, Biot, and Arago contributed much to the growth of polarimetry; Abbe improved many phases of microscopy through his researches upon better lenses and illumination. We are grateful to Frederick A. White, "A Short History of Scientific Instruments" (unpub. MS.), 235–236, for calling our attention to the valuable chronology of the important combined contributions of Abbe and Zeiss, in Felix Auerbach, *The Zeiss Works and the Carl Zeiss Foundation in Jena* . . . (London, 1927), 268.

Special applications of the refractometer created the need for special instruments, such as the butyro-refractometer (a modification of the Abbe refractometer) and the oleo-refractometer (developed by Amagat and Jean.

39 Wollaston, "Method of Examining Refractive and Dispersing Powers," *Phil. Trans.*, 9(1802): 368, referred specifically to the detection of adulterated oil of cloves, but also gave a table (370–371) of refractive indices for many other oils and drugs. Frederick A. Filby, *A History of Food Adulteration and Analysis* (London, 1934), 42–43, brought up to date a portion of Wollaston's list, but gave modern approximations only for flint and crown glass.

40 Fredrick Accum, *A Treatise on Adulterations* . . . (London, 1820), 25–27, 334–336. He made no significant additions by the time of the 4th ed. (London, 1822).

41 William Chattaway, *Digest of Researches and Criticisms bearing on the Revision of the British Pharmacopoeia, 1898, prepared by Direction of the Pharmacopoeia Committee of the General Council of Medical Education and Registration of the United Kingdom . . . 1899 to 1902 inclusive* (London, 1903), 29–40.

42 *Adulteration of Various Substances Used in Medicine and the Arts* . . . (New York, 1846), by Beck, a physician turned chemist, seems to have been the first *comprehensive* work in English devoted to the subject of drug adulteration and its detection. Beck relied heavily upon English and a few European sources, but he cited American literature as well and fully acknowledged all his sources. There is good reason to believe this work provided the necessary documentation leading to the American Drug Import Law of 1848.

43 Peirce (*Examination of Drugs, Medicines, Chemicals, Etc. as to their Purity and Adulteration* [Cambridge, Mass., 1852]), like Beck and Prescott, was an American physician.

44 Prescott, *Outlines of Proximate Organic Analysis* (1875), 105, mentioned also individual odors, physical properties (color of crude and rectified oil, specific gravity, solubility in 90 per cent alcohol), chemical reactions (with iodine and bromine, with sulfuric acid and alcohol, with sulfide of lead paper, with sodium), absorption spectra, and cohesion figures. Prescott gave details on all these tests, but merely mentioned refractive indices, absorption spectra, and cohesion figures, without further elaboration.

45 See, for example, T. H. Pearmain, "The Testing of Oils with the Oleo-Refractometer," in *Analyst*, 20(1895): 134–136. This reflects

a general upsurge of activities in the organic analysis of fats and oils. The various tests we associate with the analysis of fats and oils developed just about this time. Koettstorfer applied the "saponification number" in 1879; Benedikt and Ulzer, the "acetyl number" in 1887, with improvements by Lewkowitsch in 1897; the iodine number, by Hubl, in 1888, with improvements by Wijs and Hanus.

We are indebted to Aaron J. Ihde, Professor of Chemistry and the History of Science, University of Wisconsin, for drawing these names to our attention.

46 Chattaway, *Digest of Researches and Criticisms . . . 1899–1902*, 29–40.

47 Blyth and Blyth, *Foods* (6th ed.; 1909), 287–289, 510–512; Ernest J. Parry, *Foods and Drugs*, 2 vols. (London, 1911), 1 (*The Analysis of Food and Drugs, Chemical and Microscopical*): 96–97, 632, and 606–647 *passim*.

The bibliography given by Thurston, *Pharmaceutical and Food Analysis*, 22–23, gives an overall view of the scientific periodical literature on the subject, on both sides of the Atlantic, between 1893 and 1920.

48 Blyth, *Foods* (1882), 510–511, mentioned absorption spectra, Rousseau's diagometer (electrical conductance), cohesion figures, and specific gravity, among physical methods for detecting adulteration in olive oil.

49 Alexander Wynter Blyth, *A Dictionary of Hygiene and Public Health . . .* (London, 1876), 413. He devoted *twelve* times this space to a discussion of cohesion figures!

50 Allen, *Commercial Organic Analysis*, 1 (2nd ed.; London, 1885), 15, under the heading "Refraction and Dispersion of Organic Bodies," also discussed "several optical properties, including absorption spectra, fluorescence, double refraction, and polarization." Fully six and one-half pages were devoted to optical rotation; the remaining one and one-half pages dealt with all the other optical methods just mentioned; the discussion of refraction occupied only three lines, less than any other section.

51 Henry Leffmann, "Reviser's Note to Third Edition," in Allen, *Commercial Organic Analysis*, 2, part 1 (3rd ed.; London, 1899), vi, pointed particularly to the "important additions" in this volume of the bromine thermal method, methods for the determination of glycerol, acetyl number, and various tests for oxidation of oils. Among the physical methods mentioned (25–42) were cohesion figures, absorption spectra, viscosity, specific gravity, melting and solidifying points, and solubility. The discussion on refractive power occupied pages 71–76.

52 *Ibid.*, 73–75. The determinations of Jean and Pearmain stand out.

53 *Ibid.*, 72, 76. The reference to the bulletin of the American Association of Official Agricultural Chemists undoubtedly reflected the contribution of this volume's American editor, Henry Leffmann.

54 Allen, *Commercial Organic Analysis*, 2, part 3 (3rd. American ed.; Philadelphia, 1907), 241–242, 243 (table).

55 Arnold R. Tankard. "Preface to Volume II, Part III," in Allen,

Commercial Organic Analysis, 2, part 3 (3rd American ed.; Philadelphia, 1907), vi; see also 242, 243 (table from Parry).

56   *Ibid.,* 2, part 3 (3rd American ed.; Philadelphia, 1907), 242.

57   Vivian T. Saunders, *The Polarimeter: A Lecture on the Theory and Practice of Polarimetry* (London, n.d. [1926?]), reviewed briefly (23 pp. of text) the history of polarimetry; Edmund Oskar von Lippmann, "E. Mitscherlich und das Fünfzigjahrige Jubilaüm des Polarisations-Apparates," in *Abhandlungen und Vorträge zur Geschichte der Naturwissenschaften,* 2 vols. (Leipzig, 1906–1913), 1: 306–322, also gave a good historical account of polarimetry; while Child, *Tools of the Chemist,* 45, 60, 160–163, discussed the historical development of various types of polarimeters, and the first uses of certain instruments in the United States. Other accounts of the history of the polarization of light and polarimetry may be found in: George William Rolfe, *The Polariscope in the Chemical Laboratory: An Introduction to Polarimetry and Related Methods* (New York, 1905), 14–27, concerning a wide variety of instruments; and Florian Cajori, *History of Physics* (New York, 1924), 143–148.

Important events in the history of polarimetry are included in the chronologies of: Edmund O. von Lippmann, *Zeittafeln zur Geschichte der organischen Chemie* (Berlin, 1921); and Fr. Berger, "Kurze Notizen zur Geschichte des pharmazeutischen Handwerkzeuges . . . ," *Zentralblatt für Pharmazie,* 25(1929): 170–171.

Accounts and illustrations of historical interest concerning polarimeters and their applications in food and drug analysis, may be found in: Hans Heinrich Landolt, *Handbook of the Polariscope and its Practical Applications,* C. C. Robb and V. H. Velley, trans. (London, 1882), 98–124; *The Optical Rotating Power of Organic Substances and Its Practical Applications,* John H. Long, trans. (2nd ed.; Easton, Pa., 1902), 326–366 ("Older Forms of Apparatus"); Battershall, *Food Adulteration,* 112–120, the Ventzke-Scheibler saccharimeter (with illustration, plate X); Thurston, *Pharmaceutical and Food Analysis,* 1–15, with useful bibliography of periodical literature for period 1879–1920; Blyth and Blyth, *Foods* (1909), 116–120, Mitscherlich polariscope (with illustration, fig. 20), Soleil saccharimeter (with illustration, plate facing p. 118), Jellet saccharimeter, Saccharimètre à penombrés (Jellet principle, Duboscq constructed), etc., along with indication of types used in other countries, and comparison of scales.

A need exists for a history of polarimetry, including the development, relationships, and applications of various types of instruments. Saunders' little book, as far as we are aware the only attempt, is seriously limited by its intent to serve as a lecture (illustrations from the book were available from the publishers in slide form).

58   Jean Baptiste Biot, "Sur la construction des appareils destinés à observer le pouvoir rotatoire des liquids," *Ann. Chim. Phys.* [ser. 2], 74(1840): 401–430. Biot discovered the optical activity of sugar cane, tartaric acid, and oil of turpentine in 1815, in association

with Seabeck. Also in 1815, he noted the activity of glucose, and among other organic compounds, that of camphor, in 1852.

Biot's polarimeter consisted of a polarizer (producer) of black glass, set at 57° to the incident light to give maximum polarization, and an analyzer of Iceland spar (crystal).

59   Ventzke (in 1842) added the Nicol prism (devised from Iceland spar in 1828 by William Nicol [1761–1851]), and since then an essential part of all polariscopes. (The Nicol prism allows separation of the two beams present when light is polarized.) Mitscherlich (in 1844) introduced monochromatic light. Robiquet and Soleil (in 1845) increased sensitivity by introducing a bi-quartz plate (one dextro- and one levo-rotating, of equal thickness, cemented together) to the polarizer; used white light for illumination, and this limiting factor.

Jellet (in 1860), Cornu (in 1870), Laurent (in 1874, 1877?), Lippich (in 1880), Brace (in 1903), introduced photometric or half-shadow polariscopes to overcome limitations of the Soleil instrument, by using a more elaborate Nicol prism. Triple and quadruple field instruments followed, in an attempt to achieve more contrast and sharper divisions of field zones.

Saunders, *Polarimeter*, 16–20, discussed the essential features of most of these instruments; as did Rolfe, *Polarimeter*, 14–27, 33–37, 68–86; and Landolt, *Handbook of the Polariscope*, 98–124. Battershall, *Food Adulteration,* 112–120, treats the Ventzke-Scheibler; Blyth and Blyth, *Foods* (1909), 116–120, the Mitscherlich, and Soleil and Jellet.

Child, *Tools of the Chemist*, 162–163, pointed out that German workers made little contribution to the development of the polariscope, but Germany became the leading manufacturer of the instruments after 1860, when the Prussian government placed a tax on finished sugar and the instruments were needed to determine the purity of sugar. It is probably significant of the level of French science of the period that most of the important contributors to polarimetry we have listed here were French.

60   Biot was aware of the optical rotation of different kinds of sugars, and early suggested polarized light as a means of determining the strength of sugar solutions and juices. He realized its value to colonists and sugar refiners. The French pharmacist J. Léon Soubeiran apparently anticipated Wilhelmy (in 1851) in observing the inversion of cane sugar and in realizing its significance in refining processes.

According to Child, *Tools of the Chemist,* 60, 161, James Curtis Booth and J. S. Lovering and Co., sugar refiners of Philadelphia, first (in 1842) used the polariscope in the United States for the analysis of sugar and molasses; and a Louisiana sugar planter and refiner, Valcour Aime, probably first used it about 1850. It found first official use under the U.S. Tariff Act of 1883. See also: Charles Albert Browne, "Note on the First Uses of the Polariscope in the United States for Sugar Testing," in *Facts about Sugar*, 13(1921): 231.

The polarimeter—or more accurately, the saccharimeter—always had, and continues to have, an important application in sugar work, aside from its use for tariff purposes.

61 Biot, "Memoire sur les rotations que certaines substances impriment aux plans de polarisation des rayons lumineux," *Mém. de l'Académie Royale de Science de l'Instut de France*, 2(for 1817; published 1819): 91–93.

62 Jonathan Pereira, "On the Polarization of Light, and Its Useful Applications," *Pharm. J.*, 2(1842–43): 619–637, 681–694, 733–740; 3(1843–44): 5–13, 56–65, 150–167, 198–231. The lectures subsequently appeared in book form, and we shall refer both to the original journal series and to the book, *Lectures on Polarized Light, together with a Lecture on the Microscope, delivered before the Pharmaceutical Society of Great Britain, and at the Medical School of the London Hospital*, Baden Powell, ed. (2nd ed.; London, 1854). In the preface to the first edition (1843), Pereira explained that these lectures formed part of the course of chemistry given at the Medical School of the London Hospital (where he was lecturer in chemistry, 1832/3–1846). Pereira gave these lectures before general meetings of the Society, not in his capacity as Professor of Materia Medica (1843–1853). Perhaps his best known work was *The Elements of Materia Medica and Therapeutics* (London, 1839–40). Powell in the biographical note (xxi–xxii) on Pereira that introduced the second edition of *Lectures on Polarized Light* attempted to explain Pereira's particular interest in the subject. He concluded that his interest in chemistry led naturally to a closer investigation of crystallography and his interest in medicine explained his attention to the subject of light (the effects upon polarized light of certain physiological fluids, chemical and organic).

Pereira seems to have been familiar with the most up-to-date and pertinent literature on polarimetry. One source he cited appeared in December 1842; his lectures began early in 1843. As we noted, Pereira had given similar lectures at the London Hospital Medical School previously, so obviously he continually revised them as he went along.

63 Pereira, "On Polarization of Light," *Pharm. J.*, 2(1842–43): 620; *Lectures* (2nd ed.; 1854), 2–3 (italics added).

64 Two other interesting sources acknowledged by Pereira are: J. Léon Soubeiran, "Des changements moleculaire que le sucre éprouve sous l'influence de l'eau et de la chaleur," in *J. de pharm. et chim.* [ser. 3], 1(1842): 89–93; and M. Ventzke, "On the Application of Circular Polarization as a Re-agent," in *Annals of Chymistry and Practical Pharmacy*, 1(1842; published 1843): 316–321. Pereira, *Lectures*, viii, ix, x, 277–278; Pereira, "On Polarization of Light," *Pharm. J.*, 3(1843–44): 222–223.

65 For more general applications to various sugars and the determination of their strength or inversion (according to Soubeiran), see Pereira, "On Polarization of Light," *Pharm. J.*, 3(1843–44): 220–222; *Lectures*, 273–277. Pereira reproduced here tables of values

taken from Biot and Soubeiran. They derived some of their interest
from the cumbersome typographic method of indicating dextro-
and levo-rotation by means of arrows.

66   Pereira, *Lectures,* 273 (see also, 271–273); Pereira, "On Polarization
of Light," *Pharm. J.,* 3(1843–44): 219–220. The particular example of oil of peppermint adulterated with oil of rosemary referred to a case reported by a council member of the Pharmaceutical Society, Thomas Herring, in discussion following a paper read
before the Society by its energetic founder Jacob Bell, "On the
Adulteration of Drugs." (See *Pharm. J.,* 1[1841–42]: 262–263.)
Pereira remarked (*Lectures,* 272; "On Polarization of Light,"
Pharm. J., 3[1843–44]: 220) upon the optical activity observed in
the case of oils of turpentine, lemon, and bergamont: "isomerism
has no connection with rotatory polarization, for of three isomeric
oils . . . mentioned in this table [of Biot's], one [turpentine] is
laevogyrate, the others dextrogyrate." Pasteur made his now famous observations upon the association between optical activity
and different isomers of tartaric acid five years later (in 1848).
Pasteur did surmise some connection with molecular asymmetry,
but Van't Hoff and LeBel, independently (in 1874), related optical
activity to the presence of one or more asymmetric carbon atoms.
Pasteur was led to his discovery by crystallographic observations
that were, of course, impossible in the case of the oils. However, we
must recognize that Pereira observed differences in optical activity
between isomers, even though he could not push the matter any
further.

67   H. Bence Jones, "On M. Soleil's Polariscope for Determining the
Quantity of Sugar in a Solution," *Pharm. J.,* 11(1851–52): 455–
456; Henry Pocklington, "The Optical Analysis of Beeswax,"
Pharm. J. [ser. 3], 2(1871–72): 81–82; J. Campbell Brown, "Du-
boscq's New Polariscope:—'Saccharimètre à Penombrés'," *Pharm.
J.* [ser. 3], 7(1876–77): 839–840.

68   D. Sugden Evans, "On the Adulteration of Essential Oils with Turpentine, and the Means of Its Detection," *Pharm. J.* [ser. 2],
7(1865–66): 220–222. Originally read at the 1865 Birmingham
meeting of the British Pharmaceutical Conference, the scientific
organization of British pharmacists, Evans' paper pointed out that
different degrees of rotation were sometimes obtained from different specimens of oil and adulterants.
More curious is the apparent ignorance of the applications of the
polariscope by one of Biot's own countrymen, M. Lassaigne, "On
the Substitution in Commerce of Starch-Sugar (Glucose) for
Honey," in *Pharm. J.,* 4(1844–45): 237–238. Equally remarkable is
the fact that this notice appeared originally in the *Journal de
Chimie médicale (de pharmacie et de toxicologie . . .),* edited by
one of France's greatest protagonists against adulteration, the pharmacist Jean Baptiste Alphonse Chevallier (1793–1879).

69   C. Reich, "On the Detection of Starch-Sugar in Cane-Sugar," in
Pharm. J., 7(1847–48): 545 (reprinted from Buchner's *Reperto-
rium,* vol. 48, no. 1.), observed, "the optical sugar-test by means of

the polariscope of Biot and Ventzke is not safe enough, and, moreover, the apothecary seldom possesses this instrument."

70 Stoddart, "Report on the Purity of Sulphate of Quinine of Commerce," *Pharm. J.* [ser. 2], 6(1864–65): 242; and Henry Pocklington, "The Use of Optical Analysis in Pharmacy," *Pharm. J.* [ser. 3], 6(1875–76): 247.

71 Chattaway, *Digest* (1903), 30–40 *passim*, for instance, with respect to essential oils. *The United States Pharmacopeia* of 1890 first recognized optical rotation as a purity test.

72 Bouchardat (in 1843) noted the activity of cinchona alkaloids, Laurent (in 1845), of nicotine, and Biot (in 1852), of camphor.

73 Friedrich August Flückiger and Daniel Hanbury, *Pharmacographia: A History of the Principal Drugs of Vegetable Origin, Met with in Great Britain and British India* (2nd ed., London, 1879), 570.

74 Arthur Hill Hassall, *Adulterations Detected . . .* (London, 1859), 204, 547.

75 *Ibid.,* 204.

76 Battershall, *Food Adulteration,* 112–120.

77 Parry, *Food and Drugs,* vol. 1.

78 Blyth, *Manual of Practical Chemistry* (1879), 10–15, described (with illustrations) the instruments of Mitscherlich, Soleil, and Jellet; and the "Saccharimètre à Penombrés" of Duboscq, based on principles of Jellet; *ibid.,* 207; 219; 233.

79 Allen, *Commercial Organic Analysis,* 1(2nd ed.; London, 1885), 16–23, included a general description of the construction of the polarimeter, the special features of the Soleil, Wild, Laurent, and Jellet-Cornu (constructed by Duboscq) instruments, the determination of specific rotation, the special allowances for light of different portions of the spectrum, and the specific rotation of a number of organic substances.

80 See, for example, *ibid.,* 194–209, 189–193, 198, 236, 264, 288, 310.

81 *Ibid.,* 315 (specific rotation), 334 *et passim* (micropolariscopic examination), 435–436 *et passim* (tartaric acid).

82 *Ibid.,* 2, part 3 (3rd American ed.; Philadelphia, 1907), 241.

83 *Ibid.,* 243, 248, 501, 504–533. The author acknowledges E. J. Parry, *Chemistry of Essential Oils . . .* (London, 1899) among other sources for the table, 504–533.

84 Tankard, "Preface to Volume II, Part III," in Allen, *Commercial Organic Analysis,* 2, part 3 (3rd American ed.; Philadelphia, 1907), v. The editor noted (*ibid.,* v, vi) that as a result of this phenomenon, the text of these chapters was "almost entirely new," and the physical space occupied was respectively five and ten times as great as that in the previous edition. He also acknowledged the great contributions to the chapters on aromatic acids, resins, and essential oils by the noted English analyst E. J. Parry.

85 More detailed studies have been made of the history of the microscope than of any other scientific instrument here discussed. The two most comprehensive were both written more than twenty-five years ago: Alfred N. Disney, ed., with Cyril F. Hill, and Wilfred E. Watson, *Origin and Development of the Microscope . . .* (London,

1928); and Reginald Stanley Clay and Thomas H. Court, *The History of the Microscope Up to the Introduction of the Achromatic Microscope* (London, 1932). Both remain extremely useful, but a sufficient number of detailed monographic studies have appeared since then to warrant a modern treatment of the subject. Though limited in length (about 50 pages of text), Maria Rooseboom's *Microscopium* (Leiden, 1956) brings together the most pertinent facts more systematically and with more insight than had been done previously, and has lavish illustrations. More specialized yet excellent is Ed. Frison's *L'Évolution de la partie optique du microscope au cours du dix-neuvième siècle: les test objects, les test-, probe- et typen-platten* (Communication No. 89, Rijksmuseum voor de Geschiedenis der Natuurwetenschappen; Leiden, 1954), which presented a detailed chronology (128–133), biographical sketches of important figures in the history of microscopy for this period (134–153), and a comprehensive bibliography (154–163). Also useful is F. S. Spiers, ed., *The Microscope, Its Design, Construction, and Applications: A Symposium and General Discussion by Many Authorities* (London, 1920), 10–23, 51–59.

Many books and manuals upon the microscope and microscopy give some historical background. One of the best is Simon Henry Gage, *The Microscope: An Introduction to Microscopic Methods and to Histology* (12th ed.; n.p., 1917), 423–443 ("Brief History of Lenses and Microscopes"). *Ibid.*, 246–269, also gave useful information on the microspectroscope and the micropolariscope. A classic on the subject and now of added historical interest is James Hogg, *The Microscope, Its History, Construction and Applications* (1st ed.; London, 1854).

Wolf, *A History of Science, Technology and Philosophy in the 16th and 17th Centuries* (2nd ed.; 1950), 71–75, gave a good concise history of early microscopes. *Ibid.*, 80–82, also discussed some of the early problems of optical glass-making associated with the microscope and other optical instruments. Other discussions of this subject, aside from those referred to here, may be found in: L. M. Angus-Butterworth, "Glass," in Charles Singer, et al., *History of Technology*, 5 vols. (Oxford, 1954–1958), 4:358; and Child, *Tools of the Chemist*, 159.

The most pertinent paper for our purposes in the journal literature is Abbot P. Usher, "The Development of the Microscope and Its Application to Medicine and Public Health," in *Amer. J. Pharm. Education*, 15(1951): 319–338. Aside from his contributions to Spiers, *Microscope* (51–59), Charles Singer added to the history of microscopy in such articles as "The Dawn of Microscopical Discovery," in *J. Roy. Micr. Soc.*, 35(1915): 317–340; and "Notes on the Early History of Microscopy," in *Proc. Roy. Soc. Med.*, 7, Part 2 (1914): 247–279 (of Section of the History of Medicine).

Recent studies on the subject include H. M. Malies, "The Microscope during the Last Hundred Years," in *Microscope*, 10(1954–55): 113–121, 149–152; Arthur Hughes, "Studies in the History of Microscopy: 1. The Influence of Achromatism," in *J. Roy. Micr.*

Soc. [ser. 3], 75(1955): 1–22; Hughes, "Studies: 2. The Later History of the Achromatic Microscope," *J. Roy. Micr. Soc.* [ser. 3], 76(1956): 47–60; Edward Frison (E. F. Linssen, trans.), "Historical Survey of the Use of Divergent and Correcting Lenses in the Microscope" in *Microscope*, 8(1951): 115–120; and J. Hampton Hoch, "Fifty Years of Quantitative Microscopy," in *Economic Botany*, 3(1948): 111–116, a discussion of the late (post 1897) development of quantitative microscopy and this first in the United States.

86 *Kremers and Urdang's History of Pharmacy*, rev. by Glenn Sonnedecker (3rd ed.; Philadelphia, 1963), 316, 423; Häfliger, *Pharmaceutische Altertumskunde*, 99.

87 Powell, trans., *Pharmacopoeia Londinensis, 1809* (2nd ed.; 1809), 141 (*Hydrargyrus cum sulphure*).

88 *The Domestic Chemist* . . . (London, 1831), 93, 150.

89 *Ibid.*, 242.

90 J. F. Niemann, *Anleitung* . . . (3rd ed.; Leipzig, 1831), 100.

91 E. F. Aschoff, *Anweisung zur Prüfung der Arzneymittel* . . . (2nd ed.; Lemgo, 1835), 20.

92 Jonathan Pereira, "Introductory Lecture on Materia Medica Delivered at the Establishment of the Pharmaceutical Society," *Pharm. J.*, 1(1841–42): 572–573.

93 Jonathan Pereira, "Some Observations on Potato-Starch," *Pharm. J.*, 3(1843–44): 22, 24 (20–25, *passim*); (editor's [Jacob Bell?] comments upon) Thomas Harvey, "The Detection of Potato-Starch in Flour," *Pharm. J.*, 4(1844–45): 115; Schleiden, "On the Different Kinds of Fecula," *ibid.*, 95 (taken from *Pharmaceutisches Centralblatt*, 10 June 1844).

94 Blyth and Blyth, *Foods* (6th ed.; 1909), 32, quoted a passage from page 210 of Normandy's book: "The admixture of potato flour or fecula with wheat flour may be very well detected by the microscope." Normandy certainly was "one of the first" but other "firsts" precede him by at least nine years. (Blyth and Blyth misquoted the title of Normandy's book as "Hand-book of Commercial Analysis"; erroneously gave the page of the quotation as 210, when it was 230; and changed the word order slightly.)

95 Anon., "Reply to 'A Correspondent,'" in *Pharm. J.*, 3(1843–44): 459, suggested assistance of the microscope for the examination of the "sensible characters" of ground pepper, to determine its genuineness; Robert Warington, "Observations on the Green Teas of Commerce," in *Pharm. J.*, 4(1844–45): 33, detected sulfate of lime (calcium sulfate) in milk of sulfur (a preparation of precipitated sulfur containing some calcium sulfate); [Pereira?] "On the Adulteration of Coffee, and the Mode of Detecting the Fraud," *ibid.*, 85–87, detected chicory in coffee, and starch as one of the adulterants of chicory itself; [Pereira?], "On Chicory, or Wild Succory," *ibid.*, 121, detected "torrefied" starch grains of either corn or pulse in chicory; Anon., "Adulteration of Tea," in *Pharm. J.*, 10(1850–51): 361, extract from Dickens' *Household Words*, detected "facing" of black tea with a mixture of Prussian blue, turmeric, and

French chalk, to give it the appearance of the more-sought-after
green tea.

96 Anon., "Report 'On the Adulteration of Coffee' [paper by Arthur
Hassall read before the Botanical Society of London on Friday, 2
August, 1850]," in the *Times*, 5 August 1850, p. 7. Detailed ac-
counts surrounding this event are given by: Arthur Hill Hassall,
Narrative of a Busy Life: An Autobiography (London, 1893), 43–
44; Hassall, *Food and Its Adulterations* (London, 1855), xxxviii;
Edwy Godwin Clayton, *Arthur Hill Hassall, Physician and Sanitary
Reformer: A Short History of His Work in Public Hygiene and the
Movement against the Adulteration of Food and Drugs* (London,
1908), 14–15.

Hassall's *Narrative* appeared just a year before his death (1894)
at the age of 77 years. The key events in the autobiography took
place 40 years earlier, and consequently we may expect, and find,
some of the inevitable inaccuracies in detail to which autobi-
ographies are prone. Hassall's biographer, Clayton, was one of his
former students and obviously revered the memory of his energetic
teacher. As a result, Clayton may err in his interpretations of
certain controversial issues, but with respect to factual recorded
details may be more reliable than Hassall himself.

97 In the order mentioned, these appeared in the *Lancet*, 2(1851):
472–474, 510–511; 1(1852): 178–181, 201–203, 224–227, 525–527,
527–528, 548–551, 200–201; 1(1853): 116–117, 251–253; 1(1854):
10–14, 51–54, 77–81, 107–109, 165–168; 1(1853): 159–164, 321–
326; 2(1853): 14–18.

The majority of these drugs are also spices, which remained
among the substances most adulterated from ancient times through
the nineteenth century. The microscope provided one of the first
sure test methods for these substances. Among the drugs mentioned, opium, scammony, jalap and ipecacuanha—like the spices
—had been systematically adulterated from ancient times onward.

98 Hassall, *Food and Its Adulterations*, v, xxix, xxiv–xxxv. Hassall
(xxix) laid the chief blame on drug grinders, and of course before
the application of the microscope it was almost impossible to detect
many adulterations after the drug was reduced to a powdered state.

99 Hassall, *Adulterations Detected*, 675–690. The discussion concerning
opium, scammony, jalap, and ipecacuanha, comprised pp. 624–
675, and as in the *Lancet* series the greatest portion of space was
devoted to opium (624–647).

In the preface (vi) Hassall stated the purpose of this work to be
"to furnish plain instructions, microscopical and chemical, em-
bodying the results of extended practice and experience, for the
discovery of adulterations in Food and Medicine"; and (vii–viii) to
supply "a public want . . . [following] a suggestion for the suppression of adulteration which I made in evidence before the Select
Committee on Adulteration, in July 1855, namely, that a cheap
treatise on adulteration should be published, which 'should be
illustrated with wood-cuts showing the microscopical appearances

and structure of the different articles, both genuine and adulterated, and containing plain directions for the discovery of adulteration.' " He saw (v) this as being quite different from his earlier
Food and Its Adulterations (1855), which was intended to show
the extent of adulteration practices and the pecuniary and public
health factors involved.

100   Hassall, *Adulterations Detected*, 692. Hassall noted that many of the
adulterations listed were recorded in the *Minutes of Evidence of the
Select Committee on Adulteration* of *1855* and *1856*. Prominent
among the authorities acknowledged (aside from Hassall himself)
were: Normandy, Wakley, Postgate, Blyth, and Bastick. Chemicals
or their preparations accounted for 60 per cent of the drugs mentioned, plant or animal products for the remaining 40 per cent.

101   *Ibid.*, 44–45. Hassall discussed briefly (49–51) the cost of various
makes of microscopes, with attachments, and concluded that "if
supplied with French or German achromatic object-glasses, it
[might] be put down at about [£] 10." He described lenses of 60 to
900 diameters magnification and recommended the purchase of
polariscopic attachments for the discrimination of some starches.
He referred to the price of two "very good" German achromatic
lenses, of medium magnification, for [£] 2. 7. Henry Pocklington,
"The Microscope in Pharmacy," in *Pharm. J.* [ser. 3], 2(1871–
72): 621, quoted £6–10 for instruments of 20–200 diameters magnification.

102   Hassall, *Adulterations Detected*, 55–63, considered the microscope of
value chiefly for organic compounds for which no chemical tests
were available, but admitted (56) that "the majority of substances
injurious to health employed for adulteration [could] be detected
with certainty only by chemical methods of research." He considered the speed of microscopical tests a great advantage over chemical, but felt that it was "impossible successfully to study the subject
of adulteration without having recourse constantly both to the
microscope and chemistry." He was also fully cognizant (48) of the
technique of chemical microscopy.

103   Hassall, *Food* (1876), 464–469 (isinglass), 470–473 (gelatin),
510–528 (mustard), 554–588 (spices: ginger, cinnamon, cassia,
nutmegs, mace, cloves, and pimento), 603–604 (liquorice).

104   Hassall, *Adulterations Detected*, 52.

105   [H. Sugden Evans], "Microscopical Examination of Cinchona
Barks, Illustrated by the Aid of the Oxyhydrogen Light Applied to
an Ordinary Microscope," *Pharm. J.*, 16(1856–57): 553; George
Phillips, "Microscopic Structure of Pepper and Its Adulterants,"
Pharm. J. [ser. 2], 1(1859–60): 605–607, and 2(1860–61): 7, 9,
11; Stoddart, "Report on the Purity of Sulphate of Quinine of
Commerce," *Pharm. J.* [ser. 2], 6(1864–65): 241–244; Stoddart,
"Notes on the Use of the Microscope, and Its Crystallographic
Application," *Pharm. J.* [ser. 2], 9(1867–68): 173–176; Pocklington, "The Microscope in Pharmacy," *Pharm. J.* [ser. 3], 2(1871–
72): 621–625, continued in a truly monumental series to 5(1874–
75): 301–303, and dealing with the recognition of many botanical

classes of genuine and adulterated samples and adulterants; William Inglis Clark, "The Microscopy and Adulterations of Colocynth Powder," *Pharm. J.* [ser. 3], 7(1876–77): 509–511, with discussion, 517–518.

106 *British Pharmacopoeia, 1898*, 35. This interpretation appears borne out by suggestions in Chattaway's 1903 *Digest of Researches and Criticisms* of the 1898 edition of the *Pharmacopoeia* that microscopial observations should be incorporated into certain monographs. (See for example: 8, 10, 48, Greenish on cardamon seeds, colocynth pulp, and senna.)

107 John William Griffith and Arthur Henfrey, *The Micrographic Dictionary: A Guide to the Examination of the Structure and Nature of Microscopic Objects* (London, 1856), 13–14, acknowledged Ure, Mitchell, Normandy, and Pereira, among others; *ibid.* (4th ed.; 1883), added the reports of the Select Committee and the *Lancet* to this list. *The Tricks of Trade in Adulterations of Food and Physic; with Directions for their Detection and Counteraction* (new ed., London, 1859), 149–150, 152, 154, *et passim,* was flamboyant and popular in style.

108 Hermann Klencke,*Verfälschung der Nahrungsmittel* . . . , 2 vols. (Leipzig, 1856, 1858).

109 Chevallier, and M. W. Ernest Baudrimont, *Dictionnaire des altérations et falsifications* . . . (6th ed.; Paris, 1882), viii; Soubeiran, *Nouveau Dictionnaire de falsifications* (Paris, 1874), xii–xiii. The review of Soubeiran's book in the *Pharm J.* [ser. 3], 5(1874–75): 318, noted the reliance upon Hassall and others, and commented that the *Dictionnaire* contained little new or original work, and that some of its methods were out of date.

110 See, for example: Flückiger and Hanbury, *Pharmacographia: A History of the Principal Drugs of Vegetable Origin, Met with in Great Britain and British India;* Flückiger, *Grundriss der Pharmakognosie* (Berlin, 1884); Henry George Greenish, *The Microscopical Examination of Foods and Drugs* (London, 1903); Greenish and Eugene Collins, *An Anatomical Atlas of Vegetable Powders; Designed as an Aid to the Microscopic Analysis of Powdered Foods and Drugs* (London, 1904).

111 *Report of the Secretary of Agriculture* [for the year ending 30 June 1895] . . . (Washington, 1895), 52; we are indebted to A. Hunter Dupree, *Science in the Federal Government; A History of Policies and Activities to 1940* (Cambridge, Mass., 1957), 168, for drawing this to our attention. It had been the function of this division to make microscopical analyses for the whole department.

112 Anon., [Review] *"Science: including the Transactions of the Microscopical Society of London* (Edited by Edwin Lankester, M.D., F.R.S. and George Busk, F.R.S.)," *Pharm. J.,* 12(1852–53): 358–359.

113 Anon., [Report of lecture by H. Sugden Evans. F. C. S.], "Microscopical Examination of Cinchona Barks, Illustrated by the Aid of the Oxyhydrogen Light Applied to an Ordinary Microscope," *Pharm. J.,* 16(1856–57): 553.

114 Henry Deane and Henry B. Brady, "On Microscopical Research in Relation to Pharmacy," *Pharm. J.* [ser. 2], 6(1864–65): 232. This paper (232–240) was read at the Bath meeting of the British Pharmaceutical Conference, September 1864. At the Birmingham meeting the following year, the same authors read a paper of similar nature. See Deane and Brady, "On Microscopical Research in Relation to Pharmacy," in *Pharm. J.* [ser. 2], 7(1864–65): 183–186. Both Deane and Brady were, at one time or another, presidents of the Conference.

115 Anon., "Review [of Hogg, *The Microscope*]," in *Pharm. J.* [ser. 2], 9(1867–68): 350–351, quoted from the president of the Pharmaceutical Conference, in an 1866 paper, "On the Study of Botany in Connection with Pharmacy."

116 Stoddart, "Notes on the Use of the Microscope, and Its Crystallographic Application," *Pharm. J.* [ser. 2], 9(1867–68): 173. Stoddart was perhaps wishful when he added, "In the majority of cases the druggist will use the microscope, either for the detection of adulteration or for clinical purposes."

117 Pocklington, "The Microscope in Pharmacy," *Pharm. J.* [ser. 3], 2(1871–72): 621; Anon., "Review of Mark W. Harrington's, 'The Microscopical Examination of Crude Drugs and Other Vegetable Products,' " *Pharm. J.* [ser. 3], 6(1875–76): 899; Frederick Hoffmann, "The Application of the Microscope in Pharmacy and the Drug Trade," in *Druggists' Circular and Chemical Gazette*, 18 (1874): 58, originally presented as a lecture, 12 February 1874, before the New York College of Pharmacy, tried to appeal to the utilitarian sense of American pharmacists, when he remarked that "scientific attainments are a profitable investment nowadays." "In the examination of drugs, and many articles of commerce and domestic economy," Hoffmann considered the microscope "second in importance only to the test-tube, the burette, and the balance."

CHAPTER 6
THE APPLICATION OF CHEMICAL ANALYSIS

1 Thomas Thomson, *The History of Chemistry*, 2 vols. (London, 1830–31), 2:190.

2 We are indebted to Aaron J. Ihde, Professor of Chemistry and of History of Science, University of Wisconsin, for the many suggestions and comments he offered on the history of analytical chemistry. In addition to personal conversation, Dr. Ihde kindly made available the manuscript copy of his chapters on analytical chemistry from his *The Development of Modern Chemistry* (New York, 1964), which brought to our attention the names of certain individuals important in the development of analytical chemistry. Stieb also profited from a special seminar on the history of analytical chemistry conducted by Dr. Ihde during 1957–58.

Perhaps the most useful accounts on the subject in English are the chapters devoted to the history of analytical chemistry, in Ihde, *Development of Modern Chemistry*, 277–303, 559–584. Equally useful, though somewhat dated, are the accounts by two nineteenth-century historians, both chemists of note in their own time: Thomson, *History of Chemistry*, 2:190–250, largely inorganic analysis; and Ernst von Meyer, *A History of Chemistry from Earliest Times to the Present Day; being also an Introduction to the Study of Science*, George M'Gowan, trans. (London, 1891), 358–372, including the history of qualitative and quantitative inorganic chemistry, volumetric analysis, gas analysis, organic chemistry.

Only slightly more recent is A. Chaston Chapman, "Some Main Lines of Advance in the Domain of Modern Analytical Chemistry," in *Analyst*, 42(1917): 229–243, who concentrated more upon later developments.

More particular attention was paid to the history of analytical chemistry in its relations to food adulteration by Frederick A. Filby, *A History of Food Adulteration and Analysis* (London, 1934), *passim*, but especially 174–192 ("Food Analysis, being the Beginnings of Organic Analysis"), on mainly the period up to 1820; and Alexander Wynter Blyth, *Foods: Their Composition and Analysis* . . . (London, 1882), 32–42 ("The History of the Present Scientific Processes for the Detection of Adulteration").

Among other sources, Paul Walden, *Mass, Zahl und Gewicht in der Chemie der Vergangenheit: Ein Kapitel aus der Vorgeschichte des sogenannten quantitativen Zeitalters der Chemie* (*Sammlung chemischer und chemisch-technischer Vorträge*, new ser., No. 8 [Stuttgart, 1931]), treated the quantitative approach to chemistry, but for the most part in the period before 1800. A very specialized point of view was represented by Alcide Jouniaux, *Les Origines françaises de la chimie analytique* (*Actualités scientifiques et industrielles*, No. 707: Exposés de chimie analytique [chimie physique, minerale et industrielle] [Paris, 1838]). See also: Henry Guerlac, "Quantification in Chemistry," in *Isis*, 52(1961): 194–214; and Robert P. Multhauf, "On the Use of the Balance in Chemistry," in *Proc. Amer. Chem. Soc.*, 106(1962): 210–218.

The history of organic analysis was treated by Carl Graebe, *Geschichte der Organischen Chemie* (Berlin, 1920), and Friedrich Dannemann, *Die Naturwissenschaften in ihrer Entwicklung und in ihren Zusammenhange*, 4 vols. (Leipzig, 1910–1913), 4:118–145.

Bernard Dyer and C. Ainsworth Mitchell, *The Society of Public Analysts and other Analytical Chemists: Some Reminiscences of Its First Fifty Years; and a Review of Its Activities* (Cambridge, 1932), provides an excellent reference work for the history of the Society and of analytical chemistry applied to foods and drugs. Less connected history than chronology, the work is nevertheless of value, and has a comprehensive author and subject index. Mitchell, then editor of the *Analyst*, presented what amounted to a bibliographic essay (75–236) upon the highlights of the activities of the Society and its members, as reflected in the pages of the *Analyst*. He reviewed the material by decades, and topically within decades, so that a rather clear picture of the changing emphasis upon activities in one area of investigation or another emerged. Dyer brought authority to his contribution, by reason of his having been associated with the Society from its beginnings; however, his account

(1–72) was little more than what it purported to be—"reminiscence."

Several chronologies offer useful and varied fragments of information. The most satisfactory to use, because it has both a subject and author index, is Edmund Oskar von Lippmann, *Zeittafeln zur Geschichte der Organischen Chemie* (Berlin, 1921). Of broader scope, but containing only an author index, is Paul Walden, *Chronologische Übersichstabellen zur Geschichte der Chemie von den Ältesten Zeiten bis zur Gegenwart* (Berlin, 1952). Very specialized, but none the less useful, is Fr. Berger, "Kurze Notizen zur Geschichte des pharmazeutischen Handwerkzeuges und der pharmazeutischen Gebrauchsgegenstände," in *Zentralblatt für Pharmazie*, 25(1929): 169–171.

The excellent recent study by Marie Boas, *Robert Boyle and Seventeenth-Century Chemistry* (Cambridge, 1958) is valuable not only for the new light it throws upon the work of Boyle, but also for establishing the scope of analytical identification tests used, systematized, and invented by Boyle. See particularly 126–141, but also 205–228 *passim*.

3 Filby, *History of Food Adulteration*, 19. By way of support, he referred to his M. Sc. Dissertation (University of London, 1929), and apparently intended (though he did not say so) to prove the same thesis in his chapter (VIII, 174–192) entitled "Food Analysis, Being the Beginnings of Organic Analysis."

4 We owe the information concerning Clarke and the International Committee to Aaron J. Ihde. Clarke represented the United States on the working committee of the International Committee which included Thorpe, England; Seubert, Germany; Moissan, France.

5 The Gooch crucible was first introduced in 1878. Berzelius used filter paper of high purity, and Swedish filter paper had a reputation early in the nineteenth century, but double-washed papers were first made in Germany in 1883; hardened papers for organic analysis appeared in 1890, and ether-treated extraction thimbles in 1894. Ernest Child, *The Tools of the Chemist: Their Ancestry and American Evolution* (New York, 1940), 114, 118–120.

6 The great strides being made by inorganic, but more especially organic, analysis during this time and by English analysts independently of Continental workers is apparent from C. Ainsworth Mitchell's contribution to Dyer and Mitchell's *Society of Public Analysts*. Mitchell (75–236) analyzed the contributions to the *Analyst*, decade by decade and topically within decades.

7 Over-stepping of these boundaries and some omissions cannot well be avoided.

8 C. [Karl] Remigius Fresenius, *Anleitung zur qualitativen chemischen Analyse* (Bonn, 1843). A fourth German edition was published by the time the second English edition appeared in 1846.

9 "An Attempt to Discover the Genuineness and Purity of Drugs and Medical Preparations," *Journal of Natural Philosophy, Chemistry, and the Arts*, 2(1798): 118–122; 4(1800): 33–36, 159–163.

10 Fredrick Accum, *A Treatise on Adulterations* . . . (London, 1820), 21–23.

11   Richard Powell, trans., *The Pharmacopoeia of the Royal College of Physicians of London, 1836; M.DCCC.IX; Translated into English, with Notes, etc.* (2nd ed.; London, 1809), 59, 61–62.

12   Powell gave a few qualitative chemical tests in this edition. He mentioned (53) the reaction of calcium carbonate with acetic acid, the precipitation of sulfuric acid contaminant in citric acid by means of lead acetate (58), and the detection of calcium carbonate impurity in potassium hydroxide solution by means of lime water (80).

13   *Ibid.,* xix–xx.

14   *Ibid.,* xiv.

15   Richard Phillips, *A Translation of the Pharmacopoeia of the Royal College of Physicians of London, 1836; with Notes and Illustrations* (3rd ed.; London, 1838), xi–xii ("Advertisement [to 1st ed.]"). The Berzelius symbol for Hydrogen chloride, for instance was HCl, the Brande, (h+c), or hc, or m'; for anhydrous acetic acid, $H^3C^4O^3$, and ac', respectively; for sulphuric acid, SO^3, HO and (s'+q), respectively.

16   *Ibid.,* xi. Commenting upon these purity tests, the editor noted they were intended mainly for physicians and medical students, "if not always for the exact analysis of chemists." He also mentions (vi) having subjected the chemical preparations to especially rigid experiment.

17   Phillips was chosen both to edit and to translate this edition.

18   See, for instance, Phillips, trans., *Pharmacopoeia Londinensis, 1836* (3rd ed.; 1838), 286–287, 297–299. Complete divisions such as these appeared almost entirely under monographs dealing with chemical preparations. The separate subdivision "Adulteration" apparently appeared only for potassium sulfate (287).

19   Richard Phillips, *An Experimental Examination of the Last Edition of the Pharmacopoeia Londinensis; with Remarks on Dr. Powell's Translation and Annotations* (London, 1811), 109.

20   Phillips, trans., *Pharmacopoeia Londinensis, 1836* (3rd ed.; 1838), 30, 23–24, 44–45.

21   Robert Howard, "On Certain Precautions Necessary in Using Chemical Tests," *Pharm. J.,* 2(1842–43): 642.

22   *Ibid.;* see also, Jacob Bell and Theophilus Redwood, *Historical Sketch of the Progress of Pharmacy in Great Britain* (London, 1880), 137.

23   Richard Phillips, "Illustrations of the Present State of Pharmacy in England," *Pharm. J.,* 2(1842–43): 315–320, 396–399, 528–532, 651–652; 3(1843–44): 108–111, 244–247.

24   Phillips used specific gravity more frequently than any other analytical technique.

25   Phillips, "Present State of Pharmacy," *Pharm. J.,* 2(1842–43): 397–399; 3(1843–44): 109–110.

26   Jacob Bell, "On the Adulteration of Drugs," *Pharm. J.,* 1(1841–42): 255; George Fownes, "Precautions Necessary in the Use of Chemical Tests [Letter to editor]," *Pharm. J.,* 2(1842–43): 723; Richard Phillips, Jr., "Notes on the tests for the Presence of Time

in the Preparations of Magnesia," *Pharm. J.*, 4(1844–45): 174. Bell was one of the Society's founders, one of its most active members, and the editor of the *Pharmaceutical Journal*; Fownes was lecturer in chemistry to the Society and author of a chemistry text recommended for the use of those preparing for the Society's examinations.

27 "Regulations Adopted and Confirmed by the Council, for the Examination and Registration of Members, Associates, and Apprentices," *Pharm. J.*, 3(1843–44): 339.

28 John Attfield, *A Pamphlet on the Relation to Each Other of Education and Examination, especially with Regard to Pharmacy in Great Britain; with an Introduction, Letters from Leaders to Pharmacy, Appendices, and an Index* (2nd ed.; London, 1882), 3, 35. The first edition appeared in 1880.

29 Charles James Payne, "Address," *Pharm. J.*, 2(1842–43): 323.

30 From Kirchhoff's suggestions as to how Bunsen might improve his observations there developed the spectroscope and the full exploitation of spectral analysis as an important analytical device.

31 See, for instance, the list of apparatus considered important by John Attfield, *Chemistry: General, Medical, and Pharmaceutical . . . A Manual on the General Principles of the Science, and Their Applications to Medicine and Pharmacy* (Philadelphia, 1871, from the 2nd English ed.), vii; E. F. Aschoff, *Anweisung zur Prüfung der Arzneimittel . . .* (2nd ed.; Lemgo, 1835), 20.

32 Attfield, *Chemistry*, 497–504, 178–181, 211–212 (and fold-out, facing 211), 303.

33 L. E. Bingenheimer, Jr., "Historical Trends in Pharmaceutical Analysis as Reflected by the Official Assays," *Drug Standards*, 25(1957): 38, noted the appearance of tests of identity and purity in the second to the fifth decennial revisions of the *United States Pharmacopeia* (1840–1870), with hints of volumetric and gravimetric methods; the appearance of the term "volumetric assay," for the first time with the sixth revision (1880).

34 *British Pharmacopoeia*, 1867, xvi.

35 Attfield had been an editor, along with Redwood and Bentley, of the 1885 edition; and Redwood, along with Warington of Apothecaries' Hall, edited the 1867 edition. See *British Pharmacopoeia*, 1898, xx–xxi, acknowledging a special committee of the Pharmaceutical Society and pharmacist referees for various pharmacopoeial departments.

36 E.g., C. G. Moor, *Suggested Standard of Purity for Foods and Drugs* (London, 1902); W. Chattaway, *Digest of Researches and Criticisms bearing on the British Pharmacopoeia, 1898 . . .* [1899 to 1902 inclusive] (London, 1903). A good picture of the advances in analytical techniques and methods, decade by decade during the first fifty years of the existence of the Society of Public Analysts, as reflected in the *Analyst*, may be obtained from the topically divided discussion of these periods by C. Ainsworth Mitchell, in Dyer and Mitchell, *Society of Public Analysts*, 75–236.

37 Black used a crude pharmaceutical balance. Boas, *Boyle*, 218–221,

described Boyle's contributions to quantitative analysis and the difficulties presented by relatively inaccurate apothecaries' balances.

38   Meyer, *History of Chemistry*, 361.

39   Bergman made crude quantitative determinations on minerals. He began the practice of converting the substance being analyzed into a more suitable form of known composition, and from this calculated the weight of the test substance. Bergman first laid down rules for the systematic analysis of minerals; Klaproth brought to analytical chemistry systematic and precise procedures that made chemical analysis a science and guaranteed reproducible results by other workers. See Thomson, *History of Chemistry*, 2:198–206, and Meyer, *History of Chemistry*, 360.

40   Thomson, *History of Chemistry*, 2:212–213, commented upon the volume of Vauquelin's published work (more than any other chemist without exception) and noted the greater simplicity and precision he brought to the analytical art, but felt he stood below Klaproth, having had his German colleague's work to serve as a guide. Vauquelin received minerals for analysis from Haüy.

41   *Ibid.*, 2:230–232.

42   Proust had been aware of his law by 1797, but stated it only in 1799 and 1806. (See J. R. Partington, *A Short History of Chemistry* [2nd ed.; London, 1951], 153–154.)

43   Nils Nordenskiold, Henrich Rose, Leopold Gmelin, Eilhard Mitscherlich, Friedrich Wohler and others. Thomson, *History of Chemistry*, 2:221. See *ibid.*, 2:221–227, and Meyer, *History of Chemistry*, 361–363. Berzelius announced his electro-chemical theory in 1811 and his system of modern chemical symbolism in 1813.

44   The English edition of Fresenius' *Instruction in Chemical Analysis* (*Quantitative*) appeared the same year as the German edition (1846), and like the volume on qualitative analysis was edited by the English chemist J. Lloyd Bullock, who had spent some time in Giessen and Paris.

45   Child, *Tools of the Chemist*, 79, referred to Dalton's balance as being similar to apothecaries' balances in principle, but capable of use as a hydrostatic balance.

46   Accum, *Treatise on Adulterations* (1st ed.; 1820), 22–23.

47   *Ibid.*, 23.

48   *Ibid.*, 219–222, 286–289, and 64–73. The percentages of alcohol were stated by measure.

49   Powell, trans., *Pharmacopoeia Londinensis, 1809*, 63. See also *ibid.*, 53.

50   Phillips, trans., *Pharmacopoeia Londinensis, 1836* (3rd ed.; 1838), 21–24 *passim*.

51   *Ibid.*, 38, 42, 44, 45, 47. For instance, sodium carbonate precipitated 34 grains of magnesium carbonate from 100 grains of magnesium sulfate, indicating non-admixture of sodium sulfate adulterant; 100 parts of potassium carbonate lost 16 parts of water by strong heat; 10 grains of potassium bromide were "capable of acting upon" 14.28 grains silver nitrate; 10 grains of potassium iodide were

"sufficient to decompose" 10.24 grains of silver nitrate; 100 parts of sodium carbonate crystals yielded "62.5 parts on strong heating."

52 Mohr had come under the influence of two of Berzelius' most famous students and successors in analytical chemistry, Leopold Gmelin (1788–1853) and the pharmacist Heinrich Rose (1795–1864). The Mohr hydrostatic balance, an improved reflux condenser, and the cork borer, among numerous other pieces of equipment, are also traceable to Mohr. To volumetric analytical equipment he contributed the pinchclamp and burette tip, volumetric flasks, and volumetric pipettes; to volumetric analytical procedures he introduced back titration, normal solutions, potassium chromate as an indicator for the analysis of chloride by silver nitrate titration, oxalic acid as a primary standard for alkalimetry, and ferrous ammonium sulfate for oxidizing agents.

53 Meyer, *History of Chemistry*, 365, *n.* 2, mentioned only Sutton among "valuable books on volumetric analysis." For a detailed history of titrimetry (before 1806) see Edmund Rancke Madsen, *The Development of Titrimetric Analysis till 1806* (Copenhagen, 1958), 239 pages with summary (220–223) in Danish, and detailed bibliography (227–239).

54 Bingenheimer, "Historical Trends," in *Drug Standards*, 25(1957): 39, estimated that between the time volumetric assays were first introduced in the sixth revision (1880) of the *U.S.P.* and the eighth revision (1900), they reached their peak of importance, accounting for 80 per cent of all prescribed assays. Numerically, he showed (41) an increase from less than 100 to more than 800 volumetric assays between the appearance of the 1880 and 1945 revisions.

55 Fresenius, *Instruction in Chemical Analysis*, 354–379. An English translation (by Bullock) of Fresenius and H. Will, *New Methods of Alkalimetry*, was then already available.

56 Lewis Caleb Beck, *Adulterations of Various Substances Used in Medicine and in the Arts with the Means of Detecting Them* (New York, 1846), 170. The alkalimeter and its variations (the chlorometer and acetimeter) consisted of a graduated glass tube by means of which the neutralization of the alkali by an acid could be measured directly. It was crude, compared to methods of volumetric analysis as we know them, because the end point of the assay was observed by testing a drop on a strip of litmus paper.

57 J. B. Alphonse Chevallier, *Dictionnaire des altérations et falsifications*, 2 vols. (Paris, 1850, 1852), 1:Pl. V, fig. 29; 2:Pl. III, fig. 18; 2:Pl. V, fig. 37.

58 William Thomas Brande, *A Manual of Chemistry: containing the Principal Facts of the Science, Arranged in the Order in which they are Discussed and Illustrated in the Lectures at the Royal Institution of Great Britain*, with notes and emendations by W. J. MacNeven, 3 vols. in 1 (3rd American edition, from the 2nd London edition; New York, 1829). Brande was secretary of the Royal Society of London, Professor of Chemistry at the Royal Institution, Professor of Chemistry and Materia Medica to the Society of Apothecaries. A member of an important pharmaceutical family, with

apothecary shops in London and Hanover, Brande was a chemist of note—the first to characterize albumen. *Kremers and Urdang's History of Pharmacy*, rev. by Glenn Sonnedecker (3rd ed.; Philadelphia, 1963), 322. Accum began his career in London at the Brande pharmacy.

59   Thomas Graham, *Elements of Chemistry: Including the Application of Science in the Arts*, with notes and additions by Robert Bridges (Philadelphia, 1843), 330. See *ibid.*, 329–331, including fig. 98, illustrating the alkalimeter, and the "French" alkalimeter referred to; and 352–353, for a discussion of chlorimetry. Bridges, a physician, was Professor of General and Pharmaceutical Chemistry at the Philadelphia College of Pharmacy and one of the editors of the *American Journal of Pharmacy*. Thomas Graham (1805–1869), Professor of Chemistry at University College, London, was one of the founders of physical chemistry.

60   *Ibid.*, 331.

61   Attfield, *Chemistry* (American ed.; Philadelphia, 1871), 436–456, used a standard solution of oxalic acid for assaying alkalies (alkalimetry); a standard solution of soda, for acids (acidimetry); etc.

62   See, for example, the British *Pharmacopoeias* of 1898 and 1914 (see also p. 84 of the present work); C. G. Moor's *Suggested Standards* (1902); and Chattaway's *Digest of Researches and Criticisms* (1903).

63   This statement supports the authors' impression of the situation. Meyer, *History of Chemistry* (1891), 368, *n.* 1, referred to Allen's *Commercial Organic Analysis* (1879–1882), as one of two books incorporating qualitative organic analysis.

64   Filby, *History of Food Adulteration*, 176–177. Filby, 174–176, saw the beginnings of organic analysis in the early knowledge of processes such as the lixiviation of plant ashes, distillation, aqueous and alcoholic extraction, and expression (in the case of spices and oils). The French Academy prepared a complete natural history of plants. Lemery analyzed jalap and hellebore (1702), realized the importance of proximate as contrasted with ultimate analysis for organic chemistry (1719), and suggested the systematic investigation of organic acids (1721).

65   Marggraf for his work on plant sugars (1747); Neumann for the calcification of organic products as gums, resins, oils, camphors, etc., and for his observations upon the chemical nature of plants in general; Scheele for his isolation of many organic acids, glycerol, etc.

66   The process for estimating carbon and hydrogen involved burning a readily combustible substance in a pre-determined volume of oxygen, then estimating the carbon, hydrogen, and oxygen from the resulting carbonic acid and the residual oxygen. For substances that burned with more difficulty, he used red oxide of mercury, or other substances that freely evolved oxygen on heating, and estimated the weight of carbonic acid by means of caustic potash solution.

67   Albert Benjamin Prescott, *Outlines of Proximate Organic Analysis*

. . . (New York, 1875); Alfred Henry Allen, *An Introduction to the Practice of Commercial Organic Analysis* acknowledged his debt to Prescott; see Allen, 1(1st American ed.; Philadelphia, 1879), vi, x; 1(2nd ed.; London, 1885), 356.

68 Simon Zeisel and Adolf Lieben worked out a quantitative estimation for methoxyl and ethoxyl compounds in 1885; Josef Herzig and Hans Meyer extended their methods to ethyl and methyl groups attached to nitrogen, in 1894 and later; Koettstorfer applied (1879) carboxyl determination to fats and oils, to give our present saponification number; Arthur Freiherr von Hübl, introduced the so-called "iodine number" determinations, in 1888, with subsequent improvements being made by Wijs and Hanus; and Benedikt and Ulzer applied the "acetyl number" determinations to oils in 1887, with improvements by Julius Lewkowitz in 1897. We are grateful to Aaron J. Ihde for suggesting these names to us.

69 The French pharmacists Caventou and Pelletier isolated quinine, one of the active constituents of cinchona, that same year.

70 Accum, *Treatise on Adulterations*, 312.

71 For example, Accum detected the presence of potassium sulfate in "Prepared Kali. Ph. L. Salt of Tartar," by noting the precipitation that formed upon the addition of barium chloride or lead acetate. 100 parts of precipitate indicated 26 per cent of sulfuric acid, in the case of the barium salt; 30 per cent in the case of the lead salt. (Accum, "Attempt to Discover Genuineness and Purity of Drugs," *Journal of Natural Philosophy, Chemistry, and the Arts*, 4[1800]: 33.) We saw (*ibid.*, 34, 35) that Accum apparently used the balance for determining specific gravities of liquids.

72 N. J. B. Guibourt, *Histoire abrégée des drogues simples*, 2 vols. (Paris, 1820), 1:366–367, 376–378, 382, with fold-out charts facing 366, 377, 383. Caventou and Pelletier isolated strychnine in 1818, brucine and colchicine in 1819, and cinchonine in 1820; Sertürner, morphine, in 1805–1806. While Guibourt did not mention brucine, colchicine, quinine, or cinchonine, he did mention strychnine and morphine, reported the important investigations that Pelletier was making just then on cinchona, and noted in detail the color reactions of different varieties of cinchona with various reagents and indicators. The reports of chemical examinations—his own and those of his French and German colleagues— that Guibourt presented were quantitative as well as qualitative. For instance, he gave the analyses of Aleppo and Smyrna scammony, according to the method of Bouillon, Legrange, and Vogel, in terms of resin, gum, extract, and vegetable debris or earthly material; or cloves, by Trommsdorff's method, in terms of volatile oil, extractive and astringent material, gum, resin, vegetable fibre, and water; and of opium, in terms of acetic acid, alkaline substance (morphine), Sertürner's "acide meconique," Séguin's bitter [water-] insoluble principle (probably identical to Derosne's resin), Séguin's bitter soluble principle, oily substance, amylaceous substance, vegetable debris, and water. (*Ibid.*, 239, 74, 203. The remarks in parentheses are Guibourt's, as are the terms, which we have trans-

lated literally. Guibourt's discussion [201–204] covered the contributions of many workers to the understanding of the activity of
opium, including Séguin, Sertürner, Robiquet, and Derosne.) Guibourt was aware then of morphine, and although codeine was not
isolated until 1832, by Robiquet, the red color test with iron salts
that Guibourt mentioned as typical of the narcotic alkaline principle of opium, undoubtedly indicated codeine. (*Ibid.*, 141. Morphine gave a blue or blue-green color test with solutions of iron
salts, whereas codeine in the presence of acids resulted in a red
color.)

73 Powell, trans., *Pharmacopoeia Londinensis, 1809*, 204, 213.

74 *Ibid.*, 58. The *Pharmacopoeia* directed the preparation of calcium
citrate by the reaction of lemon juice with prepared chalk.

75 Phillips, *Experimental Examination*, 131, 7–9.

76 Phillips, trans., *Pharmacopoeia Londinensis, 1836* (3rd ed.; 1838),
21, 23, 25, 39, 46.

77 *Ibid.*, 46.

78 *Ibid.*, 31, 39, 25.

79 Jonathan Pereira, "On the Adulteration of Scammony," *Pharm. J.*,
4(1844–45): 270–272.

80 Andrew Ure, "On Potato Starch," *Pharm. J.*, 2(1842–43): 12–16. No
one seems previously to have pointed to this apparent precedent to
Fehling's work; and this point requires further investigation.

81 Theophilus Redwood, "Note on the Tests of the Purity of Balsam of
Copaiba," *Pharm. J.*, 6(1846–47): 18.

82 See, for example, Alphonse Chevallier, "On the Variable Quality and
Strength of Opium," in *Pharm. J.*, 10(1850–51): 78–79, abstracted
from the *Journal de Pharmacie*.

83 C. Fresenius, *Instruction in Chemical Analysis (Qualitative)* (2nd
ed.; 1846), 323–343.

84 C. Fresenius, *Instruction in Chemical Analysis (Quantitative)* (London, 1846), 379–433, 495–509. In *ibid.*, 509–528, Fresenius discussed soil analysis.

85 Hassall, *Adulterations Detected; or, Plain Instructions for the Discovery of Frauds of Food and Medicine* (London, 1857), 647, 655,
666, 689–690.

86 *Ibid.*, 399–401, 402. He also referred (400, *n.*) to the "improved
alkalimeter of Mohr."

87 Attfield, *Chemistry* (American ed.; Philadelphia, 1871), 315–386.
The material was divided as follows: alkaloids (315–330, of which
315–324 was devoted to the common alkaloids, morphine, quinine,
and strychnine); amylaceous and saccharine substances (331–340,
including starch, dextrin, cellulose); glucosides (340–346, including aloin, amygdalin, cathartic acid [of Senna], digitalin, elaterin,
guaiacin, jalapin, salicin, santonin, scammonin); alcohol and allied bodies (347–365, alcohol, aldehyde, ether, nitrous ether, myth-
ylic alcohol, chloroform, amylic alcohol, glycerin); albumenoid
substances (366–370); fatty bodies (370–379, soaps, solid fats,
fixed oils, volatile oils, camphor); resinoid substances (379–383,
resins, oleo-resins, balsams); coloring matters (383–386).

88 Volumetric methods were mentioned for acetic, citric, tartaric, and

hydrocyanic acids; gravimetric, for cyanides, oxalates, quinine, morphine, sugar, and alcohol.

89 Prescott, *Outlines of Proximate Organic Analysis* (1875), 5–6. Prescott wrote his preface in September, 1874; the Society held its first general meeting in August of that year.

90 In these few pages, he brought together a great deal of information on the organic acids, the fatty acids, fixed and volatile oils, gums, resins, alkaloids, glucosides, carbohydrates, and alcohols. In the case of the acids, he gave both qualitative and quantitative—gravimetric as well as volumetric—tests. (*Ibid.*, 14–72.)

Aside from the physical tests we have already mentioned, Prescott characterized the fixed oils by a wide variety of color reactions with different acids, by saponification with alkali or lead oxide, by the effect upon silver nitrate, and by the formation of elaidin upon reaction with peroxides of nitrogen. These tests were, for the most part, qualitative, but Prescott did refer to a crude quantitative method for detecting the proportion of admixture of drying oils with non-drying oils by the elaidin method. (*Ibid.*, 77. The entire section of fixed oils occupied pages 72–81.)

Most of Prescott's chemical tests for the volatile oils were entirely qualitative, depending upon their reactions with iodine, bromine, sulfuric acid and alcohol, sodium, and lead sulfide paper. Exceptions were his directions for detecting the admixture of alcohol by methods arising largely from early empirical beginnings—mixing with water, or fixed oil, or calcium chloride, or repeated distillation with water. (*Ibid.*, 106. The entire section on volatile oils occupies pages 104–116.) Individual identification was made only for the oils of turpentine, valerian, and peppermint.

Prescott brought a great variety of tests for the alkaloids, and although most of these were qualitative (color reactions), the variety of these tests and the relative space occupied by them perhaps indicated the growing interest in this class of organic compounds. A volumetric determination by means of potassiomercuric iodide, considered "somewhat unsatisfactory," was given for twelve of the most common alkaloids. (*Ibid.*, 139–140; see also 123–151, for Prescott's full characterization of alkaloids.)

91 Alfred Henry Allen, *Commercial Organic Analysis*, 1(1st American ed.; Philadelphia, 1879), v–vi.

92 *Ibid.*, 2(1st American ed.; Philadelphia, 1882), 116–256.

93 Leffmann, ed., Allen's *Commercial Organic Analysis*, 2, part 1 (3rd ed.; London, 1899), vi.

94 *Ibid.*, 53–57, 58–62, 62–66, 66–68, 80–81.

95 Announcements of English research findings in organic analysis appeared most frequently in the Society of Public Analysts' journal, the *Analyst*, and in the *Journal of the Society of Chemical Industry.*

96 Allen, *Commercial Organic Analysis*, 2(1st American ed.; Philadelphia, 1882), 54–59; *ibid.*, 2, part 3 (3rd American ed.; Philadelphia, 1907), 222–533.

97 *Ibid.*, 2(1st American ed.; Philadelphia, 1882), 402–513; *ibid.*, 3, part 2 (2nd ed.; London, 1892), 127–572; and *ibid.*, 3, part 3 (2nd ed.; London, 1896), 1–89.

98   *Ibid.,* 134–170.
99   This is particularly apparent from a comparison of the subject
     material between various decades of the Society's existence, re-
     corded in the *Analyst,* and presented by C. Ainsworth Mitchell, in
     Dyer and Mitchell, *Society of Public Analysts,* 75–236. Mitchell
     divided the material for each period topically, so it is relatively
     simple to gain an overall impression.
100 The *British Pharmacopoeia, 1914* brought, for the first time in its
     appendices, directions for the determination of acid value and
     saponification value of fixed oils, waxes, and resins; iodine value
     and unsaponifiable matter of fixed oils and fats; esters and alcohols
     of volatile oils; limits of error, of alkaloidal assays. In this same
     edition first appeared the determination of refractive indices, opti-
     cal rotation, and the quantitative limit tests for lead and arsenic.

CHAPTER 7
THE BEGINNING OF BIOLOGICAL STANDARDIZATION

1   Biological tests first entered the *United States Pharmacopeia* in
     1916, and the *British Pharmacopoeia* in 1932. The Committee on
     Physiological Testing of the Scientific Section of the American
     Pharmaceutical Association first came into being in 1910, following
     the stimulus provided by the Philadelphia chapter of the A.Ph.A.
     For information concerning the development of official physio-
     logical testing in the United States, see L. E. Bingenheimer, "His-
     torical Trends in Pharmaceutical Analysis as Reflected by the Official
     Assays," in *Drug Standards,* 25(1957): 40–42; and M. G. Allmark,
     et al., "A History of the Committee on Physiological Testing, Scien-
     tific Section, American Pharmaceutical Association," *Drug Stand-
     ards,* 24(1956): 200–205. Both articles are valuable for the infor-
     mation they provide about the late development of this test method.
     Bingenheimer gave striking graphical support to his paper; Allmark
     printed a useful bibliography of the reports of the committee,
     1910–1956. In the absence of comparable material for Britain, one
     might infer a somewhat parallel—though slightly later—develop-
     ment there compared with the United States. See also E. M. Hough-
     ton, "The Physiological Assay of Drugs," *Bulletin of Pharmacy,*
     14(1900): 370–372; Editorial, "The Doctor's Logic Limps," *Bull. of
     Pharm.,* 15(1901): 221–223; Seward W. Williams, "Physiological
     Standardization," *Bull. of Pharm.,* 13(1899): 503–505; *Modern Drug
     Standardization, with Special Reference to Physiological Methods
     and Standards* (Mulford's Working Bulletin, No. 10; H. K. Mulford
     Company, Philadelphia, after 1908); "Importance of Digitalis
     Standardization" (H. K. Mulford Co., reprint), 8 pp.; and Herbert C.
     Hamilton, "Pharmacological Assaying: Historical and Descriptive,"
     J. Amer. Pharm. Assoc., 8(1919): 49–64, a monographic approach,
     with separate sections on cannabis sativa, ergot, digitalis, pituitary
     gland, and adrenalin.
2   Anon., "Physiological Testing," *Analytical Notes 1909,* 4(1910):
     2–3. A house organ issued by Evans Sons Lescher & Webb Limited,
     Analytical Notes, brought alphabetically (and without any advertis-

ing) the analytical report upon "abnormal" or adulterated drugs and chemicals that came to its attention during the year and reported certain analytical procedures found useful in the company's laboratory. The usual constants reported included: temperature (°C); optical rotation (100 mm. tube with sodium light); specific gravity (at 15.5°C); and refractive indices (determined at 22°C, using the Amagat and Jean refractometer). In addition to these, the most pertinent particular analytical details were included according to the nature of the substances reported upon.

3   *Ibid.*, 2.

4   *Ibid.*

5   The mammalian heart method was chosen by Evans, in the cases mentioned, as affording "more accurate indications of their value under the conditions of actual practice than any method based merely upon a general toxic effect." (*Ibid.*)

6   *Ibid.*, 3.

7   E. M. Holmes, "Is Physiological Standardisation Necessary?," *Pharm. J.* [ser. 4], 22(1906): 127; and William Kirby, "Standardisation," *ibid.*, 200.

8   T. Maben, "Standardisation," *ibid.*, 62.

9   Holmes, "Physiological Standardisation," *ibid.*, 126–127. Holmes was an active figure in the Pharmaceutical Society and the British Pharmaceutical Conference.

10   Anon., "Physiological Standards and Tests," *ibid.*, 56.

11   *Ibid.*

12   Kirby, "Standardisation," *ibid.*, 200.

13   *Ibid.*, 199.

14   Fr. O. Taylor, "Forty-Five Years of Manufacturing Pharmacy," in *J. Amer. Pharm. Assoc.*, 4(1915): 473; drawn to our attention by George Urdang, "The Application of Science in Pharmacy," in *Amer. J. Pharm. Education*, 15(1951): 358, *n.* 21. This standardization of ergot and the other preparations depended on determining their total alkaloidal content.

15   W. Chattaway, *Digest of Researches and Criticisms* [1899–1902] *bearing on the Revision of the British Pharmacopoeia, 1898 . . .* (London, 1903).

16   C. G. Moor, *Suggested Standards of Purity for Food and Drugs* (London, 1902), 128, referring to a fowl-method, described by E. M. Houghton, "Therapeutic Activity of Ergot," in *Pharm. J.* [ser. 4], 7(1898): 345.

17   Alexander Wynter Blyth, *A Manual of Practical Chemistry: The Analysis of Foods and the Detection of Poisons* (London, 1879), 349.

18   Alfred Henry Allen, *Commercial Organic Analysis . . .* , 3, part 2 (2nd ed.; London, 1892), 149–150.

19   *Ibid.*

20   H. Wippell Gadd, "Some Notes on Standards for Drugs," *Pharm. J.* [ser. 4], 15(1902): 470. Gadd suggested, as a solution to the general problem of drug standards, a round-table conference comprising representatives from the General Medical Council, the Pharma-

ceutical Society, Drug Club, the Society of Public Analysts, and presided over by a member of Parliament, "representing the ignorant public."

21   W. E. Dixon and G. S. Haynes, "The Biochemical Standardization of Drugs," *Pharm. J.* [ser. 4], 21(1905): 754–755.

22   Bingenheimer, "Historical Trends," in *Drug Standards*, 25(1957): 40–42, traced (with graphs) the relative frequency of use of biological procedures in the U.S.P. and N.F. from their introduction in the ninth revision of the U.S.P. (1916), and drew the following interesting conclusion: "Biological assays, which were increasing in number relatively rapidly to 1945, have actually decreased in number since that time. Biological assays involving the use of laboratory animals have decreased sharply, having been replaced in many cases by instrumental assays, but this decrease has been offset to some extent by an increase in the number of microbiological assays." See also Charles S. Chase, "Approved Methods of Physiological Standardizations: Historical Sketch," in *J. Am. Pharm. Assoc.*, 4(1915): 1289–93.

CHAPTER 8
THE BACKGROUND

1   Arthur Hill Hassall, in *Minutes of Evidence, 4674*, in *Report from the Select Committee on Adulterations of Food, Etc.; together with the Proceedings of the Committee, Minutes of Evidence, Appendix and Index* (London, 1856), hereafter cited as *Report* (1856); *Minutes of Evidence* (1856).

2   *First and Second Report from the Select Committee on Adulterations of Food, Etc., with the Minutes of Evidence and Appendix* (London, 1855); cited hereafter as *Report* (1855); *Minutes of Evidence* (1855). Hassall's testimony was *Minutes of Evidence* (1855), 1–354, and *ibid.* (1856), 4388–4678. Hassall also received special mention in the Select Committee *Report* (1856), iii, viii.

3   George Macaulay Trevelyan, *Illustrated English Social History*, 4 vols. (London, 1949–1952), 4:5.

4   The following discussion is based mainly upon ideas and suggestions received from George L. Mosse, Professor of History, University of Wisconsin; Élie Halévy, *A History of the English People in the 19th Century*, 5 vols. (New York, 1924–1951), Vols. 1–4; William Law Mathieson, *England in Transition, 1789–1832: A Study of Movements* (London, 1920); John Theodore Merz, *A History of European Thought in the Nineteenth Century*, 4 vols. (Edinburgh, 1896–1914); Irwin T. Saunders, et al., *Societies Around the World*, 2 vols. (New York, 1953); David Churchill Somervell, *English Thought in the Nineteenth Century* (London, 1929); H. D. Traill and J. S. Mann, *Social England*, 6 vols. (New York, 1904), Vols. 5, 6; Trevelyan, *Illustrated English Social History*, Vol. 4; Trevelyan, *History of England* (London, 1952); Trevelyan, *British History in the Nineteenth Century, 1792–1901* (New York, 1930); Ernest Llewellyn Woodward, *History of England* (London, 1947); and Woodward, *The Age of Reform, 1815–1870* (Oxford, 1938).

5   The following discussion is based primarily upon the excellent over-

view found in George Rosen, *A History of Public Health* (MD Monograph on Medical History No. 1; New York, 1958), particularly pages 192–233, 259–269, and 273–274; and on biographical details (lightly documented) concerning some of the leaders of the British movement given in M. E. M. Walker, *Pioneers of Public Health: The Story of Some Benefactors of the Human Race* (Edinburgh and London, 1930), notably Sir Edwin Chadwick (71–86) and Sir John Simon (100–114). Also useful are C. Fraser Brockington, *A Short History of Public Health* (London, 1956); J. H. E. Brotherston, *Observations on the Early Public Health Movement in Scotland* (London School of Hygiene and Tropical Medicine Memoir No. 8; London, 1952); and W. M. Frazer, *A History of English Public Health, 1834–1939* (London, 1950). Valuable as publications of the period are: Sir Edwin Chadwick, *Report on the Sanitary Condition of the Labouring Population of Great Britain* (London, 1843); Benjamin Ward Richardson, *The Health of Nations: A Review of the Works of Edwin Chadwick, with a Biographical Dissertation*, 2 vols. (London, 1887); Sir John Simon, *English Sanitary Institutions, Reviewed in Their Course of Development, and in Some of Their Political and Social Relations* (London, 1890); and Simon, *Report on the Sanitary Condition of the City of London, for the Year 1850–51* (London, 1851).

6 Rosen, *History of Public Health,* 194.
7 *Ibid.,* 211.
8 *Ibid.,* 220.
9 John Roberton, *A Treatise on Medical Police, and on Diet, Regimen etc.* . . . , 2 vols. (Edinburgh, 1808–1809), 2:328.
10 *Ibid.,* 329.

CHAPTER 9
THE EXTENT AND NATURE OF THE PROBLEM

1 See particularly discussions in Chap. 12, 145–155 *passim,* and Chap. 13, 166–167, 176–177.
2 Fredrick Accum, *A Treatise on Adulterations of Food* . . . (1st ed.; London, 1820), 18.
3 *Ibid.,* 17, 20, 22, and 25. See also 166–167, in the present work.
4 Accum, "An Attempt to Discover the Genuineness and Purity of Drugs and Medical Preparations," *Journal of Natural Philosophy, Chemistry, and the Arts,* 2(1798): 121; 4(1800): 35, 36, 160.
5 [Robert?] Christison, "Observations on the Adulteration of Drugs," appendix to "Report of the Royal College of Physicians of Edinburgh on the Adulteration of Drugs," *Edinburgh Med. & Surg. J.,* 49(1838): 328; John Attfield, *Chemistry* . . . (5th ed.; Philadelphia, 1874), 271; and Friedrich A. Flückiger and Daniel Hanbury, *Pharmacographia* . . . (2nd ed.; London, 1879), 440, 441.
6 *The Tricks of Trade* . . . (London, 1859), 151–158 *passim.*
7 *Ibid.,* 152–155, 157–158.
8 Richard Phillips, "Illustrations of the Present State of Pharmacy in England," *Pharm. J.,* 3(1843–44): 247.
9 *Ibid.,* 2(1842–43): 316–320, 396–399, 529–530; and 3(1843–44): 246. The substances tested included: nitric acid, dilute nitric acid,

hydrochloric acid, potassium carbonate, liquor potassium carbonate, liquor potassae, liquor ammoniae, exsiccated sodium carbonate, and potassium tartrate.

10   *Ibid.*, 2(1842–43): 529–532, 651–652; and 3(1843–44): 108–111, 244–246.

11   *Ibid.*, 2(1842–43), 316.

12   William Ince, "On Sulphur Praecipitatum," *Pharm. J.*, 1(1841–42): 583; and Jacob Bell, "On the Adulteration of Drugs," *ibid.*, 253.

13   A. Dupré, "Correspondence," *Analyst*, 2(1877): 14–15.

14   Anon., "Adulterated Drugs," *Analyst*, 4(1879): 173; Anon., "Adulterated Drugs," *Analyst*, 5(1880): 148.

15   William Howison, "On Various Circumstances Important to be Attended to in Prescribing Medicines," *Lancet*, 1(1831–32): 913; and Review of John Short's *Practical Remarks on the Nature and Effects of the Expressed Oil of Croton Tiglium* . . . (London, 1830), in *Lancet*, 1(1830–31): 87.

16   Arthur Hill Hassall, *Adulterations Detected; or, Plain Instructions for the Discovery of Frauds in Food and Medicine* (London, 1857), 640, 652, 663, 673, 687. Essentially the same information had been published in *Lancet*, 2(1854): 81, 165; 1(1853): 164, 325–326; and 2(1853): 16.

17   Hassall, *Adulterations Detected*, 691–692.

18   *Ibid.*, 652; *Lancet*, 1(1853): 164.

19   Hassall, *Food and Its Adulterations* . . . (London, 1855), xxxv.

20   Hassall, "The Decline of Adulteration," letter to the editor, in the *Times*, 3 Sept. 1879, 8.

21   G. W. Wigner, "The Working of the Sale of Food and Drugs Act, during 1875 and 1876," *Analyst*, 2(1877): 11; Wigner, "Remarks on the Work Done by Public Analysts during 1877 under the Sale of Food and Drugs Act," *Analyst*, 3(1878): 257.

22   Hassall, in *Minutes of Evidence*, 3, 5, 149, in *First and Second Report from the Select Committee on Adulterations of Food, Etc., with the Minutes of Evidence and Appendix* (London, 1855), hereafter cited as *Report* (1855); *Minutes of Evidence* (1855); Simon, *ibid.*, 837–842; Gordon, *ibid.*, 985–997, 1018; Thomson, *ibid.*, 1456–58, 1470–71, 1526–28, 1552; Herring, *ibid.*, 1953, 2001–2002; Scanlan, *ibid.*, 2872–75.

23   Redwood, *ibid.*, 1661, 1717; Phillips, *ibid.*, 2449; and Wallington, *ibid.*, 2516–17, 2551.

24   Scanlan, *ibid.*, 2877; Herring, *ibid.*, 1990–91, 2000–2003, 2036; and Redwood, *ibid.*, 1643–45, 1658–61, 1761–88, 1791–1806.

25   *Report from the Select Committee on Adulterations of Food, Etc.; together with the Proceedings of the Committee, Minutes of Evidence, Appendix, and Index* (London, 1856), hereafter cited as *Report* (1856); *Minutes of Evidence* (1856). Challice, *Minutes of Evidence* (1856), 1536–40; Wakley, *ibid.*, 2286–87; Hassall, *ibid.*, 4391–98; Bastick, *ibid.*, 841–843.

26   Baiss, *ibid.*, 977ff., 1024, 1036; Drew, *ibid.*, 2904–07, 3031–38; Atkinson, *ibid.*, 2885, 2895–99; Allen, *ibid.*, 3862–64, 3890–96; and Bell, *ibid.*, 2315, 2319, 2334–35.

27 Gay, *ibid.*, 1707; and Postgate, *ibid.*, 4223, 4228.

28 Hassall, *ibid.*, 4452.

29 *Report* (1856), iii.

30 *Ibid.*, iv.

31 *Ibid.*, ix

32 *Ibid.*, xxiii, xxv.

33 *Report from the Select Committee on Adulteration of Food Act (1872); together with the Proceedings of the Committee, Minutes of Evidence, Appendix, and Index* (London, 1874), hereafter cited as *Report* (1874); *Minutes of Evidence* (1874). Allen, *Minutes of Evidence* (1874), 2710, 3532; Bartlett, *ibid.*, 4220; Edward Horner (wholesale druggist), *ibid.*, 2703, 2727, 2737; William Hodgkinson (wholesale druggist), *ibid.*, 2785–86, 2790–91, 2796, 2825–26; Michael Carteighe (pharmaceutical chemist, examiner and later president of Pharmaceutical Society), *ibid.*, 2842, 2845; John Williams (manufacturing chemist, member of Council and Treasurer of Pharmaceutical Society), *ibid.*, 2938, 2946; and George Webb Sandford (pharmaceutical chemist), *ibid.*, 2980.

34 Hassall, *ibid.*, 6405.

35 Those sections of the draft report that referred to drugs and the 1868 Pharmacy Act (see p. xviii of 1874 *Report*) were deleted from the final report.

36 *Report* (1874), Appendix No. 8, 373–375. See also Appendix No. 1, 360.

37 Carteighe, *Minutes of Evidence* (1874), 2920.

38 Sandford, *ibid.*, 2988–90.

39 *Report from the Select Committee on Food Products Adulteration; with the Proceedings of the Committee, Minutes of Evidence, Appendix, and Index* (London, 1894), hereafter cited as *Report* (1894); *Minutes of Evidence* (1894). Herbert Preston-Thomas, *Minutes of Evidence* (1894), 135.

40 *Ibid.*, Appendices No. 1 and 2, pp. 191, 193.

41 *Report from the Select Committee on Food Products Adulteration; with the Proceedings of the Committee, Minutes of Evidence, Appendix, and Index* (London, 1896) (hereafter cited as *Report* [1896]; *Minutes of Evidence* [1896]), xxxviii. See also Charles Umney (manufacturing chemist and wholesale druggist, supplier to British Army, and active in Pharmaceutical Society), in *Minutes of Evidence* (1895), 6376–77, 6416, in *Report from the Select Committee on Food Products Adulteration; with the Proceedings of the Committee, Minutes of Evidence, Appendix, and Index* (London, 1895), hereafter cited as *Report* (1895); *Minutes of Evidence* (1895); and Alexander Wynter Blyth (medical officer of health and public analyst, President of Society of Analysts), *ibid.*, 7706–07; and Joseph Classon Preston (wholesale druggist), *ibid.*, 6483.

42 Cecil Howard Cribb, "The Need for Fuller Statistics of Adulteration," *Analyst*, 19(1894): 273–277; with discussion, 277–279.

43 We have seen that Hassall and Wigner had estimated the overall extent of adulteration to have been about 60 to 65 per cent in the 1850's; Wigner also estimated that the Act of 1872 reduced this to

about 26 per cent. Hassall, "The Decline of Adulteration," letter to the editor, in the *Times* 3 Sept. 1879, 8; Wigner, "The Working of the Sale of Food and Drugs Act, during 1875 and 1876," *Analyst*, 2(1877): 11; 3(1878): 257.

44 *Local Government Board Report, 1877–78*, bound in *House of Commons, 1878*, Vol. 37, Pt. I.1, xciv; *LGBR, 1878–79*, in *H. of C., 1879*, 28.1, cxxx; *LGBR, 1886–87*, in *H. of C., 1887*, 36.1, cxxviii; *LGBR, 1891–92*, in *H. of C., 1892*, 38.1, cxli; *LGBR, 1896–97*, in *H. of C., 1897*, 36.1, cxl; *LGBR, 1901–02*, in *H. of C., 1902*, 35.1, clii; *LGBR, 1906–07*, in *H. of C., 1907*, 26.1, 238; and *Annual Report of Ministry of Health, 1931–32*, in *H. of C., 1931–32*, 10.1, 279. The adulteration reported for milk in the years indicated was 24.1 per cent (1877), 21.6 per cent (1878), 19.5 per cent (1881), 13.0 per cent (1886), 13.4 per cent (1891), 11.1 per cent (1896), 11.2 per cent (1901), 12.5 per cent (1906), and 6.4 per cent (1931); while for spirits during the same periods, the reported extent of adulteration was 47.6 per cent, 46.1 per cent, 28.4 per cent, 17.8 per cent, 19.1 per cent, 15.6 per cent, 12.9 per cent, 10.6 per cent, and 8.0 per cent. The results for milk must be considered perhaps more conclusive than those for any other substance examined, by the sheer numbers of samples taken. For example, in 1877 out of a total of 14,706 samples taken, fully 4,435 (or 30.2 per cent) were milk, as opposed to 503 (or 3.4 per cent) for drugs; and still in 1906, out of 90,504 samples, 42,235 (or 46.7 per cent) were milk, as opposed to 2,726 (or 3.0 per cent) for drugs. In fact more than two-thirds of all samples taken in 1906 were dairy products.

45 *Local Government Board Report, 1877–78*, in *House of Commons, 1878*, 37, Pt. I.1, xcii.

46 *Ibid.*, xcvi. See also *LGBR, 1878–79*, in *H. of C., 1879*, 28.1, cxxxiv; *LGBR, 1881–82*, in *H. of C., 1882*, 30, Pt. I.1., cvi; *LGBR, 1886–87*, in *H. of C., 1887*, 36.1, cxxxiii.

47 Wigner, "The Working of the Sale of Food and Drugs Act, during 1875 and 1876," *Analyst*, 2(1877): 13; 3(1878): 258; 7(1882): 115.

48 *Local Government Board Report, 1877–78*, in *H. of C., 1878*, 37, Part I.1, 546.

49 *Ibid.*, xciii.

50 *Local Government Board Report, 1906–07*, in *H. of C., 1906*, 26.1, 222–223.

51 For a discussion of so-called trade practices, see pages 192–194. See also "Drugs and Medicines: 9. Sale of Drugs and Medicines under Conventional Names," *Select Committee Index* (1874), 407.

52 *Local Government Board Report, 1886–87*, in *H. of C., 1887*, 36.1, cxxxiii; *LGBR, 1896–97*, in *H. of C., 1897*, 36.1, cxliv; and *LGBR, 1906–07*, in *H. of C., 1907*, 26.1, 239; *LGBR, 1895–96*, in *H. of C., 1896*, 36.1, cxxxv.

53 *Local Government Board Report, 1877–78*, in *H. of C., 1878*, 37, Pt. I.1, xcvi; *LGBR, 1878–79*, in *H. of C., 1879*, 28.1, cxvi; *LGBR, 1880–81*, in *H. of C., 1881*, 46.1, xciii; *LGBR, 1901–02*, in *H. of C., 1902*, 35.1, clv; *Annual Report of the Ministry of Health, 1931–32*, in *H. of C., 1931–32*, 10.1, 91.

54 *Local Government Board Report, 1880–81*, in *H. of C., 1881*, 46.1, xciii.

55 *Local Government Board Report, 1906–07*, in *H. of C., 1907*, 26.1, 239.

56 We reserve to Chapter 14 a more detailed discussion of trade questions. Anon., "The Birmingham Adulteration Case; Important Decision," *Analyst*, 1(1876): 57–58; Anon., "Law Reports: Castor Oil Pills," *Analyst*, 2(1877): 104–105; Anon., "Law Notes: Milk of Sulphur and Precipitate Sulphur," *Analyst*, 14(1889): 178–180; and Anon., "Legal Milk of Sulphur Prosecution," *Analyst*, 22(1897): 83–84.

57 *Local Government Board Report, 1886–87*, in *H. of C., 1887*, 36.1, cxxix; *LGBR, 1896–97*, in *H. of C., 1897*, 36.1, cxl; *LGBR, 1891–92*, in *H. of C., 1892*, 38.1, cxlvii; *LGBR, 1901–02*, in *H. of C., 1902*, 35.1, clvi; and *LGBR, 1906–07*, in *H. of C., 1906*, 26.1, xcviii.

58 Accum, *Treatise on Adulterations*, 19–20; see also *ibid.*, 18 (collectors) and 24 (vendors of medicinal herbs); and Accum, "Attempt to Discover Genuineness and Purity of Drugs," *Journal of Natural Philosophy, Chemistry, and the Arts*, 4(1800): 35 (chemists).

59 Hassall, "Jalap and Its Adulterations," *Lancet*, 1(1853): 325–326; "Scammony and Its Adulterations," *ibid.*, 164; *Adulterations Detected* (1857), 652; "Opium: Laudanum," *Lancet*, 1(1853): 117. See also *Adulterations Detected*, 9 (grinders and roasters).

60 *Minutes of Evidence* (1855), 131.

61 Warrington, *Minutes of Evidence* (1855), 460–462; Gordon, *ibid.*, 990; Redwood, *ibid.*, 1700–1704, 1710; Letheby, *ibid.*, 2776–78.

62 Thomson, *ibid.*, 1480–84; Herring, *ibid.*, 1982–86; and Letheby, *ibid.*, 2847. See also Redwood, *ibid.*, 1736.

63 Herring, *ibid.*, 1992, 1997–98, 2002–2003; and Postgate, *ibid.*, 2718–20.

64 Hassall, *Minutes of Evidence* (1856), 4399.

65 Gay, *ibid.*, 1655–57, 1659, 1667–87. For a brief review of opposing opinions see *Report* (1856), Index, 336–337: "1. As to Adulteration by Drug Grinders; exculpatory Evidence hereon."

66 *Ibid.*, 338–339: "7. As to the Propriety of a Check upon imported Drugs."

67 Horner, *Minutes of Evidence* (1874), 2704–05, 2707, 2727, 2736. While at least one witness considered that adulteration was practiced by drug wholesalers, the dealers themselves denied this and indicated how they protected the retail distributors (Allen, *ibid.*, 3643–47; Horner, *ibid.*, 2713–14; and Hodgkinson, *ibid.*, 2787). By the time of the Select Committee of 1895, one witness testified that while he still saw adulterated drugs imported, that these were by and large purchased by foreign buyers (Cameron, *Minutes of Evidence* [1895], 6414–16).

CHAPTER 10
CHANGING CONCEPTS OF DRUG ADULTERATION

1 *Report from the Select Committee on Adulterations of Food, Etc.; together with the Proceedings of the Committee, Minutes of Evi-*

dence, Appendix, and Index (London, 1856), vii, hereafter cited as *Report* (1856); *Minutes of Evidence* (1856).

2 *Report from the Select Committee on Adulteration of Food Act (1872); together with the Proceedings of the Committee, Minutes of Evidence, Appendix, and Index* (London, 1874), iii, hereafter cited as *Report* (1874); *Minutes of Evidence* (1874).

3 To add perspective to this and following chapters, we mention here in chronological order the various Parliamentary Select Committees and Acts that dealt with the adulteration of foods and drugs in Britain during the nineteenth century. Following the *Reports of Select Committees* in 1855 and 1856 there resulted an Act in 1860 (23 & 24 Victoria 1860, ch. 84) dealing specifically only with foods but affecting drugs by its incorporation into the Pharmacy Act of 1868 (31 & 32 Victoria 1868, ch. 121), then was amended in 1872 (35 & 36 Victoria 1872, ch. 74) to include drugs. Another *Select Committee Report* of 1874 gave rise to the great Act of 1875 (38 & 39 Victoria 1875, ch. 63), subsequently amended in 1879 (42 & 43 Victoria 1879, ch. 30), after the *Report of the Select Committee of 1878–79*, and in 1899 (62 & 63 Victoria 1899, ch. 51), after the *Reports of the Select Committee of 1894, 1895, and 1896.*

4 *Report* (1874), viii, continues: "Witnesses of the highest standing concur in stating that in the numerous articles of food and drink which they have analysed, they found scarcely anything absolutely injurious to health; and that if deleterious substances are occasionally employed for the purposes of adulteration, they are used in such minute quantities as to be comparatively harmless." The reference is primarily to foods, but the implication seems general.

5 Arthur Hill Hassall, *Adulterations Detected; or, Plain Instructions for the Discovery of Frauds in Food and Medicines* (London, 1857), 2; Hassall in *Report* (1856), 4424.

6 Fredrick Accum, *A Treatise on Adulterations of Food, and Culinary Poisons* . . . (London, 1820), 4, iv. These references were directed mainly to foods.

7 Anon., *The Domestic Chemist; Comprising Instructions for the Detection of Adulteration in Numerous Articles Employed in Domestic Economy, Medicine, and the Arts* . . . (London, 1831), vii–viii, referred to its principal aim as ensuring man "his health and wealth against the ravages of adulteration and disease"; Anon., *The Tricks of Trade in the Adulterations of Food and Physic: with Directions for their Detection and Counteraction* (2nd ed.; London, 1859), iii–iv.

8 *Tricks of Trade*, iv.

9 Hassall, in *Minutes of Evidence* (1856), 4425; Postgate, *ibid.*, 4238, 4248, 4249.

10 The Pharmaceutical Society's militant leaders, Jacob Bell and Theophilus Redwood, thought it particularly important to differentiate between intentional adulteration, deterioration, and contamination or impurity. See Redwood, in *Minutes of Evidence*, 1620, 1754–59, in *First and Second Report from the Select Committee on Adultera-*

tions of Food, Etc., with the Minutes of Evidence and Appendix (London, 1855), hereafter cited as *Report* (1855); *Minutes of Evidence* (1855).

J. Léon Soubeiran, *Nouveau Dictionnaire des falsifications . . .* (Paris, 1874), vii, also distinguished between accidental admixture or substitution and adulteration, which he defined as existing "each time one introduces voluntarily into a product other substances, harmful or without action, which are other than the product itself."

11 23 & 24 Victoria 1860, ch. 84, sec. 1.
12 *Report* (1856), vii–viii.
13 *Report* (1856), iv, vii. Compare Postgate, in *Minutes of Evidence* (1856), 4238, 4242, 4248.
14 *Report* (1856), viii.
15 35 & 36 Victoria 1872, ch. 74, secs. 1–3.
16 Hassall, *Adulterations Detected*, 2, defined adulteration.
17 Hassall, in *Minutes of Evidence* (1855), 150; Alphonse René le Mire de Normandy, *The Commercial Hand-Book of Chemical Analysis; or Practical Instructions for the Determination of the Intrinsic or Commercial Value of Substances Used in Manufactures, in Trades, and in the Arts* (London, 1850), iv; *Report* (1856), iv.
18 *Report* (1874), vii.
19 38 & 39 Victoria 1875, ch. 63, sec. 9.
20 Various important witnesses before the 1874 Select Committee gave slightly different views upon what they felt constituted adulteration. Hassall, in *Minutes of Evidence* (1874), 6175, considered that there was no one general definition of adulteration, but rather individual definitions for different articles; his general definition of adulteration has already been quoted. The well-known chemists Charles A. Cameron and Charles Meynott Tidy (*ibid.*, 5007, 5310), elaborated this to include fraudulent admixture for increasing weight or diminishing value, and deleterious admixture, as well as the abstraction of essential ingredients. They made exceptions in the case of non-injurious and non-misrepresented admixtures. Michael Carteighe, auditor and later president (1882–1896) of the Pharmaceutical Society stressed the fact (*ibid.*, 2835, 2838, 2893–98), that there was no such thing as absolute purity.
21 William J. Bell, *The Sale of Food & Drugs Acts and Forms, Regulations, Orders and Notices Issued Thereunder, with Notes and Cases*, Charles F. Lloyd and R. A. Robinson, eds. (7th ed.; London, 1923), 3–4, *n.* (a) mentioned sulfur, borax, carbolic acid, sulfuric acid, linseed, and liquorice as examples.

This particular definition was one suggested by the Society of Public Analysts, and the one later incorporated by the Society's secretary, G. W. Wigner, into his model Act against adulteration. (See Bernard Dyer and C. Ainsworth Mitchell, *The Society of Public Analysts and other Analytical Chemists . . .* [Cambridge, 1932], 3; Anon., "Society of Public Analysts," in *Pharm. J.* [ser. 3], 5[1874–75]: 444; Anon., "Proceedings of the Society of Public Analysts," in *Chem. News*, 31 [1875]: 59. Compare with Wigner's

Model Act, Anon., "A Model Act Against Adulteration," in the
Sanitary Record [*A Monthly Journal of Public Health and the
Progress of Sanitary Science*], 12[1880–81]: 366.)

The Commonwealth of Massachusetts followed many of Wigner's
proposals in 1882, but their definition of "drug" appeared to combine the definitions by Wigner and the American physician Edward
R. Squibb, thus overcoming some of the observed weaknesses of the
definition in the 1875 Act. Section 2 of the Massachusetts statute
defined the term "drug" to include all medicines for internal or
external use, antiseptics, disinfectants, and cosmetics." (*Massachusetts Acts* 1882, ch. 263, sec. 2.)

Squibb, on the other hand, proposed "That the term 'Medicine'
shall include every article, other than food and drink, that is used
for the preservation of health, or for the relief or cure of disease, in
man or animals, including antiseptics and disinfectants and cosmetics." (Edward R. Squibb, "Rough Draft of a Proposed Law to
Prevent the Adulteration of Food and Medicine, and to create a
State Board of Health," *New Remedies* [Supplement], 8[no. 3, whole
no. 57, March 1879], 3. See also, Squibb, *Proposed Legislation on
the Adulteration of Food and Medicine* [Economic Monographs, no.
14; reprint from *Medical Society of the State of New York, Transactions 1879;* New York, 1879], 57 pp., including short preface
[dated, 4 March 1879], proposed draft and comments [exactly as
published in *New Remedies*], "Notes in Reply to Criticisms by the
Press," and a copy of the 1875 British Act, with "Notices of Some
Rulings of the British Court.")

The first Canadian Act (1874) defined drugs to include all articles
used for curative or medicinal purposes. (Edward B. Shuttleworth,
"The Adulteration Act," *Can. Pharm. J.,* 7[1873–74]: 442.)

Squibb's definition bears a greater resemblance to the modern
American definition of the term "drug" (sec. 201, g, of the 1938
amendment), namely: "(1) articles recognized in the official
United States Pharmacopoeia, official Homeopathic Pharmacopoeia
of the United States, or National Formulary, any supplement to any
of them; and (2) articles intended for use in the diagnosis, cure,
mitigation, treatment, or prevention of disease in man or other
animals; and (3) articles (other than food) intended to affect the
structure or any function of the body of man or other animals; and
(4) articles intended for use as a component of any articles
specified in clause (1), (2), or (3); but does not include devices or
their components, parts, or accessories." (Vincent A. Kleinfeld and
Charles Wesley Dunn, *Federal Food, Drug, and Cosmetic Act:
Judicial and Administrative Record. 1953–1957* [Food Law Institute Series, New York, 1958], 465–466.)

The definition of "drug" under the 1875 Sale of Food and Drugs
Act remained unchanged in the 1879 and 1899 amendments to the
Act, although some attempts were made to alter it. A Bill of 1897
suggested the definition: "Any substance, vegetable, animal or
mineral used in the composition or preparation of medicines,

whether for external or internal use." (Anon., "The Purity of Food and Drugs," *Pharm. J.* [ser. 4], 4[1897]: 182.)

22   38 & 39 Victoria 1875, ch. 63, sec. 4. Douglas C. Bartley, *Adulteration of Food: Statutes and Cases Dealing with Coffee, Tea, Bread, Seeds, Food and Drugs, Margarine, Milk-blended Butter, Fertilizers and Feeding Stuffs, etc.* (London, 1895), 48, noted that under this section it was necessary (according to sec. 5 f.) to prove guilty knowledge, and to show injurious effect upon quality or potency. Section 5 required guilty knowledge, but according to Bell, *The Sale of Food and Drugs Acts, 1875 and 1879: with Notes and Cases; also Practical Observations Bearing upon Legal and Chemical Questions which have arisen in the Working of the Act* (London, 1886), 10, it was not sufficient for the defendant to prove ignorance of adulteration, but, in the terms of the section (5), to prove also "that he could not with reasonable diligence have obtained that knowledge."

23   38 & 39 Victoria 1875, ch. 63, sec. 6. The phrase "to the prejudice of the purchaser" caused great difficulties and was one of the main causes for the 1879 amendment of the Act. Difficulties arose because it was claimed that inspectors collecting samples for examination could not be considered prejudiced in the way an ordinary purchaser would be. Bartley (*Adulteration of Food*, 49) noted that want of guilty knowledge was no defense under this section; (50) that "prejudice" did not mean merely pecuniary prejudice; and (57) that if a purchaser demanded "mercurial ointment" and did not receive the *British Pharmacopoeia* preparation, the sale might be considered prejudicial, because this preparation was contained in the *British Pharmacopoeia*.

24   38 & 39 Victoria 1875, ch. 63, secs. 7, 27, implied strict accordance with the directions of the prescription or formula.

25   38 & 39 Victoria 1875, ch. 63, secs. 25, 8. In the case of the warranty, Bartley (*Adulteration of Food*, 103) noted that the warranty alone was insufficient, unless proof could be offered that the article was sold in the same state as it was received; and (99) that a warranty was no defense for articles coming from outside the United Kingdom, unless the defendant proved he took reasonable steps to determine the accuracy of the warranty statement. Under sec. 8, verbal notice of admixture was sufficient (63); and a label was required only to state the article to be mixed or compounded, without necessarily listing the ingredients (64).

26   It should be noted that an American law to prevent the importation of adulterated drugs had been enacted in 1848; it remained largely ineffectual, however.

27   42 & 43 Victoria 1879, ch. 30, sec. 2.

28   62 & 63 Victoria 1899, ch. 51, secs. 12, 18.

29   Hassall, in *Minutes of Evidence* (1856), 4430–31, 4440, 4444; *ibid.* (1855), 182; Hassall, *Adulterations Detected*, 24–25; Postgate, in *Minutes of Evidence* (1856), 4238, 4249.

30   Bell, *Sale of Food & Drugs Acts* (1923), 29–30; James Bell, in *Minutes of Evidence*, 138, in *Report from the Select Committee on*

Sale of Food and Drugs Act (1875) Amendment Bill; with the Proceedings of the Committee, Minutes of Evidence, and Appendix (London 1878–79), cited hereafter as *Report (1879)*; *Minutes of Evidence* (1879); and C. G. Moor, "Suggested Standards of Purity for Foods and Drugs," in *Pharm. J.* [ser. 3], 10(1900): 172.

31   31 & 32 Victoria 1868, ch. 121, sec. 15.

32   15 & 16 Victoria 1852, ch. 56, sec. 24.

33   For Canada, see A. Linton Davidson, *The Genesis and Growth of Food and Drug Administration in Canada* (Ottawa, 1949), 9. Lyman F. Kebler, for many years Chief of the Drug Division of the U.S.D.A. Bureau of Chemistry (now the Food and Drug Administration), once commented ("The Good Work of the Western Wholesale Drug Association [1876–1882] for Honest Drugs," in *J. Amer. Pharm. Assoc.*, 15[1926]: 297): "It may be said that this prize essay of Wigner's contains the essentials and is the basis of all general food and drug laws enacted in the United States, so far as concerns adulteration." See also Glenn Sonnedecker and George Urdang, "Legalization of Drug Standards under State Laws in the United States of America," in *Food-Drug-Cosmetic Law Journal*, 8(1953): 741–760. Canadian ties with British legislation—see both the Canadian Acts of 1884 and 1875—were also strong, and the first chief Dominion analyst (1884–1886) was a noted English analyst and pharmacist (president of the Pharmaceutical Society, 1869), Henry Sugden Evans.

     We do not yet find reason to attribute full credit for the New York and New Jersey laws, or for a federal bill of 1881, to Squibb, as suggested by Lawrence G. Blochman, *Doctor Squibb, the Life and Times of a Rugged Idealist* (New York, 1958), 273.

34   Dyer and Mitchell, *Society of Public Analysts*, 3; Anon., "Society of Public Analysts," *Pharm. J.* [ser. 3], 5(1874–75): 444. Anon., "Proceedings of the Society of Public Analysts," *Chem. News*, 31(1875):59.

     Compare this with Wigner's Model Act, Anon., "A Model Act Against Adulteration," *Sanitary Record*, 12(1880–81): 368:

     "An article shall be deemed to be adulterated within the meaning of this Act—

     A. In case of drugs:—

     1. If, when sold under or by a name recognised in the *United States Pharmacopoeia*, it differs from the standard of strength, quality, or purity laid down therein.

     2. If, when sold under or by name not recognised in the *United States Pharmacopoeia*, but which is found in some other pharmacopoeia or other standard work on *Materia Medica*, it differs materially from the standard of strength, quality, or purity laid down in such work.

     3. If its strength or purity fall below the professed standard under which it is sold."

Squibb, "Rough Draft of a Proposed Law . . . ," *New Remedies* (Supplement), 8(no. 3, whole no. 57, March 1879), 3, differed slightly:

"For simple articles of medicine, the standard shall be the United States Pharmacopoeia for all articles embraced by that authority. For articles not so embraced, the national pharmacopoeias of other countries.

"When not embraced in these, some commonly accepted standard authority. For compounded articles of medicine the same standards as above cited for simple articles, for all which they may embrace. For all other compound medicines the standard shall be the formula or recipe attached to the compound by label or otherwise when given, sold, offered, or held in possession; or the physician's prescription or recipe by which it shall have been compounded, or the patent or recipe to which the name or trade mark of the compound applies. In the case of proprietary or private compounds, the constituents of which are legally held secrets, the testimony of the owner of the private formulas shall be accepted as evidence of the character of the compound.

"Provided, that nothing herein contained shall be construed so as to protect or permit the issue of any compound which contains any poisonous or hurtful ingredients not publicly stated and professed by the label attached to the compound when given, sold, offered, or held in possession."

In Squibb's proposed law, these were the standards by which adulteration, or the degrees of adulteration were judged. Aside from this, he gave a definition of adulteration (with examples of each type) consisting of fully 9 separate points: 1) fraudulent admixture; 2) substitution; 3) abstraction; 4) mislabelling; 5) contamination (unusual), natural or accidental; 6) admixture of different qualities of same substance; 7) debasement or dilution; 8) coloring, coating, polishing, or powdering to conceal inferiority or deceptively improve appearance; 9) giving, or selling, or offering for sale, or possessing an adulterated article by a vendor as *prima facie* evidence of offence of adulteration.

The great American crusader for pure food and drugs, Harvey Washington Wiley (1844–1930), "Adulteration of Drugs," in reprint from *American Medicine*, 9(1905): 724–725, defined drug adulteration broadly to include the following: 1) substitution, in whole or in part, of one drug or quality of drug, for the one demanded; 2) fraudulent admixture affecting the quality of the drug; 3) extraction of valuable constituents; and 4) misbranding.

35 Bell, *Minutes of Evidence* (1879), 137, 138.
36 Herbert P. Thomas, *ibid.*, 49.
37 *Ibid.*, 64.
38 Charles Graham, "Precis of Reports on the Working of the 'Sale of Food and Drugs Act, 1875,' presented to the Justices of the Peace for Lincolnshire, during the Year 1878," *Report* (1879), appendix no. 1, 14.
39 *Ibid.*
40 See Anon., "Proceedings of the Society of Public Analysts," *Analyst*, 18(1893): 97–116; and Anon., "Draft of a Sale of Food and Drugs

Act, Prepared by the Council of the Society of Public Analysts,"
Analyst, 19(1894): 156–158. The proposed board of reference was
to be established by the Board of Trade, which was to appoint a
standing committee, to include representatives from the Local Government Board, the Board of Agriculture, the Society of Public
Analysts, the General Medical Council, the Institute of Chemistry,
and the Pharmaceutical Society of Great Britain. (See: Anon.,
"English News," in *Pharm. J.* [ser. 4], 8[1899]: 262a.)

41 Bell, *Sale of Food & Drugs Acts* (1923), 29–30; Bell, *Minutes of
    Evidence* (1879), 138; and Moor, "Suggested Standards of Purity
    for Foods and Drugs," *Pharm. J.* [ser. 3], 10(1900): 172.

42 W. D. Savage, "The Relative Positions of the Apothecaries and the
    Chemists and Druggists," *Pharm. J.* [ser. 3], 6(1875–76): 837.

43 C. R. B. Barrett, *The History of the Society of Apothecaries of
    London* (London, 1905), xxxiv, quoting the Company's charter.

CHAPTER 11
CHANGING ATTITUDES AND SANCTIONS

1   Phillips Bevan, "The Legislation to Prevent Adulteration of Food and
    Drink," *Pharm. J.* [ser. 3], 1(1870–71): 271, abstract of a paper
    presented at the 1870 Newcastle-on-Tyne meeting of the National
    Association for the Promotion of Social Science. Bevan was editor
    of the *Food Journal.*

2   Accum, *A Treatise on Adulterations of Food and Culinary Poisons*
    . . . (London, 1820), 15–16.

3   [John Dingwall Williams?], *Deadly Adulteration and Slow Poisoning
    Unmasked; or, Disease and Death in the Pot* . . . (London, 1839
    [?]), 161–162.

4   C. R. B. Barrett, *The History of the Society of Apothecaries of
    London* (London, 1905), xxxiv–xxxv.

5   Descriptions of various forms of punishment for adulteration, pri-
    marily as they related to foods and beverages, are given by:
    Alexander Wynter Blyth and Meredith Wynter Blyth, *Foods: Their
    Composition and Analysis* . . . *With an Introductory Essay on the
    History of Adulteration* (6th ed.; London, 1909), 1–14 *passim;* Jesse
    P. Battershall, *Food Adulteration and Its Detection* . . . (New
    York, 1887), 1–4 *passim;* Ward Benjamin White, "Adulteration," in
    Encyclopaedia Britannica (New York, 1952), 1: 188; Amaro Henri-
    que de Souza, "Falsificações e Penalidades à Luz da Historia," in
    Revista de Farmacia e Odontologia, 23(1957): 325–332; Henry
    Thomas Riley, *Memorials of London, and London Life, in the
    Thirteenth, Fourteenth, and Fifteenth Centuries, from the Early
    Archives of the City of London, A.D. 1276–1419* (London, 1868),
    passim.

6   Accum complained of the laxity of visitations as early as 1798.
    Accum, "An Attempt to Discover the Genuineness and Purity of
    Drugs and Medical Preparations," *Journal of Natural Philosophy,
    Chemistry, and the Arts,* 2(1798): 118. See also *Report,* ix:
    ". . . inspection by the College of Physicians, within the city of
    London takes place three times a year. The inspection however,

seems to be too cursory to be of any great utility," in *Report from the Select Committee on Adulterations of Food, Etc.; together with the Proceedings of the Committee, Minutes of Evidence, Appendix, and Index* (London, 1856), hereafter cited as *Report* (1856); *Minutes of Evidence* (1856). Lawrence Dopson, "State of London Chemists' Shops in the 18th and Early 19th Centuries," in *Chemist and Druggist*, 163 (1955): 718–721, made use of the collection of MS. reports of the Royal College of Physicians' censors on their visitations of apothecaries' and druggists' shops, from first entries (25 January 1542) to last (29 March 1856). This series of thirty-two books in the library of the Royal College of Physicians deserves further examination, especially since it refers to such noted shops as those of Accum and William Allen & Co. (Allen & Hanburys Ltd.).

7 W. S. Glyn-Jones, "The Chemist and Some of the Laws that Particularly Affect Him," *Pharm. J.* [ser. 4], 10(1900): 70. Robert Waringron, *Minutes of Evidence*, 473, 477, in *First and Second Report from the Select Committee on Adulterations of Food, Etc., with the Minutes of Evidence and Appendix* (London, 1855), hereafter cited as *Report* (1855); *Minutes of Evidence* (1855). Also Simmonds, *ibid.*, 2082; Henry Letheby, *ibid.*, 2825, 2826; *Report* (1856), ix.

8 Jacob Bell and Theophilus Redwood, *Historical Sketch of the Progress of Pharmacy in Great Britain* (London, 1880), 64–65; and Anon., "The Proper Business of the Apothecary," *Pharm. J.*, 9(1849–50): 3.

9 [Jacob Bell], Commentary to Richard Phillips, "Illustrations of the Present State of Pharmacy in England," *Pharm. J.*, 2(1842–43): 315, *n*. About a year earlier, in also commenting upon Christison's suggestions for visitations, Bell ("On the Adulteration of Drugs," *Pharm. J.*, 1[1841–42]: 257) had been less militant, but still used the phrase "invidious and unenviable" as far as pharmacist participation was concerned. At the same time he seems to have left the door open for "a friendly and habitual visitation of Druggists' shops, by medical men." See [Robert?] Christison, "Observations on the Adulteration of Drugs [appendix to Report of the Royal College of Physicians of Edinburgh on the Adulteration of Drugs]," in the *Edinburgh Medical and Surgical Journal*, 49(1838): 314–343.

10 Bell, "On the Adulteration of Drugs," *Pharm. J.*, 1(1841–42): 257.

11 [Jacob Bell?], "The Adulteration of Food and Physic, and the Pollution of Water," *Pharm. J.*, 15(1855–56): 55; [Bell?], "The Adulteration of Food, Drugs, etc.," *ibid.*, 101.

12 [Bell?], "The Adulteration of Drugs," *Pharm. J.*, 12(1852–53): 366. See also [Jacob Bell?], "Adulteration and the *Lancet*," *Pharm. J.*, 15(1855–56): 244; [Jacob Bell?], "Analysis of the Sanitary Commission," *ibid.*, 292–293, in which the author accused the *Lancet's* editor, Thomas Wakley, of selfish motives instead of public interest in the administration of his Analytical Sanitary Commission. Yet a few years earlier, Bell, commenting upon articles on adulteration that had appeared regularly in the *Pharmaceutical Journal*, threatened: "At present we confine ourselves to the statement of the

facts; but if the parties should persist in the system, and fresh
cases should come to our knowledge, we shall without the least
hesitation publish their names." "The Adulteration of Chemicals,"
Pharm. J., 9(1849–50): 346.

13   E. M. Holmes, "The Sale by Public Auction of Spurious and Worthless Drugs," *Pharm. J.* [ser. 3], 13(1882–83): 463, 477; Anon.
[Comment upon letter of A. H. Allen, Sheffield], *Pharm. J.* [ser. 3],
22(1891): 494–495.

14   Hassall in *Minutes of Evidence* (1855), 182, felt the publication of
names and offences to be more effective than punishment by
means of fines and imprisonment, although he felt all these methods necessary. Thomas Wakley in *Minutes of Evidence* (1856),
2209–10, 2215–16, 2251; John Simon (Health Officer, London), in
Minutes of Evidence (1855), 744, had a similar opinion. See also
Arthur Hill Hassall, *Adulterations Detected . . .* (London, 1857),
25; [Jacob Bell?], "The Adulteration of Food, Drugs, etc.—Result of
the Parliamentary Inquiry," in *Pharm. J.*, 16(1856–57): 153–155.

15   Accum, *Treatise on Adulterations* (1820), iv–v; *ibid.*, (4th ed.;
1822), x.

16   Anon., *The Tricks of Trade in the Adulterations of Food and Physic
. . .* (London, 1859), viii, referred to the adulteration bill introduced by the Birmingham M.P., William Scholefield, at the urging
of John Postgate. The clause providing for publication of names
disappeared from the final 1860 Act, and emerged only briefly in
the 1872 amendment, to disappear again in 1875. See also, *Report*
(1856), viii.

17   Hassall, *Adulterations Detected*, 28–29. *Ibid.*, 29, referred to laws in
other countries that included imprisonment.

18   Accum, *Treatise on Adulterations* (1820), 15–16; [Williams?],
Deadly Adulteration (1839[?]), 5: *Tricks of Trade* (1859), iv. See
also Postgate, in *Minutes of Evidence* (1855), 2131–34.

19   Hassall, *Adulterations Detected*, 29.

20   Accum, *Treatise on Adulterations* (1820), 16. See also *Tricks of
Trade* (1859), vii.

21   *Report*, viii, in *Report from the Select Committee on Adulteration of
Food Act* (1872); *together with the Proceedings of the Committee,
Minutes of Evidence, Appendix, and Index* (London, 1874), here-
after cited as *Report* (1874); *Minutes of Evidence* (1874).

22   *Ibid.*, xxiii.

23   56 George III 1816, ch. 58, sec. 3.

24   Graham, *Report*, Appendix no. 1, 14, in *Report from the Select
Committee on Sale of Food and Drugs Act* (1875) *Amendment Bill;
with the Proceedings of the Committee, Minutes of Evidence, and
Appendix* (London, 1878–79), hereafter cited as *Report* (1878–
79); *Minutes of Evidence* (1878–79).

25   [Jacob Bell?], "The Laws of Customs and Excise," *Pharm. J.*,
4(1844–45): 492. See also: Anon., "The Drug Duties," *Pharm. J.*,
1(1841–42): 608–609; Anon., "Duties of Customs, Payable on
Goods Used in Pharmacy, Imported into the United Kingdom from
Foreign Parts," *Pharm. J.*, 2(1842–43): 105–111; Anon., "The Du-

ties of Customs," *Pharm. J.*, 5(1845–46): 52; Anon., "An Act to Alter and Amend Certain Duties of Customs," *ibid.*, 87–94. The Act referred to in the last two articles repealed the duty on many drugs.

26 Thomas Herring and William Ince, in discussion following Bell, "on the Adulteration of Drugs," *Pharm. J.*, 1(1841–42): 262, 263. The sale referred to by Ince was advertised in the *Morning Herald*, to take place at the London Dock-house, upon the notice of the directors of the London Dock Company, 3 November 1841. Both Herring and Ince were council members of the Pharmaceutical Society.

27 According to Michael G. Mulhall, *The Dictionary of Statistics* (London, 1899), 580, the nominal annual wage in 1850 for a shepherd, laborer, and woman, was £25, £20, and £10, respectively; by 1880, this had risen to £36, £30, and £15. (The purchasing value was reported as the same.) From *ibid.*, 579, the weekly wage of tradesmen in 1880 ranged from 24s. for the collier to 35s. for the mason. And (*ibid.*, 470) the nominal prices, 1800–1885, for basic commodities, included 1s. for a dozen eggs or pound of butter, 7s. for 8 pounds of beef, 1.6 for a hen, £1.10 for a pig, and 1.6 for a gallon of beer.

28 31 & 32 Victoria 1868, ch. 121, sec. 26.
29 35 & 36 Victoria 1872, ch. 74, secs. 1, 2, 3.
30 *Report* (1874), iii, vi.
31 *Ibid.*, iii. See also, 38 & 39 Victoria 1875, ch. 63, secs. 3, 6.
32 38 & 39 Victoria 1875, ch. 63, secs. 7, 8, 9, 17, 27.
33 Anon., "Law and Parliamentary [Committee of the Pharmaceutical Society of Great Britain]," *Pharm. J.* [ser. 3], 5(1874–75): 811.
34 62 & 63 Victoria 1899, ch. 51, sec. 17 (2).

CHAPTER 12
THE PROFESSIONS AND THE PROBLEM

1 Albert Mathiez, "French Revolution," in *Encyclopaedia of the Social Sciences* (New York, 1951), 6:474.
2 *Report from the Select Committee on Adulteration of Food Act* (1872); *together with the Proceedings of the Committee, Minutes of Evidence, Appendix, and Index* (London, 1874), viii, hereafter cited as *Report* (1874); *Minutes of Evidence* (1874).
3 We shall limit ourselves here almost entirely to a discussion of the part played in the control of drug adulteration by the Pharmaceutical Society, the professional organization of British pharmacy.

Druggists originally were members of the Grocers' Company, which dealt in crude and unprepared drugs, while chemists prepared medicines of mineral or chemical origin. The Grocers' Company (incorporated in 1428) evolved from a guild of pepperers (dealers in spices and drugs from the East) existing in London as early as 1180. Taking their name from their use of what was later to become the avoirdupois system, the grocers (*grossarii*, associated with weighing by the Gros Beam) were largely wholesale dealers in drugs. The Society of Apothecaries was founded in 1617 as a pharmaceutical body, separate from the Grocer's Company, but eventually it became predominantly medical; the College of Physicians was founded in 1518. With the founding of the Pharmaceutical Society (in 1841) a distinction came to be made between "chemists and druggists" and "pharmaceutical chemists," the latter possessing scientific qualifications beyond those of the former. The use of the title "pharmaceutical chemist" was restricted after 1852 —and the use of both titles after 1868—to qualified practitioners, registered with the Pharmaceutical Society; chemists and druggists did not gain full membership in the Society until 1898.

For a detailed discussion of the development of English pharmacy up to the time of the founding of the Pharmaceutical Society, and for an account of the complex evolution of English medicine, including the Society of Apothecaries, see Leslie G. Matthews, *History of Pharmacy in Britain* (Edinburgh and London, 1962), 29–60, 112–131; *Kremers and Urdang's History of Pharmacy*, rev. by Glenn Sonnedecker (3rd. ed.; Philadelphia, 1963), 92–99; Jacob Bell and Theophilus Redwood, *Historical Sketch of the Progress of Pharmacy in Great Britain* (London, 1880), 1–101. We have depended largely upon these sources for this brief discussion. Also useful are: G. E. Trease, *Pharmacy in History* (London, 1964), 31–176, which outlines the evolution of the British apothecary and pharmacist, and especially useful is a flow-style diagram (32); Frederick A. Filby, *A History of Food Adulteration and Analysis* (London, 1934), 22–32, *et passim,* has interesting material upon the Grocer's Company and the early function of garbling; Cecil Wall, H. Charles Cameron, and E. Ashworth Underwood, *A History of the Worshipful Society of Apothecaries of London,* 1(1617–1815; Publications of the Wellcome Historical Medical Museum, NS, No. 8, London, 1963); C. R. B. Barrett, *The History of the Society of Apothecaries of London* (London, 1905); and D'Arcy Power, *British Medical Societies* (London, 1939), 1–11. Two excellent recent monographic studies of the early development of English pharmacy and medicine are: G. E. Trease, "The Spicers and Apothecaries of the Royal Household in the Reign of Henry III, Edward I and Edward II," in *Nottingham Mediaeval Studies,* 3(1959): 19–52; and O. M. Lloyd, "The Royal College of Physicians of London and Some City Livery Companies," in *J. Hist. Med.,* 11(1956): 412–421.

Unless we intend a special connotation, we shall use the term "pharmacist" rather than "chemist and druggist" or "pharmaceutical chemist," in the discussion that follows.

4 William Allen, "The First Annual Meeting of the Pharmaceutical Society [President's remarks]," *Pharm. J.,* 1(1841–42): 633.

5 Jacob Bell, *Observations Addressed to the Chemists and Druggists of Great Britain on the Pharmaceutical Society* (London, 1841), 5–6, 7, 14.

6 Jacob Bell, "On the Constitution of the Pharmaceutical Society of Great Britain," *Pharm. J.,* 1(1841–42): 5–6.

7   "Adulteration of Drugs:—Dr. Hassall and Dr. Redwood," *Pharm. J.*,
     15(1855–56): 252.
8   [Jacob Bell?], "The Adulteration of Drugs," *Pharm. J.*, 7(1847–48):
     249.
9   Jacob Bell, "On the Adulteration of Drugs," *Pharm. J.*, 1(1841–42):
     253–262, with discussion (262–264); originally read at a meeting
     of the Society, 10 November 1841.
10   *Ibid.*, 253. Bell reported cases of impurities (adulterations) of up to
     80 per cent, with an average of 25 or 30 per cent. See also *ibid.*,
     254, 255, 261.
11   *Ibid.*, 253.
12   *Ibid.*, 254. See also *ibid.*, 258.
13   *Ibid.*, 258, 259, 260–261, 262.
14   *Ibid.*, 262 and 256. Bell held up the Philadelphia College of Phar-
     macy and its publication, the *American Journal of Pharmacy*, as an
     example for emulation.
15   *Ibid.*, 257.
16   Adulteration remained a "trade" problem as well as a professional
     one, but the Society always tried, as much as possible, to remain
     aloof from strictly "trade" considerations in this and other matters.
     As we shall see, other organizations sprang up to deal with the
     problem of adulteration as a "trade" problem. The United Society of
     Chemists and Druggists (1860–1871), the Chemists and Druggists
     Trade Association (1876–1887), and the Chemists' Defence Asso-
     ciation (1899–present), all saw the issue in this restricted sense. In
     1921, the Chemists' Defence Association joined the parent body of
     the Retail Pharmacists' Union (re-named in 1932 the National
     Pharmaceutical Union), devoted to commercial interests of the pro-
     fession, and now to representing pharmacists in all affairs concern-
     ing the National Health Service.
17   Richard Phillips, "Illustrations of the Present State of Pharmacy in
     England," *Pharm. J.*, 2(1842–43): 315–320, 396–399, 528–532,
     651–652; 3(1843): 108–111, 244–247. Phillips had also testified
     upon the extent of drug adulteration before the Select Committee
     on the Laws, Regulations and Usages Regarding the Education and
     Practice of the Various Branches of the Medical Profession. Unfor-
     tunately, the portion of the testimony dealing with pharmacy was
     lost before publication, in a fire that destroyed the House of Com-
     mons in 1834. Phillips (*Pharm. J.*, 2[1842–43]: 315) commented
     upon this testimony: "Among others, I showed on this occasion,
     that certain medicines procured from the most respectable sources,
     were deficient both in purity and strength; notwithstanding, how-
     ever, the varied and unquestionable proofs which were adduced of
     the necessity of some guarantee for the safety of the public, and
     the reputation of the Physician, nothing whatever was then, or has
     since been, effected by the government."
18   Phillips, "Illustrations of the Present State of Pharmacy in England,"
     Pharm. J., 3(1843–44): 247.
19   [Jacob Bell?], "On the Present State of Pharmacy in England," in
     Pharm. J., 2(1842–43): 313–315, serving as an apparent editorial

"breakwater" by way of introduction to Phillips' series. See also editorial footnote to Phillips, "Illustrations of the Present State of Pharmacy in England," *ibid.*, 317; and Phillips' reply, *ibid.*, 396.

20   Bell, "On the Adulteration of Drugs," *Pharm. J.*, 1(1841–42): 253; Thomas Herring, Discussion of paper presented by Bell, "On the Adulteration of Drugs," *ibid.*, 263; Theophilus Redwood, "On Drug-Grinding," *Pharm. J.*, 8(1848–49)224; [Jacob Bell?], "The Adulteration of Food and Physic, and the Pollution of Water," *Pharm. J.*, 15(1855–56): 54, 55; [Jacob Bell?] "The Adulteration of Food, Drugs, etc.," *ibid.*, 97, 100; "Adulteration of Drugs:—Dr. Hassall and Dr. Redwood," *ibid.*, 252; Jacob Bell, in Discussion following Arthur Hill Hassall, "On the Adulteration of Annatto," *ibid.*, 309; [Jacob Bell?] "The Adulteration of Food and Drugs," *ibid.*, 445. Anon., "The Council of the Pharmaceutical Society of Great Britain, on the Education of Dispensers of Medicine and the Salt of Poisons," *Pharm. J.*, 16(1856–57): 264.

21   Bell, "On the Adulteration of Drugs," *Pharm. J.*, 1(1841–42): 253, 259, 261; Herring, Discussion of Bell, "On the Adulteration of Drugs," *ibid.*, 262; Jacob Bell, "On the Adulteration of Senna," *Pharm. J.*, 2(1842–43): 63; Anon. ["A Retail Druggist"], Letter to the Editor in "To Correspondents," *ibid.*, 731; Anon., "Remarks on the Illustrations," *Pharm. J.*, 3(1843–44): 248; [Jacob Bell?], "The Vigilance of the Government in Reference to Sanitary Regulations," *Pharm. J.*, 7(1847–48): 302; Redwood, "On Drug-Grinding," *Pharm. J.*, 8(1848–49): 224, 225; [Jacob Bell?], "Spurious Chemicals," *ibid.*, 577; [Bell?], "The Adulteration of Food and Physic, and the Pollution of Water," *Pharm. J.*, 15(1855–56): 53, 55; [Bell?], "The Adulteration of Food, Drugs, etc.," *ibid.*, 97; John Attfield, "Note on the Adulteration of Precipitated Sulphur," *Pharm. J.* [ser. 2], 10(1868–69): 472; Henry Pocklington, "The Microscope in Pharmacy," *Pharm. J.* [ser. 3], 2(1871–72): 611; Anon., "Trade Standards of Purity, Etc.," *Pharm. J.* [ser. 4], 13(1901): 75.

22   A beginning in the form of grants-in-aid of school building had been made in 1833 for distribution to the voluntary systems then operating for the education of the poor. Increasing grants in 1839 and 1858 helped, but real reform of the public education system waited until 1870, and free education only became a reality in 1898. (Raymond William Postgate and George Douglas Howard, *The British People, 1746–1946* [2nd American ed.; New York, 1947], 305–308.)

Thomas Edward Wallis, *History of the School of Pharmacy, University of London* (London, 1964), gives a somewhat limited overview of the development of the Society's school.

23   Anon., "Remarks on the Illustrations," *Pharm. J.*, 3(1843–44): 248.

24   Bell, "On the Adulteration of Senna," *Pharm. J.*, 2(1842–43): 63; [Jacob Bell?], "On Competition in the Drug Trade," *ibid.*, 562.

25   Anon. ("A Scotch Country Practitioner"), "Adulteration of Drugs," *Pharm. J.*, 6(1846–47): 230–231.

26   Redwood, "On Drug-Grinding," *Pharm. J.*, 8(1848–49): 224.

27   [Bell?], "The Vigilance of the Government in Reference to Sanitary
     Regulations," *Pharm. J.*, 7(1847–48): 302.
28   [Jacob Bell?], "Coffee and Its Adulterations," *Pharm. J.*, 10(1850–
     51): 394.
29   [Bell?], "The Adulteration of Food and Physic, and the Pollution of
     Water," *Pharm. J.*, 15(1855–56): 55; [Bell?], "The Adulteration of
     Food, Drugs, etc.," *ibid.*, 97–101; Redwood, "Alleged Adulteration
     of Annatto," *ibid.*, 200–201; "Adulteration of Drugs: —Dr. Hassall
     and Dr. Redwood," *ibid.*, 248–251; Discussion following Hassall,
     "On the Adulteration of Annatto," *ibid.*, 303–310. In the first
     Journal comment, [Jacob Bell?], "The Adulteration of Drugs,"
     Pharm. J., 12(1852–53): 364–366, upon the *Lancet* Commission's
     methods, those of Phillips for the *Journal* (1842–1844) were held
     up as emulatory.
30   "Report of the Council . . . the Adulteration of Drugs," *Pharm. J.*,
     15(1855–56): 539.
31   *Report* (1856), ix, xii, xxv (draft report), and *Minutes of Evidence*,
     passim, in *Report from the Select Committee on Adulterations of
     Food, Etc; together with the Proceedings of the Committee, Minutes
     of Evidence, Appendix, and Index* (London, 1856), hereafter cited
     as *Report* (1856); *Minutes of Evidence* (1856).
32   *Report* (1856), xxiii (draft report).
33   Attfield, "Note on the Adulteration of Precipitated Sulphur," *Pharm.
     J.* [ser. 2], 10(1868–69): 472; Pocklington, "The Microscope in
     Pharmacy," *Pharm. J.* [ser. 3], 2(1871–72): 611; Anon., "Trade
     Standards of Purity, Etc.," *Pharm. J.* [ser. 4], 13(1901): 75.
34   Bell, "On the Adulteration of Drugs," *Pharm. J.*, 1(1841–42): *pas-
     sim*, 253–262; Phillips, "Illustrations of the Present State of Phar-
     macy in England," *Pharm. J.*, 2(1842–43): 316, 532; [Bell?] "The
     Vigilance of the Government in Reference to Sanitary Regulations,"
     Pharm. J., 7(1847–48): 302; Redwood, "On Drug-Grinding,"
     Pharm. J., 8(1848–49): 224.
35   Bell, "On the Adulteration of Drugs," *Pharm. J.*, 1(1841–42): 253.
36   *Ibid.*, 262.
37   Anon., "Safeguards against Adulteration," *Pharm. J.* [ser. 4], 1
     (1895): 207; C. G. Moor, "Suggested Standards of Purity for Foods
     and Drugs," *Pharm. J.* [ser. 4], 10(1900): 173.
38   Jonathan Pereira, "On the Adulteration of Scammony," *Pharm. J.*,
     4(1844–45): 268; [Bell?], "The Adulteration of Drugs," *Pharm. J.*,
     7(1847–48): 249; [Jacob Bell?], "Impure or Adulterated Drugs,
     etc.," *Pharm. J.*, 13(1853–54): 100.
39   Bell, "On the Adulteration of Drugs," *Pharm. J.*, 1(1841–42): 253,
     258, 260; [Bell?], "Impure or Adulterated Drugs, etc.," *Pharm. J.*,
     13(1853–54): 100–101; Moor, Suggested Standards of Purity for
     Foods and Drugs," *Pharm. J.* [ser. 4], 10(1900): 173.
40   [Jacob Bell?], "Competition in the Drug Trade," *Pharm. J.*, 3(1843–
     44): 101; [Bell?], "On Competition in the Drug Trade," *Pharm. J.*,
     2(1842–43): 557–562; Pereira, "On the Adulteration of Scam-
     mony," *Pharm. J.*, 4(1844–45): 268. In 1864–65 the number

of chemists and druggists (including apprentices and assistants) known to be practicing in England was 16,026, compared to 17,981 physicians (including 3,566 medical assistants and students). See: Anon., "The Census Returns Relating to Pharmacy," *Pharm. J.* [ser. 2], 5(1864–65): 383–384.

41   [Jacob Bell?], "Medical Reform," *Pharm. J.*, 2(1842–43): 680. See also: [Bell?], "Competition in the Drug Trade," *Pharm. J.*, 3(1843–44): 99–101; [Jacob Bell?], "The Sale of Medicines by Unqualified Persons," *Pharm. J.*, 6(1846–47): 3; J. B. Barnes, "Adulteration of White Precipitate," *Pharm. J.*, 9(1849–50): 240; Anon., "The Adulteration of Food," *Pharm. J.*, 18(1858–59): 498.

42   The Pharmacy Act of 1868 restricted practice to properly qualified and registered persons. The Medical Act of 1858 made the first significant reforms among the ranks of medical practitioners.

43   Bell, "On the Adulteration of Drugs," *Pharm. J.*, 1(1841–42): 257; [Bell?], "The Adulteration of Drugs," *Pharm. J.*, 12(1852–53): 366; [Robert?] Hampson, in Discussion following E. M. Holmes, "The Sale by Public Auction of Spurious and Worthless Drugs," *Pharm. J.* [ser. 3], 13(1882–83): 478; Michael Carteighe, in Discussion following Holmes "Sale . . . ," *ibid.*, 476. Both Holmes and Carteighe were leading members of the Pharmaceutical Society and the British Pharmaceutical Conference. Carteighe was particularly interested in raising educational standards of pharmacy.

44   [Bell?], "The Sale of Medicines by Unqualified Persons," *Pharm. J.*, 6(1846–47): 4. See also: Bell, "On the Constitution of the Pharmaceutical Society of Great Britain," *Pharm. J.*, 1(1841–42): 7; [Jacob Bell?], "General Observations by the Editor," *ibid.*, 38, 42; [Jacob Bell?], "The Charter," *Pharm. J.*, 2(1842–43): 615–616; [Jacob Bell?], "Medical Reform," *ibid.*, 679–680; [Bell?], "Competition in the Drug Trade," *Pharm. J.*, 3(1843–44): 101; [Jacob Bell?], "Pharmaceutical Legislation," *Pharm. J.*, 5(1845–46): 483; Anon., "Free Trade in Medicines," *Pharm. J.*, 6(1846–47): 95; [Bell?], "The Vigilance of the Government in Reference to the Sanitary Regulations," *Pharm. J.*, 7(1847–48): 301; John Attfield, "The Future Supply of Drugs to the Public: The Relations of the State to Pharmacy," *Pharm. J.* [ser. 3], 14(1883–84): 229.

45   Moor, "Suggested Standards of Purity for Foods and Drugs," *Pharm. J.* [ser. 4], 10(1900):173. See also: Bell, "On the Adulteration of Drugs," *Pharm. J.* 1(1841–42): 258.

46   Bell, "On the Adulteration of Senna," *Pharm. J.*, 2(1842–43): 64.

47   Bell, "On the Adulteration of Drugs," *Pharm. J.*, 1(1841–42): 253, 262; Thomas Herring, in comment following Bell, *ibid.*, 262; William Allen, "The First Annual Meeting of the Pharmaceutical Society [President's Remarks]," *ibid.*, 633; Robert Howard, "On Certain Precautions Necessary in Using Chemical Tests," *ibid.*, 641–642; George Fownes, comment on Howard, *ibid.*, 646; [Bell?], "The Adulteration of Drugs," *Pharm. J.*, 7(1847–48): 249; [Bell?], "Spurious Chemicals," *Pharm. J.*, 8(1848–49): 577; [Jacob Bell?], "The Adulteration of Chemicals," *Pharm. J.*, 9(1849–50): 346; [Bell?], "The Adulteration of Coffee," *Pharm. J.*, 12(1852–53):

101; [Jacob Bell?], "Reform in the Quality of Drugs and Chemicals," *Pharm. J.*, 13(1853–54): 98–99; [Bell?], "The Adulteration of Food and Physic, and the Pollution of Water," *Pharm. J.*, 15 (1855–56): 53; "Adulteration of Drugs:—Dr. Hassall and Dr. Redwood," *ibid.*, 252; Anon., "The British Pharmaceutical Conference," *Pharm. J.* [ser. 2], 5(1863–64): 190; J. T. Miller, correspondent, "Adulteration of Powdered Gum Arabic," *ibid.*, 233; Attfield, "Adultered Drugs," *Pharm. J.* [ser. 3], 4(1873–74): 452–454; Holmes, "The Sale by Public Auction of Spurious and Worthless Drugs," *Pharm. J.* [ser. 3], 13(1882–83): 462.

48 Charles Umney, Discussion following W. S. Glyn-Jones paper at "Evening Meeting in London [of the Pharmaceutical Society]," *Pharm. J.* [ser. 4], 20(1905): 237. But see: "Report of the Committee on the Sale by Auction of Spurious and Worthless Drugs," *Pharm. J.* [ser. 3], 13(1882–83): 752.

49 [Jacob Bell?], "A Passing Sketch of the State of Pharmacy in France and in Great Britain:—The Licence in Pharmacy," *Pharm. J.*, 16(1856–57): 203; [Bell?], "The Adulteration of Food and Physic, and the Pollution of Water," *Pharm. J.*, 15(1855–56): 55; [Bell?], "The Adulteration of Food," *ibid.*, 101; Anon., "Law and Parliamentary Committee of the Pharmaceutical Society of Great Britain," *Pharm. J.* [ser. 3], 5(1874–75): 811. Compare with: [Jacob Bell?], "The Sale of Bad or Adulterated Medicines," *Pharm. J.*, 8(1848–49): 99; [Jacob Bell?], "The Substitution of One Medicine for Another," *Pharm. J.*, 9(1849–50): 101–102; [Jacob Bell?], "The Adulteration of Food, Drugs, etc.—Result of the Parliamentary Inquiry," *Pharm. J.*, 16(1856–57): 154–155.

50 [Bell?], "The Adulteration of Drugs," *Pharm. J.*, 7(1847–48): 249; [Bell?], "The Adulteration of Food and Physic, and the Pollution of Water," *Pharm. J.*, 15(1855–56): 55; Anon., "Mr. Muntz's Adulteration Bill," *Pharm. J.* [ser. 3], 1(1870–71): 791; and W. S. Glyn-Jones, "The Chemist and Some of the Laws that Particularly Affect Him," *Pharm. J.* [ser. 4], 10(1900): 71–72.

51 Hampson, discussion of "Spurious and Worthless Drugs," *Pharm. J.* [ser. 3], 13(1882–83): 373.

52 [John?] Williams, discussion of "Spurious and Worthless Drugs," *ibid.*

53 [Jacob Bell?], "The Drug Duties," *Pharm. J.* 1(1841–42): 608–609; Herring, in discussion following Jacob Bell, "On the Adulteration of Drugs," *ibid.*, 262; [Jacob Bell?], "The Duties of Customs," *Pharm. J.*, 5(1845–46): 52, commenting upon the act to repeal the duty on many drugs.

54 J. B. Brinkenhead, correspondence, *Pharm. J.* [ser. 2], 10(1868–69): 725. See also [Bell?], "The Adulteration of Food or Drink," *Pharm. J.*, 17(1857–58): 109.

55 Anon., "The Local Government Board on the Working of the Sale of Food and Drugs Act," *Pharm. J.* [ser. 3], 10(1879–80): 226; Anon., "The Local Government Board on the Adulteration of Drugs," *Pharm. J.* [ser. 3], 11(1880–81): 395–396; Anon., "The Local Government Board on the Sale of Food and Drugs Act," *Pharm. J.* [ser.

3], 12(1881–82): 187–188; 14(1883–84): 325–326; 15(1884–85): 471–472.

56 Anon., "The Adulteration of Food and Drugs Bill," *Pharm. J.* [ser. 2], 10(1868–69): 667; Anon., "The Adulteration of Food and Drugs Bill," *Pharm. J.* [ser. 2], 11(1869–70): 4; Anon., "The New Adulteration Act," *Pharm. J.* [ser. 3], 3(1872–73): 247; two other anonymous discussions entitled "The New Adulteration Act," *ibid.*, 263, 293; Anon., "Adulteration of Food and Drugs Act," *ibid.*, 266; Anon., "The Adulteration Act," *ibid.*, 427–428; Anon., "Public Analysts," *ibid.*, 509–510; Anon., "Public Analysts," *Pharm. J.* [ser. 3], 4(1873–74): 579–580; another anonymous discussion entitled "Public Analysts," *ibid.*, 618.

57 Some other preparations involved were "sweet spirit of nitre," sold in place of spirit of nitrous ether of the *British Pharmacopoeia*, and "milk of sulphur," in place of precipitated sulfur of the *Pharmacopoeia*. We shall reserve discussion of this question until our overview of problems involving official standards under the adulteration laws.

58 Glyn-Jones, "Evening Meeting in London," *Pharm. J.* [ser. 4], 20 (1905): 237.

59 Anon., "The Chemists' Defence Fund," *Pharm. J.* [ser. 4], 9(1899): 506b. The Sale of Food and Drugs Act was only one of ten or more trade Acts that the Defence Association included in its program. See also Anon., "Chemists' Defence Association [Glyn-Jones talk before North London Chemists]," *Pharm. J.* [ser. 4], 10(1900): 433. Aside from the general reasons for the formation of the Defence Association given in Glyn-Jones' talk, *Pharm. J.* [ser. 4], 11(1900): 532, pointed to the direct benefits accruing to the subscribing members. He felt this necessary in view of the feeling of many members of the Proprietary Articles Trade Association that the benefits of this organization affected the whole trade rather than merely those pharmacists who were members. Accordingly, the Proprietary Association started the Defence Association with a reserve of one thousand pounds. The close relationship between these two organizations is clear from another anonymous article entitled "Chemists' Defence Association," *Pharm. J.* [ser. 4], 10 (1900): 330; and Anon., "Proprietary Articles Trade Association Limited: Annual Meeting," *Pharm. J.* [ser. 4], 15(1902): 83.

60 Anon., "P.A.T.A. and Its Defence Fund [paraphrase of address by W. S. Glyn-Jones]," *Pharm. J.* [ser. 4], 9(1899): 517; Anon., "Manchester Pharmaceutical Association [The P.A.T.A. and Its Defence Fund]," *Pharm. J.* [ser. 4], 10(1900): 37; Anon., "Chemists' Defence Association," *ibid.*, 330; another anonymous article entitled "Chemists' Defence Association," *ibid.*, 433. Where cases were not to the interest of the Association, they considered their obligations fulfilled upon the payment of ten pounds. In those instances in which legal cases were of general interest to the trade, the Association proceeded beyond its stated maximum obligations.

61 Anon., "Chemists' Defence Association," *Pharm. J.* [ser. 4], 10 (1900): 330.

62   Anon., "P.A.T.A. and Its Defence Fund [paraphrase of W. S. Glyn-Jones]," *Pharm. J.* [ser. 4], 9(1899): 517. He referred here particularly to the defunct Chemists and Druggists' Trade Association, in precarious existence between 1876 and 1887. Upon its demise, the secretary of the Association expressed the intent of forming a Chemists' Defence Agency, but we are unaware that this ever came into being. (See: Anon., "Winding up of the Trade Association," *Pharm. J.* [ser. 3], 18[1887–88]: 6.) An equally unstable earlier organization, the United Society of Chemists and Druggists, organized under the patronage of A. C. Wootton, editor of the *Chemist and Druggist,* existed between 1860 and 1871. Its primary function had been to protect the interests of chemists and druggists, and it had entered into serious conflict with the Pharmaceutical Society during the preparation and passage of the legislation that emerged as the Pharmacy Act of 1868.

      The history of these special trade organizations of English pharmacy, as yet unwritten, forms an important chapter of the development of British pharmacy, and the need for serious studies of these groups is clear.

63   Anon., "Annotations," in *Pharm. J.* [ser. 4], 14(1902): 185, referred to an expression of interest from the grocery trade.

      The Chemists' Defence Association is now part of the National Pharmaceutical Union, having amalgamated with NPU's predecessor, the Retail Pharmacists Union, during the early 1920's. *NPU* [*National Pharmaceutical Union*], *Silver Jubilee, 1921–1946* (London, 1946), 7, touched upon this relationship. We are grateful to Miss Agnes Lothian, Librarian, The Pharmaceutical Society of Great Britain, for drawing this reference to our attention.

64   Anon., "North-East Lancashire Chemists' Association: The Chemists' Defence Association, Limited [W. S. Glyn-Jones talk]," in *Pharm. J.* [ser. 4], 19(1900): 63, admitted that the defense of some prosecutions would not be within the interest of the Society, while at the same time criticizing the Society for its apparent inaction.

65   The British Medical Association evolved in 1856 out of the Provincial Medical and Surgical Association established in 1832. The official publications of this organization include: the *Provincial Medical and Surgical Journal* (1840–1852); the *Association Medical Journal* (1853–1856); and the *British Medical Journal* (1857–present). The Association also published separate *Transactions* (1833–1853), later merged into the *Journal.*

      Ernest Muirhead Little, *History of the British Medical Association, 1832–1932* (London, 1932) and *Fifty Years of Medicine, A Symposium from the "British Medical Journal"* (London, 1950), included discussions of public health legislation and the law, in connection with the history of the association; but made no reference to any concern of the association with adulteration.

66   Anon., "Adulterations of Foods and Medicines," *Assoc. Med. J.* (1853): 116.

67   Anon., "The Week," *Assoc. Med. J.* [n.s.], 4(1856): 1001, commenting upon French laws; *ibid.,* 173; Anon., "The Adulteration of

Food," *ibid.*, 725–726; and Anon., "Adulteration of Food, etc.,"
ibid., 374. With the exception of the first reference, these articles
consisted of comments upon the current deliberations of the Parliamentary Select Committee.

68   Anon., "The Adulteration of Food," *ibid.*, 725–726; Anon., "Adulteration of Food, etc.," *ibid.*, 374.

69   Anon., "Bibliographic Notices," *Assoc. Med. J.* (1855): 157, in review of Hassall, *Food and Its Adulterations* (1855). The reviewer
took the opportunity to criticize the *Lancet's* methods in connection
with the "Analytical Sanitary Commission"; and questioned both
the wisdom of Hassall dragging up a spent subject (this work was
a reprint of the *Lancet* reports, 1851–1854), and the value of so
voluminous a work.

70   Anon., "The Week," *Br. Med. J.* (1860): 172. See also Anon., "Adulteration of Food Bill," *ibid.*, 323–324.

71   Anon., "Bibliographic Notices [review of Hassall, *Food and Its Adulterations*]," *Assoc. Med. J.* (1855): 158; Anon., "The Week," *Br.
Med. J.*, 2(1861): 536.

72   Anon., "Reviews and Notices," *Br. Med. J.*, 1(1861): 226.

73   Anon., "The Week," *Br. Med. J.*, 2(1861): 667.

74   Anon., report of meeting (July 1874) of "General Medical Council of
Education and Registration," in *Br. Med. J.*, 1(1874): 109. *Ibid.*,
35, 110.

75   Anon., "Local Government and Sanitary Department: Adulteration
Act," in *Br. Med. J.*, 2(1872): 511. Letheby, medical officer of
health and public analyst of London, and lecturer on medical
jurisprudence at London Hospital, never joined the Society of
Public Analysts, in spite of his pioneer work on the analysis of
adulterated food. (See Bernard Dyer and C. Ainsworth Mitchell,
The Society of Public Analysts . . . [Cambridge, 1932], 13.)

CHAPTER 13
INDIVIDUALS AND THE CHALLENGE

1   Arthur Hill Hassall, *The Narrative of a Busy Life: An Autobiography*
(London, 1893), 159.

2   Fredrick [Friedrich Christian] Accum, *A Treatise on Adulterations of
Food, and Culinary Poisons, Exhibiting the Fraudulent Sophistications of Bread, Beer, Wine, Spirituous Liquors, Tea, Coffee, Cream,
Confectionary, Vinegar, Mustard, Pepper, Cheese, Olive Oil, Pickles, and Other Articles Employed in Domestic Economy; and Methods of Detecting Them* (London, 1820), vi. In all his publications,
Accum signed himself with the given name Fredrick, thus apparently preferring to anglicize Friedrich, although some writers discussing him have ignored or overlooked this detail.

3   The outside covers (front and back) of the first edition, in addition
to the death's head and "death in the pot," are decorated with a
spider's web, including a large spider devouring its helpless victim;
and the whole weird panel is framed by a dozen entwined serpents
with forked tongues. Like the covers of this edition, the decorative

design of the titlepage was overladen with sinister symbolism that
changed to the macabre in subsequent editions (see Fig. 12).

4 [John Dingwall Williams?], *Deadly Adulteration and Slow Poisoning
   Unmarked; or, Disease and Death in the Pot* . . . (London, 1830
   [?]), relied heavily upon Accum's *Treatise,* as a close examination
   readily shows. This reliance is both acknowledged and otherwise;
   and Accum was constantly held up for favorable comment by
   Williams. The two most famous early works in the "Death" literature tradition were N. B. Noel's *Mors in Vitro* (Frankfurt, 1709)
   and Jo. Henr. Schulze's *Mors in Olla* (Nürnberg, 1722), which
   were discussed in Chapter 1. Accum borrowed from various sources
   (many unacknowledged), but at least a portion of the title to his
   treatise and the "death in the pot" portion of his preface appear to
   have been taken from Joseph Robertson, *An Essay on Culinary
   Poisons* . . . (London, 1781), 46 pp. Robertson, having commented upon the possible deleterious effects of certain poisons in
   foods, concluded (7): "So that, on many occasions, we may exclaim with the sons of the prophets, "There is death in the pot!' "
   Other similarities between the two works occurred in only a few
   passages. (Compare Robertson, *passim,* esp. 13–14 and 17–20, with
   Accum [1st ed.], 342–344, and 353–358.) Robertson (1726–1802)
   was an English clergyman, writer, and literary critic. His father-in-
   law was the London chemist Timothy Raikes, and Frederick A.
   Filby, *A History of Food Adulteration and Analysis* (London,
   1934), 262, suggested: "It is, then, at least possible that he derived
   some of his information from his father-in-law, but how much, or
   how little, is difficult to estimate." Filby was perhaps a little
   hypercritical of the "second-hand" nature of Robertson's material,
   in view of the fact that Robertson himself plainly stated (45) that
   the information he brought to his reader was not new and had been
   set forth by others. He hoped mainly to provide a useful compendium. Filby perhaps also overstressed (262) the connection between Accum and Robertson more than is warranted by the evidence.

5 The best and most detailed studies of Accum are those of the
   American chemist Charles Albert Browne (d. 1947), and particularly his, "The Life and Chemical Services of Fredrick Accum," in
   J. Chem. Ed., 2(1925): 829–851, 1008–34, 1140–49; also issued as
   a reprint, (n.p., 1925). We cite the reprint (which has separate
   pagination) in this discussion as: Browne, "Accum." See also
   Browne, "Prices as Considered by Accum," in *Chem. & Industry,*
   9(1931): 444–45; and Browne, "Recently Acquired Information
   Concerning Fredrick Accum 1769–1838," in *Chymia,* 1(1948):
   1–9. In spite of Browne's reputation, these accounts suffer from a
   lack of documentation; but Browne had access to unusual documents, and provided valuable illustrations. He was chief of the
   Bureau of Chemistry, U.S. Department of Agriculture (1923–
   1927).

6 Standard biographies of Accum also appear in *D.N.B.,* 1(1937–38):

57 (by George Farber Rodwell); and in *Allgemeine Deutsche Biographie,* 1(1875): 27 (by Oppenheim). See also K. D. C. Vernon, "The Library of the Royal Institution, 1799–1954," in *Nature,* 174 (1954): 244 for details concerning the charges brought against Accum by the Institution; and Anon., "Friedrich Christian Accum (1769–1838)," in *Pharm. J.,* 106(1921): 15. Anon., "Frederick Accum, Operative Chemist; A Pioneer in the Campaign against Adulteration of Food and Drugs," in *Chem. & Drugg.,* 126(1937): 767–768, adds nothing new, nor do T. D. Whittet, "Some Contributions to Pure Food and Drugs," in *Chem. & Drugg.,* 174(1960): 413–414, or "Friedrich Christian Accum (1769–1838): Ein Vorkampfer gegen Verfälschungen von Lebens—und Arzneimitteln," in *Pharmazeutiche Zeitung,* 106(1961): 581–582.

An interesting contemporary evaluation of Accum is: Anon., "Memoir of Fredrick Accum, Esq.," in *European Magazine and London Review,* 77(1820): 483–486, including a full-page portrait. Henry A. Schuette, "Death in the Pot," in *Wisconsin Academy of Sciences, Arts and Letters, Trans.,* 35(1943): 283–303, makes an interesting study of Accum's *Treatise* (and others of the "Death" school), in terms of contemporary reviews of the *Treatise.*

Browne, "Accum," 49–58; and Browne, "Recently Acquired Information . . . ," *Chymia,* 1(1948): 6–9.

7   Browne, "Accum," 2–5, 40, 42, 54, 56; Browne, "Recently Acquired Information . . . ," *Chymia,* 1(1948): 2; and Anon., "Memoir of Accum," in *European Magazine and London Review,* 77(1820): 484.

8   Browne, "Accum," 2–5; and Browne, "Recently Acquired Information . . . ," *Chymia,* 1(1948): 1–2.

9   Browne, "Accum," 5; Browne, "Recently Acquired Information . . . ," *Chymia,* 1(1948): 2; and Anon., "Memoir of Accum," *European Magazine and London Review,* 77(1820): 484.

10   Browne, "Accum," 6–7; beet sugar was discovered in 1747 by the German pharmacist Andreas Sigismund Marggraf (1709–1782).

11   Fredrick Accum, "An Attempt to Discover the Genuineness and Purity of Drugs and Medicinal Preparations," *Journal of Natural Philosophy, Chemistry, and the Arts,* 2(1798): 118–22; and 4 (1800): 33–36, 159–163.

12   Quoted in *ibid.,* 7–8, 20 (illustration) (italics added).

13   *Ibid.,* 8; and Browne, "Recently Acquired Information . . . ," *Chymia,* 1(1948): 3.

14   Browne, "Accum," 55, 9 (illustration); and Anon., "Memoir of Accum," *European Magazine and London Review,* 77(1820): 484.

15   Browne, "Accum," 10, 16, 20, 57; and Browne, "Recently Acquired Information . . . ," *Chymia,* 1(1948): 4.

16   Browne, "Recently Acquired Information . . . ," *Chymia,* 1(1948): 3.

17   Browne, "Accum," 8; and Anon., "Memoir of Accum," *European Magazine and London Review,* 77(1820): 484.

18   Browne, "Accum," 8–9, 9 (illustration). The popular and fashionable element of the lectures at the Royal Institution is mentioned by

H. D. Traill and J. S. Mann, *Social England,* 6 vols. (New York, 1904), 5:622, and 6:99; John Theodore Merz, *A History of European Thought in the Nineteenth Century,* 4 vols. (Edinburgh, 1896–1914), 1:264; and Élie Halévy, *A History of the English People in the Nineteenth Century,* 5 vols. (New York, 1924–1951), 1:493, 494, 497.

19 Browne, "Accum," 10–17, 20; and Browne, "Recently Acquired Information . . . ," *Chymia,* 1(1948): 9. Silliman was a chemist of note; Peck, a botanist; and Dana, a geologist.

20 Browne, "Accum," 22–24, 31–32. See also Anon., "Memoir of Accum," *European Magazine and London Review,* 77(1820): 484, 485.

21 Browne, "Accum," 24–31; Browne, "Recently Acquired Information . . . ," *Chymia,* 1(1948): 3–4, 9; *D.N.B.,* 1:57; and *A.D.B.,* 1:27.

22 Browne, "Accum," 28. Particularly important was his *Practical Treatise on Gas-Light* (1815), said to be the first book ever published on the subject of gas illumination, and translated into French, German, and Italian.

23 Browne, "Accum," 20, 33, 36–43; *D.N.B.,* 1:57; *A.D.B.,* 1:27; and Anon., "Memoir of Accum," *European Magazine and London Review,* 77(1820): 485–486. Among the more important and popular of his books were: *A Practical Essay on the Analysis of Minerals* (1804), then the outstanding work in English on the subject and later called *A Manual of Analytical Mineralogy* (1808); *A Manual of a Course of Lectures on Experimental Chemistry and Mineralogy* (1810); *Elements of Crystallography . . .* (1813), the first book in English on the subject; *Practical Essay on Chemical Reagents . . .* (1816), later enlarged as *Practical Treatise on the Use and Application of Chemical Tests with Concise Directions for Analyzing Metallic Ores, Metals, Soils, Manures and Mineral Waters* (1818); *Chemical Amusements, a Series of Curious and Instructive Experiments in Chemistry Which Are Easily Performed and Unattended by Danger* (1817), one of his most successful books, passing through numerous English, American, French, and Italian editions —the first English edition selling out within two months, the second within a week; *Dictionary of Apparatus and Instruments Employed in Operative and Experimental Chemistry* (1821); *Treatise on the Art of Brewing* (1820); *Treatise on the Art of Making Wines from Native Fruits* (1820); *Treatise on the Art of Making Good and Wholesome Bread* (1821); *Culinary Chemistry, Exhibiting the Scientific Principles of Cookery . . .* (1821); Anon. ("A Practical Chemist"), *An Explanatory Dictionary of the Apparatus and Instruments Employed in the Various Operations of Philosophical and Experimental Chemistry, with Seventeen Quarto Copper-Plates* (London, 1824), a reprint of his earlier *Dictionary* (1821).

24 Browne, "Accum," 5, 20–23. This included observations upon the separation of agrillaceous earth from magnesia (later the basis for the separation of aluminum and magnesium); the occurrence of benzoic acid in old vanilla pods; and the isolation and purification

of iodine (discovered by Curtois, and announced to the French
Institute in 1813)—Accum being one of the first (1814) to study
the problem in England.

25   *Ibid.*, 45. See also, *ibid.*, 45–47, 49; and Schuette, "Death in the Pot,"
in *Wisc. Acad. Sciences, Arts and Letters, Trans.*, 35(1943): 283–
303, amply illustrates this.

26   Browne, "Accum," 49. The third English edition was published in
1821; the second German edition, in 1841.

27   Accum, *Treatise on Adulterations* (1st ed.; 1820), 18; and *ibid.*,
17–26.

28   *Ibid.*, 19, 20, 23–24.

29   Browne, "Accum," 50; and Browne, "Recently Acquired Information . . . ," *Chymia*, 1(1948): 6–7.

30   Accum, *Treatise on Adulterations* (2nd ed.; 1820), x–xi.

31   Browne, "Accum," 52. See also *ibid.*, 49–54; Browne, "Recently
Acquired Information . . . ," *Chymia*, 1(1948): 6–9; *D.N.B.*, 1:
57; and *A.D.B.*, 1:27.

We have been unable to determine the source of information
leading the *D.N.B.*, 1:57, and the *A.D.B.*, 1:27, to describe the
original charge against Accum as "embezzlement." Vernon, "Library of the Royal Institution," *Nature*, 174(1954): 244, discussed
the report of these happenings found in the Minutes of the Royal
Institution for 1820, and stated that the second bill of indictment
filed against Accum was "for feloniously stealing and taking away
200 pieces of paper of the value of four pence, the property of the
members of the Royal Institution." Vernon pointed to the Institution's copy of volume five of *Nicholson's Journal*, missing an article
by Parmentier on the composition and use of chocolate, as a
present-day "evidence of these strange happenings." (The Parmentier article was the one noticed missing by the Institution's librarian, Sturt, after a prolonged watch upon Accum during one of his
visits.) See also: [Letter to the Editor], "Mr. Frederick Accum," in
the *Times*, 10 Jan. 1821, 3; and "Westminster Sessions: Mr.
Accum's Case," the *Times*, 6 April 1821, 3.

The element of revenge is usually stressed to explain the severity
of the action against Accum. However, Vernon ("Library of the
Royal Institution," *Nature*, 174[1954]: 244) pointed to very stringent early (1806) regulations instituted following the disappearance of two books from the Royal Institution's library. In the event
of theft, the managers "determine to subject such an offender to
the utmost rigour of the Law," and offered a ten guinea reward to
the informer. The size of the reward (then worth many times its
present value of roughly $30.00) suggests the seriousness with
which the misdemeanor was regarded.

32   Browne, "Accum," 53. Although there seems no clear-cut evidence,
Vernon ("Library of the Royal Institution," *Nature*, 174[1954]:
244) stated that Accum returned to Germany before the second
trial, scheduled for April, 1821. Browne, "Accum," 54–55, did not
say when Accum left England, but the implication is that it was
sometime during 1821; moreover, in 1822 Accum had assumed a

dual position in Berlin, as Professor of Technical Chemistry and Mineralogy at the Royal Industrial Institute (Gewerbe-Institute) and as Professor of Physics, Chemistry, and Mineralogy at the Royal Academy of Construction (Bau-Akademie). He held these positions until his death in 1838, and published only one other work—*Physische und Chemische Beschaffenheit der Baumaterialien, deren Wahl, Verhalten und Zweckmässige Anwendung* (1826).

33 Accum, *Treatise on Adulterations* (1st ed.; 1820), v–vi.

34 *Ibid.*, 16–17.

35 *Ibid.*, 15.

36 *Ibid.*, 157–158, 12–13.

37 Richard Phillips, "Illustrations of the Present State of Pharmacy in England," *Pharm. J.*, 2(1842–43): 315–320, 396–399, 528–532, 651–652; 3(1843): 108–111, 244–247. For biographical details see: "Obituary," *Pharm. J.*, 10(1850–51): 621, and Fritz Ferchl, *Chemisch-Pharmazeutisches Bio- und Bibliographikon* (Bavaria, 1937), 410. Aside from activities referred to, Phillips was also one of the founders of the Geological Society, chemist to the Museum of Practical Geology, editor of the *Annals of Philosophy* and the *Philosophical Magazine*, and lecturer on chemistry to the London Hospital and St. Thomas's Hospital.

38 Alphonse Normandy, *Commercial Hand-Book of Chemical Analysis* . . . (London, 1850); and John Mitchell, *Treatise on the Falsification of Food* . . . (London, 1848).

39 Arthur Hill Hassall, Letter (31 July 1855) to the Editor of the *Times*, 31 July 1855, 12; reprinted as part of "The Analytical Sanitary Commission of *The Lancet*," in *Lancet*, 2(1855): 113.

40 The standard accounts of his life and accomplishments include: Hassall, *Narrative of a Busy Life*; and Edwy Godwin Clayton, *Arthur Hill Hassall, Physician and Sanitary Reformer; A Short History of His Work in Public Hygiene and the Movement against the Adulteration of Food and Drugs* (London, 1908), 14–15. Short biographies (all except the last cited were obituaries) include: Anon., "Arthur Hill Hassall, M.D., Lond.," in *Lancet*, 1(1894): 977; Anon., "Arthur Hill Hassall, M.D.," in *Br. Med. J.*, 1(1894): 833; Anon., "Arthur Hill Hassall," in *Analyst*, 19(1894): 97–98; and Clayton, *Compendium of Food-Microscopy* . . . (London, 1909), xxv–xxix ("A Summary of the Life-Work of Dr. A. H. Hassall"). The *D.N.B.* does not mention Hassall. A modern reappraisal is seriously needed.

41 Hassall, *Minutes of Evidence*, 1–354, in *First and Second Report from the Select Committee on Adulterations of Food, Etc., with Minutes of Evidence and Appendix* (London, 1855); and *Minutes of Evidence*, 4388–4678, in *Report from the Select Committee on Adulterations of Food, Etc.; together with the Proceedings of the Committee, Minutes of Evidence, Appendix, and Index* (London, 1856), hereafter cited as *Report* (1855); *Report* (1856); *Minutes of Evidence* (1855); *Minutes of Evidence* (1856). In sheer volume of testimony, Hassall was chief witness. He was also, significantly,

the first and last witness called, and received special mention in the Committee's *Report* (1856), iii, viii.

42 Edwy Godwin Clayton, *A Compendium of Food-Microscopy with Sections on Drugs, Water, and Tobacco, Compiled with Additions and Revisions, from the Late A. H. Hassall's Works on Food* (London, 1909); Herman Klencke, *Die Verfälschung der Nahrungsmittel und Getranke, der Kolonialwarren, Drogen und Manufacte, der gewerblichen und landwichschaftlichen Producte; nach A. H. Hassall und A. Chevallier und nach eigenen Untersuchungen*, 2 vols. (Leipzig, 1856–58).

43 Hassall's early attraction to natural history developed greatly during his medical studies in Ireland, where he lived near the sea. This interest, continued on his return to England, resulted in his discovery of some new species of zoophytes and algae. The *Lepralia Hassallii* and the genus *Hassallia* (confervoid algae) attest to recognition of his work in this field. His *History of the Fresh Water Algae* (1845) was for some time a recognized authority. His skill with the microscope also served him in good stead in the preparation of the *Microscopic Anatomy of the Human Body* (1849), the first book in English of its scope on the subject. The book contained four hundred microscopic illustrations, prepared under Hassall's direction by an artist who was to provide similar valuable services in Hassall's later publications on the adulteration of food and drugs. The book also contained a description of the so-called "Hassallian corpuscles," among other original observations. About the same time, Hassall began his work as a sanitary reformer in his microscopic investigation of London drinking water, which led to the Parliamentary investigation of 1850. It has been suggested that Hassall anticipated Koch's discovery of the comma bacillus (1884), by observations made while he was Medical Inspector under the General Board of Health during the cholera epidemic of 1853–54: "Although Hassall did not express a positive opinion as to the significance of the vibriones, his observations went far beyond those of his contemporaries." (Clayton, *Hassall*, 4, 6–9; Clayton, *Compendium of Food-Microscopy*, xxvii.)

This information has been abstracted from Hassall, *Narrative*, 12–20, 23–24, 30–36, 40–41, 58–70, 157; Clayton, *Hassall*, xiii–xiv, 2–9, 60–62; Clayton, *Compendium of Food-Microscopy*, xxvii; Anon., "Arthur Hill Hassall," *Br. Med. J.*, 1(1894): 833.

44 Hassall's grandfather, father, and elder brother, Richard, were all members of the medical profession, as was his distinguished uncle, Sir James Murray, the prominent Irish physician.

45 Hassall, *Narrative*, preface (unnumbered page 2). Hassall studied at the Dublin School of Medicine between 1834 and 1837, returning to England with a diploma in midwifery, where he became a member of the Royal College of Surgeons of England (1839) in order to practice medicine. Then to "qualify for higher branches of medical profession," he received M.B. (1848) and M.D. (1851) degrees from the University of London and a license ("Member" 1851)

from the Royal College of Physicians of London. He began general practice in 1843. For further details, and a list of the various positions he held, see: Hassall, *Narrative*, 10, 22–23, 26–30, 70–73; Clayton, *Hassall*, 2, 756; Anon., "Hassall," in *Br. Med. J.*, 1(1894): 833; Anon., "Hassall, M.D., Lond.," in *Lancet*, 1(1894): 977.

Aside from his notable contributions to biology and the pure food and drug movement, Hassall made several important contributions to medicine. Clayton (*Hassall*, 55) characterized *The Urine in Health and Disease* (London, 1859) as a book containing "much original matter connected with the chemistry of the urine"; and Clayton (*ibid.*, 52) described *The Inhalation Treatment in Diseases of the Organs of Respiration, including Consumption* (London, 1885), as "one of the very few works in the English tongue devoted to the subject of inhalation." An attack of pulmonary tuberculosis, in 1866, led Hassall to conceive and later to found the Royal National Hospital for Consumption and Diseases of the Chest at Ventnor, on the Isle of Wight, built on the "separate system."

For further details, see: Hassall, *Narrative*, 96–116; Clayton, *Hassall*, xv, 45–50, 117–141; Anon., "Hassall," *Br. Med. J.*, 1 (1894): 833; Anon., "Hassall, M.D., Lond.," *Lancet*, 1(1894): 978.

46   Hassall, *Narrative*, 42–43.

47   "Supply—Adulteration of Coffee," in 111 *Hansard's Parliamentary Debates*, (ser. 3, 14 May–17 June 1850): 276. See also Hassall, *Narrative*, 44; Clayton, *Hassall*, 14.

48   Hassall's paper on coffee was read 2 August, notices appeared in the public press 5 August, and by 13 August 1850 an agreement had already been made between Hassall and Wakley; the first reports appeared in the *Lancet* in January 1851. See Clayton, *Hassall*, 15; Hassall, *Narrative*, 44; and the *Times*, 5 August 1850, 7.

49   Full title under which reports appeared was: "The Analytical Sanitary Commission. Records of the Results of Microscopical and Chemical Analysis of the Solids and Fluids Consumed by all Classes of the Public."

50   Hassall, *Narrative*, 45. See also Clayton, *Hassall*, 15, *n.* 2. Hassall, himself, and others readily admitted the responsibility assumed by Wakley. See, for instance, Hassall, *Narrative*, 45, 51–52, 53–54; Clayton, *Hassall*, 109, 111, 113, 115; Hassall, *Food and Its Adulterations* (London, 1855), xxxvii–xxxviii; Hassall, Letter to the *Times*, 26 July 1855, 12, and reprinted, "Analytical Sanitary Commission," in *Lancet*, 2(1855): 111.

51   Hassall, *Narrative*, 45–46.

52   Hassall, *Adulterations Detected*, viii, said that he had used only the conclusions and results of the earlier analyses made for the *Lancet* and that for the present work he had made "several hundreds" of analyses, between 1855 and 1856, never published in the *Lancet*.

53   Hassall, *Narrative*, 46–47, 53–54; Clayton, *Hassall*, 28–29, 35; Anon., "Dr. Arthur Hill Hassall," *Lancet*, 2(1866): 499.

54   Hassall, "Adulteration and Its Remedy," *Cornhill Magazine*, 2 (1860): 96. A committee of this organization, Hassall felt, should

issue periodic reports of the results of analyses. Hassall, in the same article, also suggested the public demand warranties of purity with their purchases.

55 Anon., "The Week," *Br. Med. J.*, (1860): 172, replying to an attempt to leave the operation of the proposed Act entirely in the hands of the public, who were to submit samples for analysis.

56 Hassall, "The Adulteration of Food and Drink Act," *Lancet*, 2 (1860): 272–273.

57 Hassall, *Narrative*, 126.

58 The *British Food Journal* (founded 1899), with its "British Analytical Control" and the *Revue internationale des falsifications* (founded 1887), with its laboratory, inaugurated such systems of guarantee later. In the area of drugs, this resembles the suggestion for a company to specialize in the manufacture of strictly standardized pharmacopeial preparations by Anon. ("Facts and Fancies by an Ordinary Pharmacist"), "B.P. Standards for Drugs," in *Pharm. J.* [ser. 4], 10(1900): 24, 122.

59 Hassall, *Food and Its Adulterations* (1855); Hassall, *Adulterations Detected* (1857).

60 Anon., "Hassall, M.D., Lond.," *Lancet*, 1(1894): 978. Although this necrology is replete with the usual eulogies, it departs from custom by introducing a long and somewhat ungallant discussion of the credit due Hassall, as compared to others such as Wakley, Letheby, and Postgate.

61 [Thomas Wakley?], Editorial, in *Lancet*, 2(1855): 83; Anon., "The Analytical Sanitary Commission of 'The Lancet' correspondence reprinted from London *Times* [July 1855]," *ibid.*, 111–114; Anon., "Hassall, M.D., Lond.," *Lancet*, 1(1894): 978; Hassall, *Narrative*, 52–53; Clayton, *Hassall*, 36–38, 40. See also the *Times* (1855): July 26, p. 12; July 27, p. 10; July 30, p. 7; July 31, p. 12; Aug. 2, p. 12.

For a brief review of this controversy, see: Hassall, *Adulterations Detected* (1857), viii–x.

62 *The Correspondence relating to the Lancet Sanatory Commission (which appeared lately in the Times), examined by James Caesar Durnford, Esq., John A. Power, L.M., M.A., Cantab., and Raymond S. Daniel, M. A., Oxon; with an appendix* (London, 1856).

63 John Postgate, letter (24 August 1860) addressed to Thomas Lloyd, Mayor of Birmingham, upon the occasion of the passage of the 1860 Adulteration Act, reprinted in "The Week," *Br. Med. J.* (1860): 746. The letter stressed the need for local authorities to take seriously their responsibilities as administrators of the new legislation, if anything was to come of the measure.

64 [Jacob Bell?], "The Adulteration of Food, Drugs, etc.," *Pharm. J.*, 15(1855): 95–101; [Jacob Bell?], "Adulteration and The Lancet," *ibid.*, 244; "Adulteration of Drugs:—Mr. Hassall and Mr. Redwood," *ibid.*, 248–254; Redwood, Bell, et al. Discussion following Arthur Hill Hassall, "On the Adulteration of Annatto," *ibid.*, 303–310.

65 *Report* (1856), iii, viii. Clayton (*Hassall*, 34–37, 82–92, 95–103)

amply showed the recognition given by the press, including appropriate abstracts from these notices; *ibid.*, 41–42, 104–116; and
Hassall, *Narrative*, 52–53. A further tangible evidence of the general recognition of Hassall's achievement took the form of a £100
per annum pension granted him by the British Government in 1866
"in consideration of his public services," and £50 per annum for his
widow upon his death in 1894. (Clayton, *Hassall*, 42, 44.) Clayton
concluded here, "That the Sovereign's Ministers, acting officially as
chiefs of the Imperial Government, showed more discernment and
a truer sense of proportion than did some who might have been
expected to excell in warm appreciation of the subject of this
memoir."

The Society of Public Analysts honored him by choosing him one
of their first vice-presidents, at the time of its founding in 1874.
(Bernard Dyer and C. Ainsworth Mitchell, *The Society of Public
Analysts* . . . [Cambridge, 1932], 3.) In his autobiography, Hassall erroneously stated: "Of this Society I was appointed, naturally
enough perhaps, the first President . . . I looked upon the appointment as merely honorary and complimentary and intended as a
recognition of what I had done in the past." For this reason, and
because he never regarded himself "as a permanent and professional analyst," Hassall tells us he never occupied the chair, although he cannot fully recall the details of this negligence of his
duties. (Hassall, *Narrative*, 58.) Whether we should attribute this
lapse of memory to old age, or to something more than that, is
difficult to decide. Hassall was justly proud of his achievements
and made no efforts at modesty, but perhaps he could not bring
himself to remember that the man selected as first president of the
Society was in fact Theophilus Redwood, probably one of Hassall's
most outspoken critics. Clayton made an almost equally untenable
statement, in pointing to the founding of the Society as "directly
traceable to Dr. Hassall's investigations." (Clayton, *Hassall*, 33.)
Hassall's obituary in the Society's official organ, the *Analyst*,
pointed to his election as vice-president "in recognition of his great
services," but added that "he never took any active interest in the
formation or actual working of the Society." Anon., "Arthur Hill
Hassall," *Analyst*, 19(1894): 98.

66 Anon., "Arthur Hill Hassall," *Analyst*, 19(1894): 98. Hassall, *Narrative*, 58, commented on the subject of his being an analyst: "I
scarcely regarded myself as a permanent and professional analyst.
I became one rather by accident than design, my profession having
always been that of medicine." Cf. *Ibid., preface* (unnumbered
p. 2).

67 Epitaph to Postgate cited by Thomas Seccombe, "John Postgate," in
D.N.B., 16:204. Details of Postgate's early medical training and
qualifications prior to 1854 were given in a brief article by G. K.
Keeston, "A Brief History of the Inauguration of Food and Drug
Legislation in Great Britain," *Food-Drug-Cosmetic Law Journal*, 8
(1953): 495–498. Unfortunately, the article was undocumented,
although the author apparently used original documents in the

hands of Postgate's descendants. On the basis of our own investigation, we believe Keeston gives undue emphasis to Postgate's role in the over-all development of anti-adulteration legislation in England. The same is true of T. D. Whittet, "Some Contributions of Pharmacy to Pure Food and Drugs," *Chem. & Drugg.*, 174(1960): 441–442, who has relied heavily upon Keeston and upon Postgate's obituary in *Br. Med. J.*, 2(1881): 651. We also believe Whittet is somewhat misleading when he refers to Postgate as an "apothecary" in a manner which suggests he was a pharmacist, at a time when British apothecaries were essentially medical practitioners. A definitive biography of this important figure is needed.

68   William Scholefield (1809–1867) was Liberal Member of Parliament (1847–1867) for Birmingham. Aside from Scholefield's part in bringing the adulteration issue before the government, his biographer Samuel Timmins "William Scholefield," in *D.N.B.*, 17:911, noted: "He was one of the twelve members of parliament who voted for the people's charter, and actively supported bills for repealing the paper duties and taxes on knowledge, [and] for lowering the income tax."

  George Frederick Muntz (1794–1857), political reformer and Member of Parliament (1840–1857). See Samuel Timmins, "George Frederick Muntz," in *D.N.B.*, 13: 1210–12.

69   Anon., "Appointment of Public Analysers," *Lancet*, 1(1854): 321; [Thomas Wakley?], Editorial, *ibid.*, 477–478; Anon., "Birmingham: The Adulteration of Food and Drugs," *ibid.*, 480–481; Anon., "Adulteration of Food and Drugs," *Lancet*, 2(1854): 471; [Thomas Wakley?], Editorial, *ibid.*, 489; Anon., "Adulteration of Food," *Lancet*, 1(1855): 353; Anon., "Adulteration of Food and Drugs. Meeting at Scarborough," *Lancet*, 2(1855): 334. See also Postgate, *Minutes of Evidence* (1856), 4424; and Postgate, "The Legislation on Adulteration of Food, Drink, and Drugs," in *Trans. National Association for the Promotion of Social Science* (1868): 507.

70   Anon., "Adulterated Food," *Lancet*, 1(1854): 293.

71   Anon., "Birmingham: The Adulteration of Food and Drugs," *Lancet*, 1(1854): 480–481. See also Postgate, *Minutes of Evidence* (1856), 4426.

72   Anon., "Adulteration of Food and Drugs," *Lancet*, 2(1854): 492–493.

73   *Ibid.*, 493.

74   Anon., "The Adulteration of Food [report of a lecture delivered by John Postgate at Bridlington, England]," *Br. Med. J.*, 1(1862): 123; John Postgate, "The Adulteration of Food and Drink Act [Letter dated August 1861]," *Br. Med. J.*, 2(1861): 241; John Postgate, Letter (dated 24 August 1860) to Thomas Lloyd, Mayor of Birmingham, reprinted in "The Week," *Br. Med. J.* (1860): 746. In these letters and this lecture, Postgate repeatedly charged local authorities with their responsibilities to make the 1860 Act effective. See also Postgate, "The Legislation on Adulteration of Food, Drink, and Drugs," in *Trans. National Association for the Promotion of Social Science* (1868): 507.

75 The 1872 amendment was introduced by Muntz at Postgate's urging, and Postgate made further suggestions toward the 1875 Act. Clayton (*Hassall*, 21, 41) acknowledged the part played by Postgate, but, we think correctly, pointed to the priority of the *Lancet* Commission. The obituary of Postgate appearing in the London *Times* (September 30, 1881) attributed the control of adulteration to Postgate's crusade and aroused some severe criticism; see Anon., "Adulteration of Food and Drugs," *Lancet*, 2(1881): 638–639. Summing up the contributions of the *Lancet* and of Hassall, the writer (*ibid.*, 638) concluded: "Mr. Postgate, no doubt, used his influence at an advanced period of the inquiry with Mr. Scho[le]-field in furtherance of useful legislation, and thus far he is entitled to credit and praise." Postgate's biographer in *D.N.B.*, 16:204 complained that "Postgate obtained no public recognition of any kind for his services," yet the *D.N.B.* failed to mention Hassall, although it did include Wakley, Scholefield, and Letheby, in addition to Postgate.

76 Edward Irving Carlyle, "Thomas Wakley," in *D.N.B.*, 20:465. *Ibid.*, 461–465, gave a detailed account of his life and activities, but the major biography was by Samuel Squire Sprigge, *Life and Times of Thomas Wakley Founder and First Editor of the "Lancet"* (London and New York, 1897). Obituaries appeared in *Lancet*, 1(1862): 609; and *Gentleman's Magazine*, 2(1862): 364. See also an article by Stieb, "Thomas Wakley, Nineteenth-Century Food and Drug Reformer," in *J. Amer. Pharm. Assoc., Pract. Pharm. Ed.*, 21(1960): 777–778, which has been adapted for this work, with permission.

77 The Medical Act of 1858 first satisfactorily solved the problems plaguing organized English medicine during the first half of the nineteenth century. The Act creating the General Council of Medical Education and Registration of the United Kingdom was responsible, among other things, for the publication of the *British Pharmacopoeia*. About this same time (1856) the British Medical Association evolved out of the Provincial Medical and Surgical Association, dating back to 1832, perhaps significantly the same year in which the first Reform Act passed.

78 W. B. O'Shaugnessy, "Poisoned Confectionary," *Lancet*, 2(1830–31): 193–198. See: Anon., "Adulterations of Drugs," in *Lancet*, 2(1825–26): 413; E. Moore, "Tests of Adulterated Quinine," *Lancet*, 2(1828–29): 80; M. Auguste Delomel, "Tests for the Sulphate of Quinine," *ibid.*, 365; Anon., "Adulteration of Bread," *ibid.*, 607–608, 657; Abraham Booth, "On Prussic Acid," *ibid.*, 575–576; Anon., "Review of Michael John Short's *Practical Remarks* . . . (1830)," *Lancet*, 1(1830–31): 87; Anon., "*Review of Deadly Adulteration* . . . (1830)," *ibid.*, 485–487; M. Robiquet, "On the Adulteration of Strychnine [from the *Journal de Pharmacie*]," *ibid.*, 6; and M. Valet, "Mode of Detecting the Adulterations of Some Essential Oils with Essence of Turpentine [from *Arch. de Brandes*]," *ibid.*, 7.

79 Thomas Wakley, Letter (dated 28 July 1855) to the *Times*, reprinted in *Lancet*, 2(1855): 112. For discussions of priority, see also Anon., "Hassall, M.D., Lond.," *Lancet*, 1(1894): 978.

80 Wakley, 28 July 1855 Letter to the *Times, Lancet,* 2(1855): 113.
81 *Ibid.*
82 Anon., report "On the Adulteration of Coffee paper read by Hassall before the Botanical Society of London, 2 August 1850," in the *Times,* 5 August 1850, 7.
83 [Thomas Wakley?], Editorial, in *Lancet,* 1(1851): 18.
84 Anon., "The Analytical Sanitary Commission: Records of the Results of Microscopical and Chemical Analyses of the Solids and Fluids Consumed by All Classes of the Public," *Lancet,* 1(1851): 20.
85 Part of general introductory title for the reports of "The Analytical Sanitary Commission," *Lancet,* 1(1853): 321.
86 Anon., "Bibliographic Notices [review of Hassall's *Food and Its Adulterations,* 1855]," *Br. Med. J.* (1855): 157. See also pp. 150–151, 158, 159, of the present work.
87 Anon., "Bibliographic Notices," *Br. Med. J.* (1855): 157, commenting upon the *Lancet's* "ferocious onslaught upon the peccant tradesmen of London." The increased subscription list is mentioned by [Thomas Wakley?], Editorial in *Lancet,* 1(1852): 16.
88 [Wakley?], Editorial in *Lancet,* 1(1851): 72.
89 "Mr. Mortar on the Adulteration of Drugs," Letter in *Lancet,* 1 (1851): 172, *n.****.
90 *Ibid.*
91 Anon., "Bibliographic Notices," *Br. Med. J.* (1855): 158.
92 Anon., "The Week," *Br. Med. J.,* 2(1861): 536. This broad evaluation of the good accomplished by the *Lancet* was based upon the analysis of one particular substance only. See also pages 158, 159 of the present work.

CHAPTER 14
THE ROLE OF THE GOVERNMENT

1 The German government consulted the Society of Public Analysts on the administration of the British law. See Anon., "German Government and Adulteration," in *Analyst,* 2(1877): 171–172; and Anon., "Replies to the Inquiries by the German Government as to the Working of the Sale of Food and Drugs Act," *ibid.,* 173–175.
2 Arthur Hill Hassall, *Minutes of Evidence* (1855), 182, 4440, 4444, in *First and Second Report from the Select Committee on Adulterations of Food, Etc., with the Minutes of Evidence and Appendix* (London, 1855), hereafter cited as *Report* (1855); *Minutes of Evidence* (1855); and Hassall, *Adulterations Detected; or, Plain Instructions for the Discovery of Frauds in Food and Medicine* (London, 1857), vii–viii, 31–37.
3 John Postgate, *Minutes of Evidence* (1856), 4238; Wakley, *ibid.,* 2213, 2227–28, 2250, in *Report from the Select Committee on Adulterations of Food, Etc.; together with the Proceedings of the Committee, Minutes of Evidence, Appendix, and Index* (London, 1856), hereafter cited as *Report* (1856); *Minutes of Evidence* (1856).
4 Wallington, *Minutes of Evidence* (1855), 2611–12, 2649–50, 2666–68; Simon, *ibid.,* 795, 797, 814–822.

5 Theophilus Redwood, *ibid.*, 1619, 1938–42, referred repeatedly to the efforts of the Pharmaceutical Society. See also Jacob Bell, *ibid.* (1856), 2315, 2319.

6 *Report* (1856), viii.

7 Hassall, *Adulterations Detected,* 31; and *Report* (1856), 30–37. Hassall noted that the Excise commanded a force of 60 or 70 analytical chemists, along with 4000 officers scattered about the country. He felt that, with the proper reorganization, this body could well serve in the administration of adulteration legislation, a task it was at that time not fulfilling, even in connection with the revenue.

8 *Report* (1856), ix; see also draft *Report* (1856), xxii, xxiii, xxv.

9 Hassall, *Adulterations Detected,* 30–31.

10 35 & 36 Victoria 1872, ch. 74, sec. 5. Frederick A. Filby, *A History of Food Adulteration and Analysis* (London, 1934), 195, failed to make clear the special circumstances under which the Act "made the appointment of analysts and inspectors compulsory"; although he quoted the pertinent section in his appendix (245).

11 *Report from the Select Committee on Adulteration of Food Act (1872); together with the Proceedings of the Committee, Minutes of Evidence, Appendix, and Index* (London, 1874), iii, viii; cited hereafter as *Report* (1874).

12 Bernard Dyer and C. Ainsworth Mitchell, *The Society of Public Analysts* . . . (Cambridge, 1932), 16; see also *ibid.*, 14–16. Dyer intended no criticism of Sir James Bell, head of Somerset House, but considered that Bell felt obligated to keep himself aloof from outside connections, in view of the laboratory's function as an independent referee; and commended his efforts, in the remark (15) that "[Dr. James Bell,] brought up in the traditions of the Civil Service, whose practical scientific knowledge had been gathered in a somewhat narrow channel, but who, although past his prime, threw himself eagerly into the task of qualifying himself and his staff for their new duties as referees under the Act."

13 Dyer and Mitchell, *Society of Public Analysts,* 16, commented that some members of the Somerset House staff "grew to regard the Public Analyst as a kind of generic enemy, and this personal feeling was not unreciprocated by many Public Analysts."

14 *Ibid.*, 17–18.

15 The Society of Public Analysts originally proposed a board of reference including the chief chemical officer of the Inland Revenue Laboratory, three public analysts appointed by the Local Government Board, and a nominee of the Board of Agriculture. Aside from definitions and standards, the Society proposed such a board should investigate analytical processes and devise new ones; and should examine and report on the composition of food and drugs. (See: Anon., "Draft of a Sale of Food and Drugs Act Prepared by the Council of the Society of Public Analysts," *Analyst,* 19[1894]: 165.) Similar recommendations had been made to the Select Committee (1896) by Otto Hehner, for the Society of Public Analysts; and by Charles R. C. Tichborne, chemist to the Apothecaries' Hall of

Ireland, president of the Pharmaceutical Society of Ireland, a member of the General Council of Medical Education and Registration of the United Kingdom, and a prolific contributor to the *Pharmaceutical Journal* on pharmacopeial preparations. See *Minutes of Evidence* (1896), 269, 131, 134–136, 140–144, 1489–94; and *Report* (1896), xviii–xx, in *Report from the Select Committee on Food Products Adulteration; with the Proceedings of the Committee, Minutes of Evidence, Appendix, and Index* (London, 1896), hereafter cited as *Report* (1896); *Minutes of Evidence* (1896). Bernard Dyer, Edward Bevan, and Charles E. Cassall, "Report of the Council of the Society of Public Analysts on the Sale of Food and Drugs Bill Introduced in the House of Commons . . ." *Analyst*, 23(1898): 31–33; Dyer and Mitchell, *Society of Public Analysts*, 39–40.

16 38 & 39 Victoria 1875, ch. 63, sec. 10; italics added.

17 *Ibid.*, sec. 10. Section 11 permitted the town council of any borough to use the services of an analyst in a neighboring borough, or in the same county. In 1899, metropolitan boroughs, rather than vestries and district boards, were designated; and in 1888, county councils, rather than quarter sessions. See William James Bell, *The Sale of Food and Drugs Acts; and Forms, Regulations, Orders and Notices Issued Thereunder, with Notes and Cases*, Charles F. Lloyd and R. A. Robinson, eds. (7th ed.; London, 1923), 47, *nn.* (a), (b).

18 38 & 39 Victoria 1875, ch. 63, sec. 13.

19 *Ibid.*, sec. 10.

20 *Report* (1896), iv–vi; Anon., "The Local Government Board on the Sale of Food and Drugs Act," *Pharm. J.* [ser. 3], 14(1883–84): 325–326.

21 *Local Government Board Annual Report* (1892), 9; cited by H. Mansfield Robinson and Cecil H. Cribb, *The Law and Chemistry of Food and Drugs* (London, 1895), 19, *n.* 2, who also commented: "The Sale of Foods and Drugs Acts seem to be used very little in securing the purity of drugs." See also pp. 120–123 of the present work.

22 62 & 63 Victoria 1899, ch. 51, secs. 2, 3.

23 *Ibid.*, sec. 3, subsec. 1. Bell, *Sale of Food and Drugs Acts*, 144, *n.* (a), confirms our conviction, by his statement: "This is the first time in the Sale of Food and Drugs Acts that a positive duty is cast upon local authorities to see to the proper execution of the Acts, and a remedy provided in case they make default. Prior to the passing of this Act there were no means of compelling a negligent local authority to do its duty."

24 62 & 63 Victoria 1899; compare secs. 2 and 3 (subsec. 2) with sec. 3 (subsec. 1).

25 *Report* (1874), vii; see also *ibid.*, iii.

26 *Ibid.*, vii.

27 Anon., "Meeting of Public Analysts," *Pharm. J.* [ser. 3], 5(1874–75): 121; Anon., "Meeting of Public Analysts," *Chem. News*, 30 (1874): 73–74. The references to proposed interference include the Committee suggestion that Somerset House be designated a court of

reference for disputed cases; and the suggestion that compulsory examination of qualifications be instituted at South Kensington.

28   Anon., "Society of Public Analysts," in *Pharm. J.* [ser. 3], 5(1874–75): 443.

29   35 & 36 Victoria 1872, ch. 74, sec. 5.

30   Anon., "The Adulteration of Food and Drink Bill," *Pharm. J.*, 19 (1859–60): 586; Anon., "The Adulteration of Food and Drugs Bill," *Pharm. J.* [ser. 2], 10(1868–69): 667; Anon., "The Adulteration of Food and Drugs Bill," *Pharm. J.* [ser. 2], 11(1869–70): 4; Anon., "The New Adulteration Act," *Pharm. J.* [ser. 3], 3(1872–73): 247; two other anonymous discussions entitled "The New Adulteration Act," *ibid.*, 263, 293; Anon., "Adulteration of Food and Drugs Act," *ibid.*, 266; Anon., "The Adulteration Act," *ibid.*, 427–428; Anon., "Public Analysts," *ibid.*, 509–510; Anon., "Public Analysts," *Pharm. J.* [ser. 3], 4(1873–74): 579–580; another anonymous discussion entitled "Public Analysts," *ibid.*, 618.

31   We have taken this account of the qualifications of public analysts before the formation of the Society of Public Analysts, largely from Dyer and Mitchell, *Society of Public Analysts*, 5.

32   Dyer and Mitchell, *ibid.*, mentioned G. W. Wigner and Alfred H. Allen, among the few almost purely chemical consultants in practice.

33   Dyer and Mitchell, *ibid.*, mentioned: Dr. Thomas Stevenson, Professor J. A. Wanklyn, Dr. (later Sir) Charles A. Cameron, Alexander Blyth, and Dr. C. Meymott Tidy, as examples of chemists who became physicians in order to do public health work, because of limited opportunities in chemistry. We see no reason for mentioning Hassall in the latter connection, for he entered medicine directly, and his limitations with respect to chemistry drew sharp criticism in connection with his investigations for the *Lancet* Commission. Most of the chemical work for the *Lancet* investigation seems to have been done by others, notably Letheby. Of this group, Letheby and Tidy never joined the Society of Public Analysts; Wanklyn, though like Hassall a vice-president, left the Society in the second year after its formation, never to rejoin; all the others held positions as officers or members of the Society's council.

34   Frederick Parsons, "The Adulteration Muddle [Letter to the editor]," *Pharm. J.* [ser. 3], 4(1873–74): 508; Professor Marreco [?], "The Position of Professional Chemists, as Affected by the Adulteration Act," *Pharm. J.* [ser. 3], 5(1874–75): 18–19; Anon., "The Meetings of the Medical Council," *ibid.*, 71–72.

35   38 & 39 Victoria 1875, ch. 63, sec. 10.

36   Anon., "The Local Government Board on the Sale of Food and Drugs Act," *Pharm. J.* [ser. 3], 14(1883–84): 325–326; 62 & 63 Victoria 1899, ch. 51, sec. 3 (subsec. 5); Anon., "The Competency of Public Analysts," *Pharm. J.* [ser. 4], 10(1900): 293. See also Bell, *Sale of Food and Drugs Acts*, 45–48, 140–145, 213–214, 262–263.

37   Dyer and Mitchell, *Society of Public Analysts*, 7, 10, 36.

38   *Ibid.*, 34.

39   *Ibid.*, 36; Anon., "Proceedings of the Society of Public Analysts,"

Analyst, 18(1893): 115–116. See also *Report* (1896), xx–xxi.

40 62 & 63 Victoria 1899, ch. 51, secs. 2, 3.

41 Henry Chaplin and S. B. Provis, "Regulation as to Competency of Analysts [circular letter from Local Government Board, 7 March 1900, signed by the Board president and secretary, respectively]," in Bell, *Sale of Food and Drugs Acts,* 213–214.

42 S. B. Provis, "Public Analysts: Regulation as to Competency [circular letter from Local Government Board, 8 March 1900, signed by the Board secretary]," in Bell, *Sale of Food and Drugs Acts,* 262–263.

43 Anon., "Institute of Chemistry [Annual Report of the Council]," *Pharm. J.* [ser. 4], 20(1905): 307. The special requirements instituted by the Local Government Board in 1900 did not extend to persons appointed, with Board approval, between January 1891, and March 1900. (See Bell, *Sale of Food and Drugs Acts,* 214.)

44 Original requirements for membership included election upon nomination by 4 members, at least 2 of whom could testify to the nominee's qualifications. In 1899, the Society removed the restriction limiting membership to appointees under the Sale of Food and Drugs Acts. Thereafter any candidate with a *"bona fide* interest in analytical chemistry" was admitted. This change was subsequently reflected in the change in the Society's name, at the time of its incorporation in 1907, to "Society of Public Analysts and Other Analytical Chemists." For details, see Dyer and Mitchell, *Society of Public Analysts,* 2, 42, 46–47; Anon., "Meeting of Public Analysts," *Pharm. J.* [ser. 3], 5(1874–75): 131; Anon., "Society of Public Analysts," *Pharm. J.* [ser. 4], 21(1905): 306.

45 For more detailed discussion of the problems connected with definitions of adulteration, standards of purity, delegation of administrative authority, enforcement of the laws, and competency of analysts, the reader is referred to sections dealing individually with these topics.

46 31 & 32 Victoria 1868, ch. 121, sec. 24.

47 35 & 36 Victoria 1872, ch. 74, secs. 1, 2, 3; italics added.

48 38 & 39 Victoria 1875, ch. 63, sec. 5; italics added. Sections 3 and 4 preceding, to which this section refers, dealt with foods and drugs, respectively, treated in the manner here described, and with the *intent* of selling them in this state.

49 See also Douglas A. Bartley, *Adulteration of Food: Statutes and Cases . . .* (London, 1895), 48; and Bell, *Sale of Food and Drugs Acts,* 8.

50 38 & 39 Victoria 1875, ch. 6, secs. 6, 7, 24. See also Bartley, *Adulteration of Food,* 49; and Bell, *Sale of Food and Drugs Acts,* 10, *n.* (b), 33.

51 38 & 39 Victoria 1875, ch. 83, secs. 8, 27.

52 Bell, *Sale of Food and Drugs Acts,* 6, 9, 11–13 (*n.* [b]); Bartley, *Adulteration of Food,* 60, interpreted sec. 6 differently.

53 Anon., "Adulteration of Food Act," *Pharm. J.,* 20(1860–61): 393; Anon., "The Adulteration of Drugs," *Pharm. J.* [ser. 2], 10(1868–69): 618; and Anon., "Adulteration," *Pharm. J.* [ser. 3], 1(1870–71): 687.

54   [Jacob Bell?], "The Adulteration of Food, Drugs, etc.—Result of the
      Parliamentary Inquiry," *Pharm. J.*, 16(1856–57): 155. See also,
      Anon., "Mr. Muntz's Adulteration Bill," *Pharm. J.* [ser. 3], 1(1870–
      71): 791; *Report* (1874), *passim*, *Minutes of Evidence* (1874), for
      Horner, Carteighe, Sandford.

55   Anon., "Adulteration of Food, Drugs, etc.," *Pharm. J.* [ser. 3], 3
      (1872–73): 129; Anon., "Meeting of the Council of the Pharmaceu-
      tical Society," *Pharm. J.* [ser. 3], 4(1873–74): 897.

56   G. W. Wigner, "The Adulteration Act," in *Pharm. J.* [ser. 3], 5
      (1874–75): 759. Wigner was one of the prime movers for the
      founding of the Society of Public Analysts, one of its honorary
      secretaries (1874–1882), one of its presidents (1883–84), and
      editor of its journal, the *Analyst*. Wigner participated in the So-
      ciety's first attempts to frame definitions of adulteration and to set
      standards; and framed the model adulteration law, influential upon
      early American state adulteration acts. He unfortunately died at
      the age of 42, while the Society and English legislation on adultera-
      tion were both still in their infancy.

57   38 & 39 Victoria 1875, ch. 63, sec. 6; 42 & 43 Victoria 1879, ch. 30,
      preamble, and sec. 2; Bell, *Sale of Food and Drugs Acts*, 20–21 (*n.*
      [c]).

58   Bartley, *Adulteration of Food*, 57; Bell, *Sale of Food and Drugs Acts*,
      29–30.

59   Bell, *Sale of Food and Drugs Acts*, 29–30.

60   In the case of the so-called "citrate of magnesia" the difficulty was of
      course with the name, because on analysis the preparation would
      show not a trace of the substance (i.e., magnesium citrate) which
      its name suggested it should contain. "Milk of sulfur" and "sweet
      spirit of nitre" are today considered synonyms of precipitated
      sulfur and spirit of nitrous ether, respectively, but in this earlier
      period there was some difference depending upon different for-
      mulas carried over from previous pharmacopeias. "Castor oil pills"
      consisted of rhubarb, aloes, and soap, but contained no castor
      oil.

61   Anon., "The Operation of the Adulteration Act in the Drug Trade,"
      Pharm. J. [ser. 3], 4(1873–74): 363. For an account of the sweet
      nitre dilemma, see Anon., "The Adulteration Act in Its Relation to
      Druggists," *ibid.*, 443, and for an account of the court trial, with
      full testimony, *ibid.*, 454–465. The milk of sulfur controversy raged
      in the following articles: Anon., "Alleged Adulteration of 'Milk of
      Sulphur,' *Pharm. J.* [ser. 3], 6(1875–76): 717–718; Anon., "Milk of
      Sulphur Case," *ibid.*, 840; Anon., "Important Decision under the
      Sale of Food and Drugs Act: The Sale of Milk of Sulphur," *ibid.*,
      975–977; Anon., "Prosecution of a Chemist and Druggist under the
      Sale of Food and Drugs Act," *ibid.*, 1039; Anon., "Milk of Sulphur,"
      Pharm. J. [ser. 3], 7(1876–77): 9, 459; Anon., "More Milk of
      Sulphur Prosecutions," *ibid.*, 539; Anon., "The Sale of Milk of
      Sulphur," *ibid.*, 579–586; another anonymous article entitled "Milk
      of Sulphur," *ibid.*, 645–647. See also, Anon., "Prosecution for the
      Sale of Adulterated Cream of Tartar," *Pharm. J.* [ser. 3], 10(1879–
      80): 257.

62   38 & 39 Victoria 1875, ch. 63, sec. 6.

63   42 & 43 Victoria 1879, ch. 30, sec. 2. See also Bell, *Sale of Food and Drugs Acts,* 22.

64   35 & 36 Victoria 1872, ch. 74, secs. 1, 2; 38 & 39 Victoria 1875, ch. 63, sec. 4; 31 & 32 Victoria 1868, ch. 121, sec. 24; Bell, *Sale of Food and Drugs Acts,* 8.

65   Bell, *Sale of Food and Drugs Acts,* 14, 20–22, *n.* (c); Bartley, *Adulteration of Food,* 50.

66   Bell, *Sale of Food and Drugs Acts,* 7.

67   The law itself referred only to giving notice by means of a label or other printed notice accompanying the mixed drug. The courts accepted verbal notice as well, probably in consequence of some prosecutions attempted on the grounds that the container, though labelled, was covered by an opaque wrapper. Possible abuses of the clauses that allowed warranties and labels as a defense against conviction were covered by making false labelling and false warranties punishable offenses. See 38 & 39 Victoria 1875, ch. 63, secs. 8, 25, 27; Bartley, *Adulteration of Food,* 63, 99, 103; Bell, *Sale of Food and Drugs Acts* (London, 1886), 35, 58; *ibid.* (7th ed.; 1923), 14–20, 36–40, 79–93, 94–96. The restriction upon the use of the warranty, and the addition of the meaning "willful" to the use of a false warranty, were incorporated into 62 & 63 Victoria 1899, ch. 51, sec. 20.

68   The amending Act of 1899 qualified the meaning of "distinctly and legibly" to include "not obscured by other matter on the label." At the same time, the new regulation did not hinder the use of a registered trade mark, or of a label in continuous use for seven years before the law became effective. It did, however, prevent the approval of any newly designed labels not conforming to these specifications. 38 & 39 Victoria 1875, ch. 63, sec. 8; 62 & 63 Victoria 1899, ch. 51, sec. 12. See also Charles Graham, *Report* (1879), appendix, 13–14, re: mixtures, in *Report from the Select Committee on Sale of Food and Drugs Act (1875) Amendment Bill; with the Proceedings of the Committee, Minutes of Evidence, and Appendix* (London, 1878–79), hereafter cited as *Report* (1879); *Minutes of Evidence* (1879).

69   38 & 39 Victoria 1875, ch. 63, sec. 6 (subsec. 3), and sec. 7. See also *ibid.,* sec. 4.

70   Bell, *Sale of Food and Drugs Acts* (1923), 8, *n.* (a), 34, *n.* (1), 35.

71   Bartley, *Adulteration of Foods,* 59.

72   31 & 32 Victoria 1868, ch. 121, sec. 15.

73   *Ibid.,* sec. 24; 35 & 36 Victoria 1872, ch. 74, sec. 4.

74   38 & 39 Victoria 1875, ch. 63, sec. 1.

75   Bartley, *Adulteration of Foods,* 59.

76   Bell, *Sale of Food and Drugs Acts* (1923), 29–30, and 30–33, *passim.*

77   *Ibid.,* 30, in reference to two cases involving mercury ointment and liniment of soap, not prepared according to the *British Pharmacopoeia* but claimed by the defendants to have been prepared accord-

ing to commercial standards. See also James Bell, *Minutes of Evidence* (1879), 138; and C. G. Moor, "Suggested Standards of Purity for Foods and Drugs," *Pharm. J.* [ser. 4], 10(1900): 172.

78 *Report* (1856), ix.

79 *Minutes of Evidence* (1879), 49.

80 Graham, *Report* (1879), appendix, 14. See pp. 132–133 of the present work.

81 C. G. Moor, *Suggested Standards of Purity for Foods and Drugs* (London, 1902); William Chattaway, *Digest of Researches and Criticisms . . . of the British Pharmacopoeia, 1898* (London, 1903); Robinson and Cribb, *Law and Chemistry of Food and Drugs*. W. S. Glyn-Jones, "The Chemist and Some of the Laws that Particularly Affect Him," in *Pharm. J.* [ser. 4], 10(1900): 72; Moor, "Suggested Standards of Purity for Foods and Drugs," *ibid.*, 172; Anon., "The Standards of Purity for Drugs," *ibid.*, 202; H. Wippell Gadd, "Standards for Drugs," *Pharm. J.* [ser. 4], 15(1902): 214; Glyn-Jones, "Evening Meeting in London of the Pharmaceutical Society," *Pharm. J.* [ser. 4], 20(1905): 237; John C. Umney, and H. Wippell Gadd, Discussion following Glyn-Jones, *ibid.*, 238–239; Anon. ("A Pharmacist"), "The Sale of Food and Drugs Acts; Some Defects and Suggested Remedies," *Pharm. J.* [ser. 4], 23(1906): 237; John C. Umney, "A Few Difficulties of the British Pharmacopoeia, 1898," *Pharm. J.* [ser. 4], 10(1900): 8; C. G. Moor, in Address before "Chemists' Defence Association," *ibid.*, 330. Moor was a noted analyst and author, and official analyst to the Chemists' Defence Association.

82 Robinson and Cribb, *Law and Chemistry of Food and Drugs*, 391–394.

83 Bell, *Minutes of Evidence* (1879), 138; Anon., "Pharmacopoeia Standards," *Pharm. J.* [ser. 4], 2(1896): 491. A similar feeling concerning the *United States Pharmacopeia* found expression about this same time by John Uri Lloyd, in a paper read before the Philadelphia College of Pharmacy. See Lloyd, "The Pharmacopoeial Standard," in *Amer. J. Pharm.*, 68(1896): 297.

84 H. Wippell Gadd, in discussion following Glyn-Jones, "Evening Meeting in London," *Pharm. J.* [ser. 4] 20(1905): 329; see also Glyn-Jones, *ibid.*, 236; Anon., "The Sale of Food and Drugs Acts; Some Defects and Suggested Remedies," *Pharm. J.* [ser. 4], 23(1906): 237.

85 *British Pharmacopoeia, 1898*, xx–xxi.

86 *British Pharmacopoeia, 1914*, xviii–xx.

87 Anon., "Annotations," *Pharm. J.* [ser. 4], 9(1899): 150; Anon., "The Standards of Purity for Drugs," *Pharm. J.* [ser. 4], 10(1900): 202; Charles Umney, "The Pharmacopoeia and Its Relations to Pharmacists," *ibid.*, 2; Anon., "Trade Standards of Purity, Etc.," *Pharm. J.* [ser. 4], 13(1901): 75.

88 Anon., "Parliament and Its Work in 1897," *Pharm. J.* [ser. 4], 6(1897): 18; Anon., "Public Health Congress [paraphrase of Charles R. C. Tichborne]," *Pharm. J.* [ser. 4], 7(1898): 244–245; Anon., "English News," *Pharm. J.* [ser. 4], 8(1899): 262a; Glyn-

Jones, "The Chemist and Some of the Laws that Particularly Affect Him," *Pharm. J.* [ser. 4], 10(1900): 72; Gadd, "Standards for Drugs," *Pharm. J.* [ser. 4], 15(1902): 470; Glyn-Jones, "Evening Meeting in London," *Pharm. J.* [ser. 4], 20 (1905): 236; Dyer and Mitchell, *Society of Public Analysts*, 36, 38; Anon., "Proceedings of the Society of Public Analysts," *Analyst*, 18(1893): 97; Anon., "Draft of a Sale and Drugs Act, Prepared by the Council of the Society of Public Analysts," *Analyst*, 19(1894): 165; Dyer et al., "Report of the Council . . ." *Analyst*, 23(1898): 31–33.

89   Anon., "Facts and Fancies by an Ordinary Pharmacist: Pharmacists and the Pharmacopoeia," *Pharm. J.* [ser. 4], 10(1900): 24; Nestor Tirard, "Pharmacy and the British Pharmacopoeia," *Br. Med. J.*, 2(1899): 1787.

90   Glyn-Jones, "Evening Meeting in London," *Pharm. J.* [ser. 4], 20 (1905): 237.

91   C. G. Moor and C. H. Cribb, "Suggested Standards of Purity for Foods and Drugs," *Pharm. J.* [ser. 4], 9(1899): 129; Moor, "Suggested Standards of Purity for Foods and Drugs," *Pharm. J.* [ser. 4], 10(1900): 172; Moor, *Suggested Standards of Purity for Foods and Drugs*. Informal standards, through agreement between chemists and analysts, of the sort proposed by Moor, were endorsed in an editorial, "The Standards of Purity for Drugs," in *Pharm. J.* [ser. 4], 10(1900): 202.

92   Anon., "Pharmacopoeia Standards," *Pharm. J.* [ser. 4], 2(1896): 491; Anon., "Pharmacists as Traders," *Pharm. J.* [ser. 4], 9(1899): 631.

93   J. Eagle, "The Pharmacopoeia as a Standard [Letter to the Editor]," *Pharm. J.* [ser. 4], 10(1900): 52–53.

94   Anon., "Facts and Fancies by an Ordinary Pharmacist: The Pharmacopoeia as a Standard," *Pharm. J.* [ser. 4], 10(1900): 75; H. Wippell Gadd, "The Pharmacopoeia as a Standard [Letter to the Editor]," *ibid.*, 78.

95   William Bastick, *The Pharmacopoeia a Dead Letter; or, an Exposure of the Systematic and Fraudulent Adulteration of the Preparations of the Pharmacopoeia, with Suggestions for Its Prevention* (London, 1845), 15 pp., published by the author, and addressed to the Royal College of Physicians of London.

96   *Ibid.*, 6.

97   *Ibid.*, 7, 9.

98   Anon., "Facts and Fancies by an Ordinary Pharmacist: wanted, A New Apothecaries' Hall," *Pharm. J.* [ser. 4], 10(1900): 75; Anon., "Facts and Fancies . . . B. P. Standards for Drugs," *ibid.*, 122. The author felt strongly (122) that current drug price lists belied the purity of the preparations contained therein; and pointed (75) to the open substitution of pareira root by another root of unknown botanical origin: "To such an extent has the custom developed that wholesale druggists now ignore the falsification and boldly offer the substitute as Rad. Pareirae."

99   Bastick, *The Pharmacopoeia a Dead Letter*, 13–15.

100   Gadd, "Standards for Drugs," *Pharm. J.* [ser. 4], 15(1902): 215.

101   *Report* (1856), vii.

CHAPTER 15
THE EMERGENCE OF SPECIAL SOCIETIES AND PUBLICATIONS

1   Bernard Dyer and C. Ainsworth Mitchell, *The Society of Public Analysts and other Analytical Chemists: Some Reminiscences of Its First Fifty Years* [Dyer], *and a Review of Its Activities* [Mitchell] (Cambridge, 1932). Dyer first became associated with the Society only a few months after its formation in 1874. Mitchell was, when this book was written, editor of the Society's periodical, the *Analyst*. Though both men perhaps stood too close to the phenomena they were examining, contemporary records attest to the accuracy of the most significant events they record. Dyer's account by its very nature—reminiscences of his fifty-year association with the protagonists in the Society's drama—is the more interesting. Mitchell lends authority to Dyer's picture, for Mitchell's contribution consists almost entirely of a topically divided bibliography, with only brief comment, of the most significant papers to appear in the *Analyst* from the time of its founding in 1877.

2   The requirement for membership that stipulated "actual practice" was dropped in 1902, as the Society prepared for incorporation, so that many who might make valuable members would not be prevented from joining. This broader membership policy was reflected in the organization's changed name—"Society of Public Analysts and other Analytical Chemists"—first adopted at the time of incorporation in 1907.

3   The Society passed these resolutions at its founding meeting, 7 August 1874, at the same time that it faced problems of organization. Redwood acted as chairman of the organization committee, of which Heisch and Wigner were secretaries. The Committee's first duties were to draw up a constitution, a code of rules, and to draft definitions of adulteration, and suggestions for limits of purity or standards. The Committee's suggestions were reported to the Society's first meeting in December 1874, when the questions of standards and definitions were delegated to the Society's newly elected Council. In the course of several meetings in succeeding months, the Council set forth definitions for what constituted adulteration in food and drugs, and set various limits in connection with certain foods. We have seen that Wigner's participation in these proceedings was significant. The definition of drug adulteration, for instance, may be traced to Wigner's model adulteration law and subsequently to American and Canadian food and drug legislation, which accepted the definition, while the British Parliament largely ignored the Society's definitions and suggested standards.

4   Contrary to the Society's suggestions, Somerset House, the laboratory of the Department of Inland Revenue, became the court of reference in cases of dispute. The arrangement hindered rather than helped the operation of the Act until the end of the century. The Society's definition of "drug" as a medicine for internal or external use, did find its way into the Act.

5   Anon., "Society of Public Analysts," *Pharm. J.* [ser. 3], 5(1874–75): 443.

6   Dr. Rottenburgh, commissioner for the German government, officially consulted with the Society's Council upon questions of the administration of British law. See: Anon., "German Government and Adulteration," in *Analyst*, 2(1877): 171–172; Anon., "Replies to the Inquiries by the German Government as to the Working of the Sale of Food and Drugs Act," *ibid.*, 173–175.

7   At first (1875–76) Society proceedings appeared in *Chemical News*, through the courtesy of its editor William (later Sir William) Crookes. This happy arrangement terminated when friction developed between Crookes and the Society's Council and consequently the *Analyst* first appeared in March 1876, under the joint editorship of the Society's secretary, G. W. Wigner, and John Muter. Between 1877 and 1891 the journal was privately owned (by Wigner and Muter to begin with), but published with increasing subsidies from the Society. As a result, the Society's Council had no control over the contents of the *Analyst*, during this period, and the candid reporting of controversies within the Society's ranks, and with outside bodies such as Somerset House, gives a valuable insight into the growing pains of this vigorous organization.

8   Dyer and Mitchell, *Society of Public Analysts*, 34, 36.

9   *Ibid.*, 7, 10, 36.

10 Alfred Hill, "What is Milk of Sulphur," *Analyst*, 1(1877): 63–76 (including discussion); Anon., "Law Reports: Sale of Paregoric Containing No Opium," *Analyst*, 5(1880): 189–190; Anon., "Law Reports: Castor Oil Pills," *Analyst*, 2(1878): 104–105; John Muter, "On the Commercial Analysis of Cinchona Barks," *Analyst*, 5 (1879): 223–225; Alexander Wynter Blyth, "The Estimation of Quinine in Quinine Wine, Tinctures, etc.," *Analyst*, 6(1881): 162–164; and J. Carter Bell, "Iodic Acid Test for Morphia," *Analyst*, 4(1879): 181.

11 See the *Analyst, passim*.

12 Aside from those members of the Pharmaceutical Society of British Pharmaceutical Conference who were also public analysts, there seems to have been no formal co-operation between organized pharmacy and the Society of Public Analysts until 1905, when the former president of the Pharmaceutical Society, Michael Carteighe, suggested a conference between its law committee and the Council of the Society of Public Analysts. The outcome was the formation of an advisory committee with representatives from both organizations, with the purpose of giving opinions and advice in cases of difficulties relating to the composition of drugs.

13 During a period from February 1880 to January 1882, the title was augmented by "and Household Cistern Cleansing."

14 After January 1882, "*and Food Journal.*" This periodical seems to have been preserved only in the British Museum, and its holdings are incomplete. A comparative study of the *Review* with two American publications, *Anti-Adulteration Journal* (Philadelphia and Williamsport, 1886–1891) and *Purity: A Magazine and Bulletin of Health, Food, and Drugs* (title varies; Lowell, Mass., 1907–1909), should prove interesting.

15   Only volumes 11 and 12 (1898) have, according to our information, been preserved, in the National Library of Medicine, Bethesda, Md.

16   *Anti-Adulteration Review* 1(November 1871): 13.

17   *Ibid.*

18   *Ibid.*, 9; and *ibid.* (January 1874): 11; *ibid.* (December 1880): 112.

19   *Ibid.* (January 1873): 9, and (April 1873): 10.

20   *Ibid.* (November 1871): 13, and (September 1872): 14.

21   "Miscarriage of Justice," *ibid.* (April 1879): 1; and "The Anti-Adulteration and Household Cistern Cleansing Company," *ibid.* (February 1871): 1.

22   "Our Definition of Adulteration," *ibid.* (January 1874): 8. Compare with Arthur Hill Hassall, *Minutes of Evidence* (1856), 4424, in *Report from the Select Committee on Adulterations of Food, Etc.; together with the Proceedings of the Committee, Minutes of Evidence, Appendix, and Index* (London, 1856); and Hassall, *Adulterations Detected . . .* (London, 1857), 2.

23   We may mention a few exceptions involving a citrate of magnesia conviction: "First Case of Adulterated Drugs," *Anti-Adulteration Review* (November 1873): 9; and "Trade Conference of Chemists and Druggists," *ibid.* (December 1873): 5.

24   "The Anti-Adulteration Association (Limited)," *ibid.* (January 1874): 11–12.

25   "The Why and Wherefore," *ibid.* (May 1876): 1; Phillips Bevan, "Legislation to Prevent Adulteration of Food and Drink," *ibid.* (December 1871): 19; "1880," *ibid.* (December 1880): 111; and "The Main Cause of Adulteration," *ibid.* (November 1871): 9.

26   "Introduction," *British Food Journal*, 1(1899): 1. Title varies: *British Food Journal and Analytical Review* and *British Food Journal and Hygienic Review*.

27   *Ibid.*

28   "The British Analytical Control," *ibid.* 7–8; "The Prevention of Adulteration by a Permanent Analytical Control," *ibid.*, 6–7; "The British Analytical Control and Its Critics," *ibid.*, 63; "The British Analytical Control," *ibid.*, 161–162; "Purity by Control," *ibid.*, 162–163; "The British Control Analytical," *ibid.*, 10(1908): 202; and "British Analytical Control," *ibid.*, 27(1925): 87.

29   Beginning in 1914, it was also official organ of the "Pure Food and Health Society of Great Britain."

30   This was an outgrowth of the International Congress of Hygiene held in Madrid in 1898, at which the Report of the International Commission on Adulteration recommended that the editors of the *Revue* "have power to publish Reviews or Journals to be written and published in conformity with the customs and requirements of the countries where they may appear." (*British Food Journal*, 1[1899]: 30.) Articles had appeared in English, as well as French and German, from the very beginning of the *Revue*, though French remained the principal language. English collaborators for the *Revue* included such well known British chemists as Charles E. Cassall, W. H. Corfield, and E. Frankland.

31 *Maandblad tegen der vervalsching van levensmiddelen*, published in Amsterdam beginning in 1884.

32 *Compte-rendu, Sixième Congrès international pharmaceutique* (Brussels, 1885), 748–750, 874–877; and Van Hamel Roos, "Preface," *Revue internationale des falsifications*, 1(1887): 3.

33 "Proposed International Action with Regard to Adulteration," in *Pharm. J.* [ser. 3], 18(1887–88): 255–256. From 1887 to 1888 the full title was *Revue internationale scientifique et populaire des falsifications des denrées alimentaires*.

34 "Résultats," in *Revue internationale des falsifications*, 1(1887–88): 33.

35 Subtitle, vols. 1–9: "Bulletin international de la repression des fraudes alimentaires et pharmaceutiques."

36 The Society also sponsored two international congresses "for the repression of alimentary and pharmaceutical frauds," the first at Geneva in 1908 and the second at Paris in 1909.

37 *Revue internationale des falsifications*, 10(No. 1, January–February 1897), facing p. 1.

38 Anon. [Arthur Hill Hassall], "Adulteration and Its Remedy," *Cornhill Magazine*, 2(1860): 86–96. See also Edwy Godwin Clayton, *Arthur Hill Hassall . . .* (London, 1908), 31.

39 [Hassall], "Adulteration and Its Remedy," *Cornhill Magazine*, 2 (1860): 86.

40 *Ibid.*, 96.

41 *Ibid.*

42 *Ibid.*

43 *Punch, or the London Charivari*, 21(1851): 196.

44 "What to Eat, Drink and Avoid," *ibid.*, 29(1855): 45.

45 *Ibid.*, 29(1855): 105.

46 *Ibid.*, 66(1874): 255.

47 *Ibid.*, 29(1855): 79. Other comments alluded to the Reform Bill and Gladstone. The reference to absolute purity was probably a snide poke at the testimony of the well-known pharmacist Theophilus Redwood before the 1855 Select Committee. Russell (1792–1878) was a prominent British statesman (serving as prime minister, 1845–1851, 1851–1852) often involved in political controversies. The allusion to Vienna refers to his part as British representative in the fruitless Congress at Vienna concerning the Crimean War then in progress. Disapproval of his role in the proceedings led to his resigning from political life for a time.

48 [Editorial], 20 August 1856, 6.

49 [Editorial], 25 August 1856, 6.

INDEX

Accum, Fredrick [Friedrich Christian]: tests for adulteration, 32, 37, 41, 43, 79, 86, 92; compared with Guibourt, 92; misjudged British laissez faire, 105–106, 168; on extent of adulteration, 114, 166; accused drug grinders, 124; distinguished forms of adulteration, 127; on punishment for adulteration, 135, 138; on publicity as deterrent, 138, 141; significance of, 161–169, 300n23; *Treatise on Adulterations*, character and success of, 161, 166–169; favored government control, 166, 168; charges against him, 168; on war as factor in adulteration, 169; mentioned, 48, 60, 69, 112, 113, 159, 176, 180, 198, 211, 216

Acetyl value, 96

Acid reactions: mentioned by Pliny, 7

Acland, Henry W.: on qualifications of public analysts, 159

Admixture: fraudulent and willful, defined as drug adulteration, 4, 128–29; exemption of, 130; declaration of, 130, 205; punishment for, 140; as problem in administering legislation, 194–195

Adulteration: history of food, ix; antiquity of, 4; and fraud, 4; caused by avarice, according to Pliny, 6; extent of, 51, 86, 114–121; 150–152; guild control of, 106–107; nature of, 122–123; movements against, 159,

172; International Commission on, 211; attention to by public press, 212–216. *See also* Intentional adulteration

—definition of: for this book, 3; general, 3–4, 281–282nn20–21; effect on administration of legislation, 122, 133; by Society of Public Analysts, 131–132, 205–207 *passim;* by Edward R. Squibb, 132; in American legislation, 132; by G. W. Wigner, 132; by Charles Heisch, 132; by Theophilus Redwood, 132; need for board of reference to set, 133; by Apothecaries' Company, 134; problem of recognized by Select Committee of 1874, 184; by Anti-Adulteration Association, 210

—detection of: in Greco-Roman period, 4–9; by specific gravity method, 5; earliest, credited to Archimedes, 5; nature of first certain, 51; first certain, with microscopy, 175–176; by Society of Public Analysts members, 208. *See also* Drug adulteration; and names of specific drugs

Age of drugs: effect on quality, according to Theophrastus, 4

Alcoholometer: mentioned by Aschoff, 38

Alkalimetry: development of, 87–90 *passim*

Alkaloids: development of analysis of, 97

323